NUCLEAR PULSE SPECTROMETRY

NUCLEAR PULSE
SPECTROMETRY

ROBERT L. CHASE

Associate Head, Instrumentation Division
Brookhaven National Laboratory

McGRAW-HILL BOOK COMPANY, INC.

New York   Toronto   London   1961

NUCLEAR PULSE SPECTROMETRY

THE MAPLE PRESS COMPANY, YORK, PA.

PREFACE

The great upsurge in nuclear technology, during and after World War II, has been associated with substantial development in its techniques and tools.   Nuclear reactors and particle accelerators of many types and sizes are supplying nuclear data in ever-increasing quantities, and electronic devices are being built for collecting, recording, and processing these data in ever more refined and elaborate ways.

During the war the designers of electronic circuits for nuclear experiments borrowed very heavily from the wealth of pulse circuitry growing out of the development of radar.   Making only minor modifications to adjust to the aperiodic nature of most nuclear events, nucleonic designers were able to adapt many of the radar timing, gating, and amplitude-selecting systems to nuclear data collection.   These systems, added to some original circuit developments, particularly in the fields of pulse counting, stable pulse amplification, and high-speed coincidence measurements, resulted in equipment capable of making accurate pulse-height and pulse-time measurements.

Measurements in nuclear physics tend to differ rather considerably from measurements in sciences dealing with macroscopic objects.   It follows from the quantum-mechanical uncertainty principle that a single observation on a submicroscopic physical system yields at best an approximate picture of the system.   If a precise description of a nuclear reaction is desired, it is necessary to make a large number of observations and to draw conclusions on the basis of a statistical analysis of large quantities of data.   As physicists attempt more sophisticated experiments demanding higher standards of statistical accuracy, they require measuring instruments capable of recording and classifying very considerable quantities of data.   In many cases, conventional pulse-counting circuits capable of storing these large quantities of data are too costly to build and maintain or too full of fallible components to operate reliably.

Similar problems of data storage have been encountered and solved in the development of large digital computing facilities.   Nucleonic designers are now actively adapting digital computer memory and data handling systems to nuclear data collection, with considerable success. Nuclear instruments have been built with acoustic delay-line memories, with magnetic-core and magnetic-drum memories, with cathode-ray-tube electrostatic memories, with magnetic tape, punched paper tape, and punched-card storage systems, and it is likely that, as new computer memory devices are developed, they will be employed in nuclear instruments.

Research in nuclear physics makes use of a relatively small number of basic measuring tools, most of which can be grouped into four general classes.

1. Track-recording devices: Included in this class are cloud chambers of the expansion and diffusion type, bubble chambers, and photographic emulsions.

2. Magnetic and electrostatic deflection devices: These devices separate charged particles according to their momenta, and include magnetic lens and electrostatic beta-ray spectrometers as well as several types of mass spectrometers.

3. Diffraction devices: Neutron diffraction spectrometers sort neutrons according to their energy. They make use of regular crystal lattices to diffract neutrons, much as a diffraction grating is used in an optical spectrometer.

4. Counter and ionization-chamber devices: This class includes radio-assay and radiation-dose measuring devices that use Geiger counters, proportional counters, scintillation counters, and ionization chambers. Also included are two types of spectrometric devices that take advantage of the relations between pulse-amplitude or pulse-detection time in these counters and incident particle energy.

The four classes of nuclear devices are not, of course, distinct and unrelated. Counters, for example, are commonly used in association with all of the other devices mentioned. We make use of this perhaps arbitrary division to define the scope of this volume. We shall be concerned primarily with devices in the fourth class and, more specifically, with the electronic systems and circuits that make up these devices. Our objectives are to acquaint practicing experimental nuclear physicists with the capabilities, limitations, operating principles, and future prospects of counter instrumentation; to introduce electronic design engineers to some of the problems of nuclear circuit design in order to encourage their interest and participation in future developments; and to present, in a single volume, a study of the present status of nuclear pulse-height and pulse-time-distribution spectrometers.

The author wishes to express his sincere appreciation to William A. Higinbotham and Brian D. Pate for their numerous suggestions during the preparation of this volume and for their help in editing the manuscript.

Robert L. Chase

CONTENTS

INTRODUCTION

Most of our knowledge of nuclear structure is derived from studies of nuclear reactions and radioactivity. The characteristics of nuclear forces and energy states of nuclei are deduced from the nature, energy, and angular distribution of radiations emitted as a result of these processes. In the course of this volume we shall discuss many of the electronic pulse techniques that have been applied to the study of these radiation characteristics.

Electronic pulse techniques have also been applied to the measurement of radiation for other purposes. For example, radioactive tracers can be located in chemical and biochemical systems and identified by their characteristic alpha, beta, or gamma radiation as measured with a pulse spectrometer. Also, exceedingly small quantities of many elements can be identified and measured by activation analysis. The unknown material is made radioactive by exposure to neutrons, after which its chemical nature is determined from the character and intensity of the resulting radiation.

Whether the application be basic nuclear research or chemical analysis, the pulse spectrometers used have many characteristics in common. All of them start out with one or more radiation detectors capable of producing electrical impulses, some characteristic of which, for example, pulse height or time of arrival, is related to the energy of the incident radiation. Because the detector signals are usually quite small, the detectors are generally followed by pulse amplifiers which serve both to increase the amplitude of the signals and to provide them with a shape suitable for analysis. The last and usually most complex component of a pulse spectrometer is a sorting and tallying device which catalogs the input signals according to some significant parameter, such as amplitude or time of arrival.

In the chapters that follow each of these components of pulse spectrometers will be discussed in some detail. We begin with a study of radiation detectors and their characteristics.

CHAPTER 1

RADIATION DETECTORS AND THEIR CHARACTERISTICS

Nuclear radiations are detectable by virtue of their interactions with matter. The character of the interaction is dependent upon the type of radiation (beta particles, gamma rays, etc.), the energy of the radiation, and the physical and chemical properties of the detecting medium. A detailed discussion of all the interactions of nuclear radiations with matter is beyond the scope of both the author and this volume. We shall restrict ourselves to a consideration of electrons, gamma and X rays, alpha particles, and neutrons, although much of what we say about alpha particles will also apply to other heavy charged particles (protons, deuterons, etc.). Furthermore, we shall only be concerned with those interactions which can be translated into electrical impulses.

1.1 Electrons (Beta Rays)

The electrons emitted in nuclear beta decay are limited to the energy range below 15 Mev. Electrons in this energy range are not able to penetrate atomic nuclei. Furthermore, because of the large difference in mass between electrons and nuclei, an electron can transfer very little energy to a nucleus. The principal interaction between electrons and nuclei, therefore, is elastic scattering in which the electrons are deflected, but transfer essentially no energy to the scattering nuclei. However, when an electron is accelerated in the Coulomb field of a nucleus, it loses energy because of radiation (bremsstrahlung). For low-energy electrons in light materials, the energy loss due to bremsstrahlung is usually negligible compared with that lost in interactions with other electrons [1,2].* However, the energy radiated varies as the square of the atomic number Z and, for relativistic electrons, approximately linearly with energy, so that in lead, for example, 6.9-Mev electrons lose about as much energy due to bremsstrahlung as they do in collisions with other electrons.

As far as the detection of energetic electrons is concerned, the most important interactions are with other electrons. Most of the interactions are characterized by the transfer of very little energy, and an energetic

* Numbers in brackets refer to references at the end of the chapter.

electron usually makes a very large number of inelastic collisions in the process of losing its energy. Most of the collisions result in the excitation of the atomic electrons, but in a smaller number of cases enough energy is transferred to an electron to break it loose from the atom, producing an electron–positive-ion pair. The secondary electrons released in the ionization process (delta rays) have, on the average, enough kinetic energy to produce one or two additional ion pairs, so that ion pairs are usually formed in small clusters along the path of the primary electron.

TABLE 1.1

Gas.........................	A	He	H₂	N₂	Air	O₂	CH₄
Energy per ion pair, W, in electron volts..................	27.0	32.5	38.0	35.8	35.0	32.2	30.2

The relationship between the incident electron energy and the number of ion pairs produced is an important one, because it offers a means of determining the electron energy. This relationship has been studied by several investigators [3–6] for a number of gases, and it has been found that the energy lost per ion pair, W, not only is nearly independent of the energy of the incident electron, but its value is very nearly the same for all gases. Table 1.1 shows some representative values of W as summarized by Siegbahn [7].

1.2 Gamma Rays and X Rays

Gamma rays and X rays are both forms of electromagnetic radiation and differ only with respect to origin, gamma rays being produced in transitions between nuclear states and X rays resulting from transitions between atomic electron states. Since they are, in other respects, indistinguishable, we shall confine our discussion to gamma rays, with the understanding that the same remarks apply equally well to X rays.

Although gamma rays are known to induce nuclear reactions, and these reactions may be useful in some cases for the determination of gamma-ray energies [8] it is, however, the atomic processes of photoelectric conversion, Compton scattering, and pair production that are of interest in pulse spectrometry.

Photoelectric Effect. Photoelectric conversion occurs when a gamma ray transfers all of its energy, $h\nu$, to an electron and disappears. Photoelectric conversion is not possible with free electrons, because another body must be present if momentum is to be conserved. An electron bound in an atom by the Coulomb field of a nucleus can participate in photoelectric conversion, and the more tightly the electron is bound, the more probable is the process.   Photoelectric conversion, therefore, most commonly occurs with the K electrons (provided that the gamma-ray energy exceeds the K binding energy), and its probability increases rapidly with atomic number, varying approximately as Z^5.

The variation of the photoelectric conversion cross section with gamma-ray energy is fairly complex [9].   For low-energy gamma rays (below 100 kev), the cross section varies approximately as the inverse third power of the energy.   In the energy range between 100 and 500 kev, it varies more nearly as the inverse square of the energy, and above 500 kev, it varies inversely as the first power of the energy.

If a gamma ray interacts with a K electron by the photoelectric process, part of the gamma-ray energy is used up in separating the electron from the nucleus, so that the kinetic energy of the photoelectron is the gamma-ray energy less the K binding energy.   The process is followed immediately by the emission of a K X ray, which may either interact in the detector or escape.   Since the X-ray energy is smaller than that of the incident gamma ray, the probability of its interaction is relatively greater.   If it interacts by the photoelectric process with an L electron, an L X ray is produced and the K minus L energy difference is carried off as kinetic energy by the second photoelectron.   The L X ray may also be absorbed, producing a still lower energy X ray, and so on, the net result being a family of photoelectrons of progressively decreasing energy, the sum of whose energies will be equal to the incident gamma-ray energy. Of course, any of the X rays may escape from the detector volume or interact by Compton scattering (see below), but because each successive X ray has a lower energy, the probability of escape becomes small very quickly.

Compton Scattering.   As an alternative to the photoelectric effect, gamma rays may interact with electrons by Compton scattering, whereby the gamma ray is deflected and decreased in energy, the energy loss being taken up by the scattering electron which recoils at an angle appropriate to the conservation of momentum.   If, in Fig. 1.1, E_g represents the energy of the incident gamma ray, E_g' the energy of the scattered gamma ray, and E_e the energy of the recoiling electron, then it follows from the law of conservation of momentum that

$$E_g' = \frac{E_g}{1 + \alpha(1 - \cos\theta)} \tag{1.1}$$

$$E_e = E_g \left[1 - \frac{1}{1 + \alpha(1 - \cos\theta)} \right] \tag{1.2}$$

where α is the ratio of the gamma-ray energy to the energy equivalent of the rest mass of the electron, E_g/mc^2.

All values of the scattering angle θ are possible, their relative probability being dependent on the gamma-ray energy. High-energy gamma rays tend to scatter through small angles, giving only a small fraction of their energy to the scattering electron, whereas low-energy gamma rays (below 50 kev) scatter forward and backward with almost equal probability.

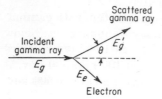

Scattered gamma ray

Incident gamma ray

E_g

θ E_g'

E_e

Electron

Fᴵɢ. 1.1 Typical Compton scattering event. The incident gamma ray is deflected through an angle θ and imparts some of its energy to the scattering electron.

Although the energy transferred to the scattering electron can have a continuous range of values starting from zero, it can never equal the gamma-ray energy. When the gamma ray scatters directly backward $(\theta = \pi)$, the residual gamma-ray energy is a minimum. These minimum values are plotted in Fig. 1.2 as a function of incident gamma-ray energy. It is interesting to note that, as gamma-ray energy increases, the energy of the backscattered gamma ray approaches half the electron rest energy (255 kev) and that for a wide range of gamma-ray energies, it has a value near 200 kev.

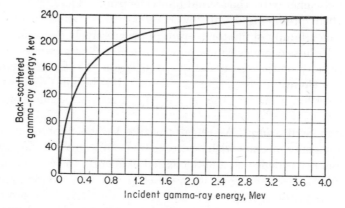

Fᴵɢ. 1.2 The energy retained by a gamma ray that Compton-scatters in the backward direction $(\theta = \pi)$ as a function of the incident gamma-ray energy.

Pair Production. A gamma ray whose energy exceeds $2mc^2$ (1.02 Mev) can, in the field of a nucleus, spontaneously convert to an electron-positron pair, the excess energy being carried off as kinetic energy of the two particles. The probability of the process increases roughly linearly with gamma-ray energy starting from zero at the threshold energy, 1.02 Mev. Pair production is much more likely in heavy materials than in light ones, the probability varying approximately as Z^4.

The electron and positron lose energy by inelastic collisions with other electrons and ultimately come to rest, at which time the positron inter-acts with a neighboring electron. The electron and positron mutually annihilate, usually giving rise to a pair of gamma rays,[1] each with an energy of 510 kev, that leave the scene in opposite directions (to conserve momentum). A typical pair-production and annihilation process is diagramed in Fig. 1.3.

If the electron-positron pair is created in an energy-sensitive electron detector, then an impulse is produced proportional to the gamma-ray energy less $2mc^2$. In addition, one or both of the annihilation gamma rays may be detected because of photoelectric conversion or Compton scattering, so that the net impulse can represent a whole range of energies between $E_g - 2mc^2$ and E_g. Usually three peaks can be recognized in the pulse distribution, corresponding to $E_g - 2mc^2$ when both annihilation gamma rays escape, to $E_g - mc^2$ when one annihilation gamma ray escapes and the other is photoelectrically converted, and to E_g when both annihilation gamma rays are photoelectrically

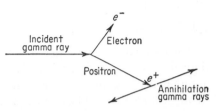

FIG. 1.3 Typical pair-production event. An incident gamma ray decays sponta-neously into an electron-positron pair. The positron interacts with another elec-tron, leading to their mutual annihilation and the production of a pair of 510-kev gamma rays.

converted. This last peak is, of course, indistinguishable from that which results from the photoelectric conversion of the incident gamma ray.

1.3 Alpha Particles

Most of the alpha particles produced in the decay of radioactive nuclei fall in the energy range between 4 and 10 Mev. Because of their con-siderable mass (almost 7,300 times that of an electron), an alpha particle, even at 10 Mev, has a velocity less than one-tenth the speed of light. In contrast, a 73-kev electron has a velocity half that of light. Because alpha particles spend considerable time in passing through a unit length of matter, they make many exciting and ionizing collisions per centimeter traveled and, therefore, can penetrate relatively little matter before they dissipate their energy. The average amount of energy lost in each collision is, however, quite small because of the large mass difference between alpha particles and electrons. The average energy lost by an alpha particle per ion pair formed is very nearly the same as for electrons, being 32.5 ev for alpha particles in air and 35.0 ev for electrons in air (see Table 1.1). The ionization produced by alpha particles is, however, much more dense than that produced by electrons and increases in density

[1] A small fraction of the time three gamma rays are produced.

toward the end of the track, as the particle slows down and makes more collisions per centimeter.

Alpha particles are capable of making inelastic collisions with atomic nuclei, but because nuclear dimensions are small compared with their separation, the mean free path between such collisions is large. In the case of alpha particles with energies less than 10 Mev, the mean free path between nuclear interactions in matter is much larger than the range of the alpha particles, so that it is only the interactions with electrons that are significant with respect to the detection of alpha particles in this energy range.

1.4 Neutrons

Because neutrons are uncharged and very much heavier than electrons, they do not interact significantly with electrons, and we must depend upon nuclear interactions for their detection. Since they are not repelled by nuclear electric fields, even very low energy (thermal) neutrons readily penetrate and react with nuclei, so that one has a host of reactions to choose from. To be suitable for the detection of neutrons, a nuclear reaction must have a reasonably high probability and must result in the production of some other form of easily detectable radiation, such as charged particles or gamma rays. Suitable reactions fall into four general categories: activation reactions, transmutation reactions, fission, and scattering.

Activation Reactions. Activation reactions are those which result in the production of excited nuclei with reasonably long lifetimes. Samples of suitable materials (usually thin foils) are exposed to neutron irradiation. They are then removed from the neutron flux and their radioactivity is measured, usually by beta or gamma counting. From a knowledge of the reaction cross section, the exposure time, and the intensity and lifetime of the radioactivity produced, the intensity of the neutron flux can be inferred. Two reactions commonly used for this purpose are

$$Rh^{103} + n \rightarrow Rh^{104}(44 \text{ sec}) + \gamma$$
$$In^{115} + n \rightarrow In^{116}(54 \text{ min}) + \gamma$$

Rh^{104} and In^{116} both decay with the production of beta and gamma rays which are easily detectable.

Activation reactions are very useful for the detection of neutrons even in the presence of intense gamma radiation which may interfere with other detection techniques, but since they do not play a role in pulse spectrometry, we shall not consider them further.

Transmutation Reactions. Neutrons may be captured by nuclei and cause the prompt emission of charged particles such as protons, deuterons,

or alpha particles.   In most such cases the reaction energy is negative.
The incident neutron must supply sufficient energy to overcome the
force binding the charged particle to the compound nucleus for the
reaction to take place.   Selected reactions of this type can be used to
determine the number of neutrons with energies exceeding the reaction
threshold energy.

There are some neutron-induced transmutation reactions which have
positive reaction energies, and these can be used for the detection of
neutrons of all energies.   Two very useful reactions are

$$B^{10} + n \rightarrow Li^7 + \alpha + 2.5 \text{ Mev}$$
$$Li^6 + n \rightarrow H^3 + \alpha + 4.5 \text{ Mev}$$

Reactions of this type can also be used in the determination of neutron
energies, both by time-of-flight and pulse-height analysis techniques.
The detection of the excitation or ionization produced by the alpha
particle and the recoiling daughter nucleus can mark the time of arrival
of a neutron at the end of a measured flight path (see Chap. 8).   Alternatively, if the total energy of the alpha particle and the recoiling nucleus
is determined by measuring the amount of excitation or ionization produced, the incident neutron energy can be determined by subtracting
the reaction energy.   The time-of-flight technique is most useful for
slow neutrons whose flight times can be measured accurately.   The pulse-
height technique gives useful energy information only for fast neutrons
with energies comparable to the reaction energies.

Fission.   The fission process provides a technique for detecting neutrons in the presence of very intense gamma radiation.   Because of the
large amount of energy given to the fission fragments (about 200 Mev),
the amount of ionization resulting from the fission process is very large
compared with that produced by gamma-ray photoelectrons.   An
impulse produced by fission can be distinguished from that resulting
from the pile-up of a considerable number of nearly simultaneous gamma-
ray pulses.   Fission detectors can be made sensitive to either fast or
slow neutrons by the proper choice of target material.   Slow neutrons
induce fission in U^{235}, U^{233}, and Pu^{239} while fast neutrons (above 1 Mev)
induce fission in U^{238}, Th^{232}, and Pa^{231} in addition.

Scattering.   The elastic scattering of neutrons from light nuclei
(notably protons) provides a useful method for detecting moderately fast
neutrons.   Because protons and neutrons have approximately the same
mass, the energy transferred from an energetic neutron to a proton at
rest may have any value up to the full neutron energy, all values of
energy transfer in this range being equally likely.   The energy of the
recoiling protons can be determined by measuring the ionization or
excitation produced in a suitable detector (ionization chamber or scintil-

lation counter), and from the distribution of proton energies the incident neutron energies can sometimes be inferred. The technique is very useful in the case of monoenergetic neutrons, where the spectrum of recoil proton energy is flat up to a definite end point (the neutron energy) but yields confusing results with complex neutron spectra.

1.5 Detectors

Our discussion of radiation detectors will be confined to those which give rise to measurable electrical impulses, and we shall, therefore, exclude such devices as cloud chambers and photographic emulsions. The detectors to be considered fall into three general categories: (1) gas-filled devices in which electric charges are transported between a pair of electrodes as a result of ionization produced by radiation; (2) scintillation counters in which excitation by radiation gives rise to small flashes of light; and (3) conduction counters in which the electrical conductivity of insulators or semiconductors is temporarily increased by the passage of ionizing radiation.

1.6 Ionization Chambers

Ionization chambers are the simplest and oldest form of radiation detector. Figure 1.4 shows an ionization chamber in its simplest form.

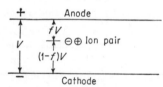

FIG. 1.4 A simple ionization chamber consisting of an anode and a cathode with a gas between them. A single ion pair is shown at a point in the chamber which differs in potential from the anode by a fraction f of the total chamber voltage V.

It consists of a gas and a pair of electrodes with an electric potential difference between them. When an energetic charged particle passes through the gas, it ejects electrons from some of the gas molecules producing electron–positive-ion pairs. The electrons and positive ions are accelerated in opposite directions by the electric field between the electrodes, the electrons being attracted to the positive electrode (anode) and the positive ions to the negative electrode (cathode). As the charges move apart in the electric field, they induce image charges on the electrodes. If the electrodes, which can be considered as the plates of a capacitor, have a capacitance C, then the induced charge Q produces a change in the voltage between the electrodes, $\Delta V = Q/C$. To determine the relation between the induced charge and the motion of the charges in the gas, let us consider the motion of a single electron with a charge e, through a fraction f of the total voltage between the electrodes V. It will be assumed that V is very large compared with the induced voltage change ΔV. If we equate the work done on the electron in falling through the voltage fV to the change in energy stored on the capacitor C, we obtain

$$efV = \tfrac{1}{2}CV^2 - \tfrac{1}{2}C(V - \Delta V)^2 \qquad (1.3)$$
$$efV = CV\,\Delta V - \tfrac{1}{2}C(\Delta V)^2 \approx CV\,\Delta V \qquad (1.4)$$

from which
$$\Delta V = \frac{fe}{C} \qquad (1.5)$$

In other words, the image charge induced by an electron moving in the electric field between the electrodes is equal to the charge on the electron (1.6×10^{-19} coulomb) multiplied by the fraction of the total voltage through which it has moved. The same argument, of course, applies to the positive ion produced in conjunction with the electron, the positive ion making a contribution to the induced charge proportional to the fraction of the field through which it moves. Suppose that an ion pair is created at a point between the electrodes differing in potential by fV with respect to the anode. The electron then falls through a potential fV inducing a charge fe which produces a voltage change fe/C. The positive ion falls through a potential $(1 - f)V$, inducing a charge $(1 - f)e$ and a voltage change $(1 - f)e/C$. The net voltage change, $fe/C + (1 - f)e/C = e/C$, is independent of the position in the field at which the ion pair is formed.

The mechanics of the motion of charged particles in gases is fairly complex, and we shall not attempt a complete discussion here. (For a more thorough discussion of the motion of electrons and ions in gases, the reader is referred to Refs. 10 and 11.) The motion of charged particles is influenced by the size and mass of the particle, the chemical composition of the gas, the pressure, and the electric field strength. In the usual pressure range for practical ionization chambers (about $\tfrac{1}{10}$ to 10 atm), the electrons and ions make many collisions with gas molecules on their way to their respective electrodes, collisions in which the particles lose some or all of the energy gained from acceleration in the electric field. The motion of a particle is the resultant of a random thermal agitation velocity, whose average value is zero, plus a drift component due to the action of the electric field. The mobility of electrons in gases depends critically on the probability of electron attachment to atoms of the gas. Electron attachment leads to the formation of heavy negative ions with mobilities about a thousand times lower than those of free electrons, so that, in pulse-ionization chambers in which fast electron collection is desirable, electronegative gases such as oxygen, water vapor, and the halogens are generally excluded.

In most gases used in ionization chambers, the electron mobility is two or three orders of magnitude greater than that of the positive ions, so that the voltage pulse appearing across the chamber capacitance has a fast part due to electron collection and a slow part due to positive-ion collection. In an ionization chamber with plane parallel electrodes, in which the electric field is uniform and the drift velocities constant, the voltage signal resulting from a single ion pair may have any of the shapes shown in Fig. 1.5, depending on where in the chamber the ion pair was

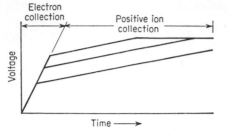

FIG. 1.5 Typical voltage signals induced in an ionization chamber with plane parallel electrodes by a single ion pair. The three curves correspond to three different locations of the ion pair in the chamber volume.

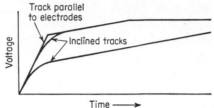

FIG. 1.6 Voltage signals induced in an ionization chamber with plane parallel electrodes as a result of ionization trails produced with various orientations and locations in the chamber. The three curves correspond to the same number of ion pairs, so the final values of all three signals are the same.

formed. The signal resulting from a number of ion pairs is a composite of curves like those of Fig. 1.5 and may look like any of the curves of Fig. 1.6, depending on the location of the ionization track and its orientation with respect to the electrodes. The curves of Fig. 1.6 are drawn for the same total number of ion pairs, so that they all ultimately achieve the same voltage value. Also, they all start with the same initial slope, but as some or all of the electrons are collected, the slope falls (gradually or abruptly, depending on the track orientation) to a lower value corresponding to the lower positive-ion mobility.

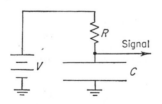

FIG. 1.7 An ionization chamber connected to a source of voltage through a leak resistor R which allows the signal charge to leak off.

The voltage waveforms of Figs. 1.5 and 1.6 are an oversimplification because they show the signals rising but not falling. If the signals did not decay, the voltage across the chamber would ultimately drop to zero and charge collection would cease. To prevent this effect, pulse-ionization chambers are normally connected to a voltage source through a resistor R (Fig. 1.7) which allows the signal charge to leak off the chamber capacitance at a rate governed by the time constant RC. In addition, the signal shapes as they appear after amplification are altered by coupling and integrating time constants and pulse-shaping networks in the amplifier, so that a wide variety of output-pulse shapes is possible.[1]   Normally the pulse-shaping time constants are long compared with the electron collection time, but they may or may not be long compared with the positive-ion collection time.   If all of the significant time constants are very long, then the pulse shapes will be rather like those in Figs. 1.5 and 1.6 and the pulse amplitude will be a measure of the total amount of ionization produced in the chamber by the detected event. However, since each pulse will be quite long (several hundred microseconds, typically), the system counting rate will be limited to low values if the pulses are to be resolved from one another.   If short time constants are used for pulse shaping, then high counting rates will be possible; but each pulse amplitude will represent only that portion of the signal due to electron collection, and its relation to the total ionization produced will depend on the location and orientation of the original ionization trail.

If the pulse amplitude is to represent the total ionization unambiguously at moderately high counting rates, it is necessary to depart from the simple configuration of Fig. 1.4.   One possibility is to use a cylindrical chamber with a fine axial wire as the positive electrode.   The electric field configuration is such that most of the voltage drop is confined to the immediate neighborhood of the center wire.   When ionization is produced in the main volume of the chamber outside of this region,

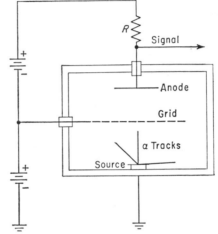

FIG. 1.8   Frisch grid ionization chamber.

the positive ions fall through only a small fraction of the total field and contribute little to the signal.   The electrons, which fall through the major portion of the field, are responsible for nearly all of the pulse.

A disadvantage of this arrangement is that the electric field in the main volume of the chamber is necessarily low if multiplication and breakdown effects in the high field region near the center wire are to be avoided. The low drift velocity imparted to the electrons allows more time for electron attachment, which may decrease the pulse height and spoil the resolution if electronegative impurities are present in the counter gas. An alternative arrangement, which is generally preferred for high-resolution alpha-particle-energy measurements, makes use of the Frisch grid chamber [12] (Fig. 1.8).   The Frisch grid chamber has a highly

[1] For more about pulse shaping see Chap. 2.

transparent fine wire grid, which is mounted between the main chamber electrodes and maintained at an intermediate electric potential. The alpha-emitting source is placed on or near the cathode. The gas pressure and source-to-grid spacing are chosen so that the most energetic alpha particles of interest will have a range less than this distance, so that all of the ionization is produced in the lower part of the chamber. The electrons are accelerated toward the grid, but because of its high transparency and the higher potential on the anode, nearly all of them pass through and are collected on the anode. The positive ions travel to the cathode, but because of the shielding effect of the grid, they induce almost no image charge on the anode. The output signal results almost entirely from the motion of the electrons between the grid and the anode,

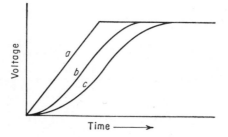

Fig. 1.9   Typical voltage signals from a Frisch grid ionization chamber.   Curve *a* corresponds to an initial ionization trail parallel to the electrodes; curve *b* corresponds to an inclined ionization trail; curve *c* corresponds to an ionization trail normal to the electrodes.

since the shielding effect of the grid prevents their motion in the lower portion of the chamber from affecting the output. Since all electrons fall through the full grid-to-anode potential, they all contribute the same amount to the output signal, regardless of track orientation. Because the positive ions contribute practically nothing to the output signal, the signal rises rapidly and does not contain a slow part.

While the signal rise time in a Frisch grid chamber is relatively short, usually of the order of 1 or 2 μsec, the detailed shape of the signal rise is dependent on the track orientation. If the ionization trail is parallel to the electrodes, the electrons enter the upper portion of the chamber at about the same time, drift together to the anode, and are collected at about the same time, giving rise to a signal like Fig. 1.9*a*. If the ionization trail is normal to the electrodes, the electrons enter and leave the upper portion of the chamber separately, producing a signal like Fig. 1.9*c*. Figure 1.9*b* represents the case of an inclined track. These pulse-shape differences are not in themselves important, since it is generally only the final pulse height that is significant, but unless the subsequent pulse-shaping circuits are properly designed, differences in rise time can lead to differences in measured pulse height. The usual practice is to integrate the signal with a time constant equal to several times the signal rise time, to reduce the effect of variations in rise time on the output-signal amplitude.[1]

[1] For a more detailed discussion of the effect of signal rise time variation, see Ref. 13, pp. 69ff.

1.7 Proportional Counters

A proportional counter is a gas-filled, two-electrode device similar to an ionization chamber, except that it takes advantage of the process of gas multiplication.   It produces an output pulse many times larger than would be obtained from an ionization chamber for the same initial ionization.   Gas multiplication results whenever the electric field strength in the counter is sufficient to give free electrons enough energy between collisions with gas molecules to cause additional ionization. If the geometry of the chamber is such that each initial ion pair results in the production of a specific average number of collected ion pairs, the output signal is proportional to the initial ionization.

In the most common proportional counter configuration (Fig. 1.10) the electrodes are coaxial cylinders, the anode being a fine wire of radius a and the cathode being a much larger hollow cylinder of radius b.   In this configuration the electric field E, at a distance x from the center of the counter, is

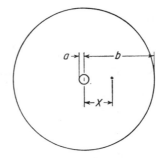

$$E = \frac{V}{x \log_e (b/a)} \qquad (1.6)$$

FIG. 1.10   Cross section of a cylindrical proportional counter.

where V is the total counter voltage.   At the usual counter pressures the mean free path of an electron is small compared with the radius of the center wire, so that, if the electric field in the immediate neighborhood of the center wire is large enough for gas multiplication to occur, each electron, as it passes through this region, may give rise to a large number of additional ion pairs.   Since the multiplication is confined to the immediate neighborhood of the center wire, with half of the ion pairs being formed within a mean free path of the center wire and more than 99 per cent being formed within seven mean free paths, the electrons, in being collected, fall through a very small fraction of the total applied voltage.   This is in spite of the fact that the field strength is high near the center wire.   For example, in a 1-in. counter with a 1-mil center wire ($b/a = 1,000$), an electron moving from a distance $2a$ to the center wire falls through only $\frac{1}{10}$ of the field, and the majority of secondary electrons are produced well inside this distance.   It follows, therefore, that electron collection contributes very little to the output pulse, the major portion of which is due to the motion of the positive ions.   One might, therefore, expect the signal rise to be slow because of the low mobility of positive ions, but this is not in fact so, because the ions fall through most of the total voltage drop while moving in the high field region near

the center wire.   Wilkinson [11] shows that the voltage signal induced
on the center wire due to the motion of a single positive ion moving from
the wire to the cathode varies with time according to

$$P(t) = \frac{e}{C} \frac{\log \left[\dfrac{2VKt}{a^2 \log{(b/a)}} + 1 \right]}{2 \log{(b/a)}} \tag{1.7}$$

until
$$t = \frac{(b^2 - a^2) \log{(b/a)}}{2VK} \tag{1.8}$$

when the positive ion is collected and the signal $P = e/C$.   The constant K is the ion mobility and e represents the ionic charge (equal to
the electron charge for a singly ionized molecule).   Figure 1.11 is a
normalized plot of $P(t)$, for a positive ion collected in unit time, for a
counter with a b/a ratio of 100.   The value of the total collection time
depends on the counter gas and the pressure and may vary considerably,
but a collection time of about 100 μsec may be considered typical.   It is

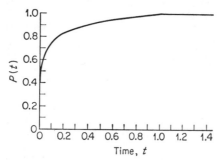

seen from Fig. 1.11 that the signal
rises to half amplitude rapidly, the
second half being relatively slow.

Figure 1.11 shows the pulse
shape for a single ion or for a
number of ions produced at the
same distance from the anode.
When the initial ionization has an
appreciable radial distribution in
the counter, the output signal will
be a composite of curves like Fig.
1.11, each starting at a different
time, corresponding to the time at
which the various initial electrons
drift into the multiplication region.
This gives rise to an uncertainty in
the early part of the signal rise

FIG. 1.11   Normalized plot of the voltage signal from a proportional counter
with a ratio of outer to inner radius, b/a,
of 100.   The signal rises rapidly at first
and then more slowly as the positive ions
drift out of the high field region near the
anode.

time, much like that in the Frisch grid ionization chamber, making it
advisable to integrate the signal somewhat in the pulse amplifier, so that
the subsequent differentiation will not introduce an appreciable artificial
pulse-height variation.

Proportional counters can be operated over a wide range of gas multiplication factors.   The multiplication depends on the counter geometry,
the nature of the gas filling, and the applied voltage.   Since, in the
multiplication region, the number of ion pairs very nearly doubles for
every mean free path, the gain is 2^n, where n is the extent of the multiplication region measured in mean free paths.   From Eq. (1.6) it is seen

that the size of the multiplication region is proportional to the applied voltage V. If $n = fV$, then the gain is 2^{fV}. Typical values of f fall in the range of 0.01 to 0.02, so that the gain of a typical proportional counter doubles for voltage increments of 50 to 100 volts.

Proportionality between initial ionization and output-pulse height in a proportional counter may extend over a considerable gain range, being ultimately limited at high gains when the positive-ion space charge significantly depresses the electric field strength near the center wire. When the initial ionization trail is a dense one, like those produced by heavy charged particles, proportionality may begin to fail at gains of about 10^4, while for minimum ionizing particles proportionality may extend up to gains of 10^7.

1.8   Geiger Counters

Although historically the Geiger-Müller counter, or Geiger counter as it is frequently called, antedates the proportional counter by many years, its operation is not nearly so well understood. Associated with the electron avalanches that produce gas multiplication in proportional counters there is always a great deal of excitation, some of it followed by the emission of visible and ultraviolet photons. The vast majority of these photons are absorbed or escape from the counter without producing any electrical effects, but a small fraction may eject photoelectrons from the gas or the counter wall. As the gas multiplication is increased, the number of photons produced by each avalanche increases and, eventually, reaches a value at which each avalanche, on the average, gives rise to the production of a photoelectron somewhere in the counter. Since each photoelectron leads to a new avalanche, the process is regenerative and leads very quickly to a discharge along the entire length of the counter anode. This spread of the discharge along the anode is what characterizes Geiger counter operation and distinguishes it from proportional counter operation. In a Geiger counter a single initial ion pair is enough to produce complete discharge, so that the output-signal amplitude is no longer a measure of the initial ionization. For this reason, Geiger counters play very little part in pulse spectrometry, and there is little point in our discussing them further here.

1.9   Scintillation Counters[1]

The one detector that is presently used more than any other for energy measurements is the scintillation counter. There are a number of reasons for this, the most important of which are the high efficiency and fast response of a number of scintillating phosphors.

[1] For a thorough treatment of the scintillation process and scintillation counters, see Ref. 14.

The operation of scintillation counters is based on the fact that, in some materials, an appreciable fraction of the energy dissipated by charged particles is converted to visible and ultraviolet light. When a charged particle passes through an inorganic crystalline material, it may elevate some of the loosely bound valence electrons to the conduction band. The electrons then return to the ground state by several mechanisms at imperfections in the crystal: (1) Some of the lattice defects act as quenching centers at which the excess electron energy is converted to heat. (2) Others act as luminescence centers at which the transition to the ground state is accompanied by the emission of photons. (3) Still others can trap electrons in metastable energy levels. The trapped electrons may acquire additional energy from thermal lattice vibrations and return to the conduction band, or they may fall to the ground state by radiationless transitions.

The second mechanism is responsible for fluorescence effects in inorganic solids and is also the basis for inorganic scintillation detectors. The third mechanism accounts for the delayed emission of light (phosphorescence) of some materials and is important to scintillation counting only as an undesirable nuisance.

Some of the inorganic phosphors that have been used in scintillation counters are zinc sulfide (activated with silver or manganese), sodium iodide (activated with thallium), lithium iodide (activated with thallium, tin, or europium), and calcium and cadmium tungstate. Zinc sulfide is used mostly for the detection of heavy charged particles, its fluorescent efficiency being very much greater for heavily ionizing particles than for electrons. Lithium iodide has been used as a neutron detector because of the $Li^6(n,\alpha)H^3$ reaction. However, by far the most generally useful inorganic scintillator is sodium iodide, because of its high fluorescent efficiency, its high transparency to its own radiation, and the relatively high atomic number of its iodine component ($Z = 53$). The high Z makes sodium iodide particularly useful as a gamma-ray detector, because it increases the probability of the photoelectric process relative to Compton scattering.

In organic materials the scintillation process is somewhat different, fluorescence being a property of individual molecules rather than of the crystal lattice. Organic substances which form useful solid scintillating crystals frequently turn out to be useful in solution and even in the gas phase. Inorganic phosphors, on the other hand, are highly dependent on the crystal form and its detailed imperfections, and the fluorescence properties of such materials are altered and frequently enhanced by the inclusion of specific impurities or activators.

The first organic phosphor to be used in a scintillation counter was naphthalene, but it has been almost entirely superseded by other phosphors with higher luminescent efficiency, such as anthracene, stilbene, and terphenyl.   Liquid organic phosphors have also been used extensively, largely because of the ease with which they can be formulated in all sizes and shapes.   In some cases it is possible to add radioactive sources, in suitable chemical forms, directly to liquid scintillators, without seriously decreasing their luminescent efficiency.   Efficient detectors for the soft beta rays of C^{14} and tritium have been made in this way. Organic phosphors have also been made in the form of scintillating plastics, which have reasonably high luminescent efficiency, are available in large sizes, and are easily machined into complex shapes.

An important characteristic of scintillating phosphors, in addition to luminescent efficiency and atomic number of the constituents, is the characteristic luminescent decay time.   In some phosphors in which several mechanisms compete, there may be fast and slow decay components, but in most cases there is one dominant decay time.   In nearly all cases the light intensity is maximum immediately after passage of the ionizing particle, after which it decays exponentially with time.   The characteristic decay time constants of the organic phosphors are all quite short, having values in the range of 10^{-8} sec.   The inorganic phosphors, as a group, have larger decay time constants in the neighborhood of 10^{-6} sec.   NaI(Tl) at room temperature has a dominant luminescent decay time constant of 2.5×10^{-7} sec.

A scintillation counter consists of a suitable scintillating phosphor optically coupled to a sensitive light-detecting device, which is nearly always a photomultiplier tube.   Photomultiplier tubes are vacuum tubes containing a photoemissive cathode surface and a number of secondary emission electron multiplying electrodes (dynodes).   The electrons from the photocathode are electrostatically focused and accelerated, so that they arrive at the first dynode with sufficient energy to eject, on the average, more than one (in some cases as many as five or six) secondary electrons.   The secondary electrons are accelerated to the second dynode by an appropriately shaped electrostatic field, where each gives rise to additional secondary electrons.   The process is repeated at each of the dynodes (from 10 to 14 in commercially available photomultiplier tubes), the electrons from the last dynode being collected on the photomultiplier anode.   The secondary emission multiplication factor at each dynode increases slowly with the energy of the incident electrons and, therefore, with the interdynode voltage, but the over-all gain, which is a high power of the individual-stage gain, varies very rapidly with the over-all applied voltage.   In 10-stage photomultipliers the gain varies approximately as the seventh power of the over-all applied voltage over the useful range of multiplication values (about 10^3 to 10^7); it varies still more rapidly in 14-stage photomultipliers, which are sometimes operated with gains as high as 10^9.

The voltage signal at the photomultiplier anode, following the passage of a charged particle through the phosphor, is equal to the charge carried by the secondary electrons collected at the anode, divided by the capacitance of the anode circuit, and is proportional to the intensity of the light impulse over a wide range of photomultiplier gain. At very high values of gain, proportionality fails because of space-charge saturation effects in the last stages of the photomultiplier. In the case of the relatively slow inorganic phosphors the signal rise time at the photomultiplier anode is determined almost entirely by the characteristic decay time constant of the phosphor. However, with the faster organic phosphors the rise time is determined both by the phosphor decay time and by the electron transit time dispersion in the photomultiplier tube. Transit time dispersion results from the fact that the various possible electron paths from photocathode to anode are not all of the same length and because the potential gradients along the various paths are also different. The value of transit time dispersion depends on the interdynode voltages and on the photomultiplier geometry and, with present-day photomultipliers, is usually between 1 and 10×10^{-9} sec.

1.10   Cerenkov Counters

Cerenkov counters, like scintillation counters, make use of photomultiplier tubes and media which respond to the passage of charged particles by the emission of light. They are, however, based on an entirely different physical principle. When a charged particle traverses a medium at a velocity exceeding that of light in that medium, it radiates light at a particular angle with respect to the direction of the particle, the angle being dependent upon the particle velocity and the index of refraction of the medium. The effect was first observed by P. A. Cerenkov in 1934 [16] and was explained in 1937 by Frank and Tamm [17] on the basis of classical electromagnetic theory. Cerenkov radiation can be considered as a sort of optical shock wave somewhat analogous to the acoustical shock wave accompanying an object traveling at a velocity exceeding that of sound, its intensity and angular distribution being governed by the following equations:

$$I = \frac{2\pi Z^2 \, \Delta\nu}{137c} \sin^2 \theta = \frac{2\pi Z^2 \, \Delta\nu}{137c} \left(1 - \frac{1}{\beta^2 n^2} \right) \qquad (1.9)$$

$$\cos \theta = \frac{1}{\beta n} \qquad (1.10)$$

where I is the intensity of light in a frequency range $\Delta\nu$; θ is its angle with respect to the direction of the particle; β is the ratio of the velocity of the particle to c, the velocity of light in vacuum; n is the index of refraction of the medium in the frequency range of interest; and Z is the charge of the particle in units of the electronic charge. If the particle velocity is great enough to excite Cerenkov radiation, βn is, of course, greater than 1.

All Cerenkov counters are threshold detectors in that they respond only to particles exceeding a specific velocity, the velocity threshold being determined by the index of refraction of the radiator. Equations (1.9) and (1.10) show that both the intensity and the direction of Cerenkov radiation are related to the particle velocity, and both have been used for its determination. However, directional measurements [18] are usually much more satisfactory, because the very small amount of light produced in a radiator of reasonable size makes accurate measurement of its intensity very difficult.

Cerenkov counters are exceedingly fast particle detectors. While scintillation counters are limited by the characteristic decay time of the phosphor, in Cerenkov counters the light is emitted instantly, so that the only time uncertainties result from the dispersion in light collection time (only important with large radiators) and the transit time spread in the photomultiplier tube.

1.11 Conduction Counters

When energetic charged particles pass through crystalline materials, they may elevate some of the more loosely bound electrons to the conduction band. In practical scintillating phosphors these electrons are very quickly trapped at crystal imperfections, a substantial number of which are luminescent centers. However, in some very pure crystals there are so few traps that electrons may remain in the conduction band for an appreciable length of time. If an electric field is applied to the crystal via a pair of electrodes on opposite surfaces, these free electrons will move under the influence of the field and induce image charges on the electrodes much like the moving charges in gaseous ionization chambers. In small, nearly perfect, crystals with high electric fields the electrons may move all the way to the positive electrode and be collected, but in most conduction counters made with insulating crystals many of the electrons are trapped before they reach the anode. As with ionization chambers, the induced signal then depends upon the fraction of the electric field through which the electrons fall. The positive vacancies left in the crystal lattice by the removal of electrons (holes) can also move under the influence of the electric field, if electrons in the valence band are free to move from atom to atom. In some crystals, notably the semiconductors, hole migration may account for an appreciable part of the signal, while in others (cold silver chloride, for example) hole mobility is negligible.

To be useful as a conduction counter a crystal must have negligible natural conductivity; otherwise statistical fluctuations in this conductivity will obscure the conductivity induced by radiation. Good insulators like sulfur and diamond, zinc, and cadmium sulfides have all been used as conduction counters at room temperature. Other crystals, such as silver and thallium chloride, have too high conductivity at room temperature, but they can be used as conduction counters at liquid nitrogen temperature (77°K).

Since none of these materials has a significant number of free electrons or holes at the operating temperature, those charges which are produced by radiation but trapped before collection at the electrodes cannot be neutralized by recombination. After prolonged irradiation these trapped charges accumulate in the body of the crystal and set up a polarization field in opposition to the applied electric field, ultimately reducing the net field to a value at which conduction signals can no longer be observed. The amount of irradiation required to produce significant polarization effects depends upon the radiation energy, its distribution in the crystal, the energy dissipated per ion pair, the electric field, and the dimensions of the crystal. Most conduction counters made with insulating crystals can detect only a few million events before significant polarization effects are observed. However, by periodically reversing the polarity of the electric field, polarization effects can be made to cancel at least approximately and the useful life of the counter can be considerably extended. Infrared radiation has also been used [19] to release trapped electrons which ultimately find the trapped holes and neutralize them.

In most crystal counters only a small amount of energy is required to produce an ion pair. Silver chloride requires about 5 ev per ion pair [20], and those diamonds that work require about 10 ev per ion pair [21], both figures comparing favorably with the 30-ev-per-ion-pair characteristic of gaseous ionization chambers. This, combined with high density, the possibility of high Z, and the fact that working counters can be made very small, makes crystal counters attractive in some applications despite the problems associated with polarization, refrigeration, and the difficulty in obtaining crystals of adequate purity.

But in pulse spectrometry, conduction counters made with insulating crystals have been used very little, because polarization effects and the nonuniform distribution of traps lead to large uncertainties in the energy-pulse-height relationship. However, recent work on semiconductors as conduction counters [22] has renewed interest in their use in spectrometry.[1] Germanium and silicon are particularly promising because of

[1] For an extensive bibliography on conduction counters including recent work on semiconductors, see Ref. 23.

the highly developed purification techniques, because the energy per ion pair is low (about 3.5 ev), and because of the high concentration of carriers (electrons and holes) at room temperature which prevents polarization effects.

Of course, intrinsic semiconductors are useless as conduction counters at room temperature because of their low resistivity (47 ohm-cm for germanium, 63,000 ohm-cm for silicon). It is necessary to reduce the quiescent current so that statistical fluctuations in it will be small compared with the signal current, and this is done by forming rectifying P-N junctions and operating them reverse-biased. The electric field in the main body of the semiconductor is practically zero, because of the high carrier concentrations (electrons in N-type material and holes in P-type), except at the depletion layer marking the P-N junction, where the carrier concentration is low and the field high. When electron-hole pairs are produced on either side of the junction, those minority carriers that diffuse to the depletion layer are accelerated across it, falling through practically the entire applied voltage and inducing a signal at the electrodes. Those minority carriers that do not reach the junction are ultimately trapped at recombination centers and do not contribute to a signal pulse. Whether the minority carriers reach the junction or not depends on how far from the junction they are produced, their diffusion velocity, and their lifetime (before being trapped). The diffusion velocity and lifetime combine to determine a diffusion length[1] for minority carriers. If the signal pulse is to correspond to the total ionization (as it must for good resolution in a spectrometer), nearly all of the ionization must be produced well within a diffusion length of the junction. Since the diffusion lengths in semiconductors are small (less than 1 mm for moderately doped germanium), efficient charge collection is possible only with short-range particles (e.g., alpha particles), and the particles must enter the crystal in the immediate neighborhood of the depletion layer. It is necessary, therefore, that the depletion layer be very close to the working surface of the semiconductor. This is true of the surface barrier diode [24] in which a thin film of a suitable metal is deposited on the specially prepared surface of a doped semiconductor.

If all of the ionization is produced in the depletion layer, the charge collection is very rapid. However, if some of the ionization is produced beyond the depletion layer but within a diffusion length of it, then part of the signal rise is slow because of the appreciable diffusion time (of the order of 100 μsec in germanium). Low-energy alpha particles may dissipate all of their energy in the depletion layer while more energetic particles may pass beyond it by an appreciable fraction of a diffusion length. Therefore, if proportionality between signal size and particle

---

[1] If the concentration of carriers in a small region is d, the diffusion length is the distance from this region at which the concentration falls to d/e.

energy is to be preserved into the high-energy region, the signal integration time must be long.[1]

The signal amplitude with a semiconductor counter, as with an ionization chamber, depends upon the collected charge and the counter capacitance. The capacitance of a *P-N* junction is inversely proportional to the thickness of the depletion layer, which is in turn directly proportional to the square root of the applied voltage. The signal is therefore proportional to the square root of the applied voltage. Also, because of the greater thickness of the depletion layer, the counter is linear up to higher particle energies at higher voltages, even with short amplifier differentiating time constants. It is, therefore, advisable to operate semiconductor counters at as high a voltage as possible without causing avalanche breakdown or excessive noise due to increased reverse leakage current.

REFERENCES

1. Siegbahn, K.: "Beta- and Gamma-ray Spectroscopy," p. 13, Interscience Publishers, Inc., New York, 1955.
2. Heitler, W.: "Quantum Theory of Radiation," Oxford University Press, New York, 1948.
3. Curran, S., J. Angus, and A. Cockroft: *Phil. Mag.*, vol. 40, p. 36, 1949.
4. Valentine, J., and S. Curran: *Phil. Mag.*, vol. 43, p. 964, 1952.
5. Pontecorvo, B.: *Helv. Phys. Acta*, vol. 23, suppl. III, p. 97, 1950.
6. Weiss, J., and W. Bernstein: Energy Required to Produce One Ion Pair for Several Gases, *Phys. Rev.*, vol. 98, p. 1828, 1955.
7. Siegbahn: "Beta- and Gamma-ray Spectroscopy," p. 168.
8. Siegbahn: "Beta- and Gamma-ray Spectroscopy," pp. 192ff.
9. Davisson, C., and R. Evans: *Revs. Modern Phys.*, vol. 24, p. 79, 1952.
10. Rossi, B., and H. Staub: "Ionization Chambers and Counters: Experimental Techniques," McGraw-Hill Book Company, Inc., New York, 1949.
11. Wilkinson, D.: "Ionization Chambers and Counters," Cambridge University Press, New York, 1950.
12. Frisch, O.: Isotope Analysis of Uranium Samples by Means of Their Alpha-ray Groups, British Atomic Energy Project, BR 49, 1944.
13. Gillespie, A.: "Signal, Noise and Resolution in Nuclear Counter Amplifiers," Pergamon Press, Inc., New York, 1953.
14. Birks, J.: "Scintillation Counters," Pergamon Press, Inc., New York, 1953.
15. Marshall, J.: Cerenkov Counters, *Ann. Rev. Nuclear Sci.*, vol. 4, p. 141, 1954.
16. Cerenkov, P.: *Compt. rend. acad. sci. U.R.S.S.*, vol. 2, p. 451, 1934.
17. Frank, I., and I. Tamm: *Compt. rend. acad. sci. U.R.S.S.*, vol. 14, p. 109, 1937.
18. Wiegand, C.: Cerenkov Counters in High Energy Physics, *IRE Trans. on Nuclear Sci.*, vol. NS-5, p. 77, 1958.

[1] This is unfortunate because it implies a low value of amplifier low-frequency cutoff, which tends to emphasize the noise associated with the residual reverse junction saturation current. This residual current produces noise similar to that resulting from grid current in the amplifier input tube (see Chap. 2).

19. Chynoweth, A.: Removal of Space Charge in Diamond Crystal Counters, *Phys. Rev.*, vol. 76, p. 310, 1949.
20. Hofstadter, R.: Crystal Counters, *Proc. IRE*, vol. 38, p. 726, 1950.
21. McKay, K.: Electron Bombardment Conductivity in Diamond, *Phys. Rev.*, vol. 74, p. 1606, 1948.
22. Gossick, B., and J. Mayer: Use of Gold-Germanium Broad Area Barrier as an Alpha Particle Spectrometer, *Rev. Sci. Instr.*, vol. 27, p. 407, 1956.
23. Blankenship, J.: Bibliography on Semiconductor Nuclear Radiation Detectors, *Oak Ridge Natl. Lab. Rept.* 2583, 1958.
24. Schwarz, R., and J. Walsh: The Properties of Metal to Semiconductor Contacts, *Proc. IRE*, vol. 41, p. 1715, 1953.

CHAPTER 2

LINEAR AMPLIFIERS

The signals produced by radiation detectors fall in the range between 10^{-15} and 10^{-10} coulomb per pulse. The charge collection time (signal rise time) usually lies in the range of a few millimicroseconds to several microseconds. Most present-day pulse-height analyzers measure pulses in the 0- to 100-volt range. Their requirements with respect to pulse duration vary from instrument to instrument, but pulse lengths of the order of one to several microseconds are most common.

It is the purpose of a linear amplifier to transform the detector signals into signals suitable for pulse-height analysis. This transformation will be considered in terms of its two principal parts, pulse shaping and amplification.

2.1 Pulse Shaping

To maximize the signal amplitude at the amplifier input, and therefore the signal-to-noise ratio, it is customary to integrate the signal charge on the smallest practical amount of capacitance, usually the stray capacitance associated with the counter itself and the amplifier input. The associated leak or discharging resistance is made sufficiently large so that the resultant input time constant is long compared with the signal rise time. In this way the signal is allowed to approach a peak amplitude determined only by the signal charge and the integrating capacitance. The signal then has the general appearance of a step function (Fig. 2.1a) except that the rise time is greater than zero.

If the measurement of individual signals is to be independent of previous ones, the signals must be permitted to decay in a reasonable time. "Reasonable time" has various interpretations depending on the application, but in general the decay time must be short compared with the average interval between pulses if the distortion due to pile-up is to be small. At the same time the signal duration must be longer than the rise time if the peak height is to be representative of the total collected charge.

There are two important reasons why the peak signal height should represent, as nearly as possible, the total collected signal charge.   First, the accuracy with which the signal height represents the energy dissipated in the counter is limited by the statistical uncertainty in the number of ion pairs or photoelectrons produced in the detector.   Each signal represents a statistical sampling of some fraction of these ion pairs or photoelectrons, and the larger the fraction, the smaller is the uncertainty compared to the signal size. The total signal charge is the largest statistical sample available and yields the most accurate energy measurement and, therefore, the best resolution in a nuclear spectrometer.   Secondly, the signal rise time with some detectors (notably proportional counters and pulse-ionization chambers) varies from pulse to pulse.   This results from the fact that the charge collection time

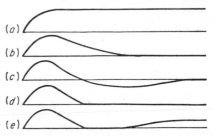

FIG. 2.1   (a) Integrated input signal; (b) after single-RC differentiation; and (c) after double-RC differentiation. (d)   Double-RC-differentiated   signal with undershoot removed by properly located d-c restoring diode and (e) by improperly located d-c restoring diode.

depends on the location and orientation of the incident particle track in the detector.[1]   If the signal duration is too short to represent the total signal charge, the amplifier output-pulse height will represent an uncertain fraction of the energy dissipated in the counter and the system resolution will be poor.   Therefore, in all cases where good resolution is required, it is important that the signal duration be at least several times the rise time.

Single-RC Differentiation.   Single-RC differentiation is the simplest pulse-shaping system in current use [1,2].   The signal is passed through a single high-pass resistance-capacitance coupling circuit (differentiating circuit) (see Fig. 2.2).   The differentiating time constant RC is chosen to produce a moderately short pulse consistent with the

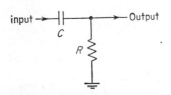

FIG. 2.2 RC differentiating circuit.

requirement that the pulse duration be long compared with the rise time. Time constants of 0.2 to 10 μsec are most common.   All of the other coupling time constants in the amplifier are made very long compared with the short differentiating time constant so that the resultant pulse (Fig. 2.1b) is unipolar.   The choice of the location of the single short differentiating (clipping) time constant is influenced by two more or less conflicting

[1] See Arts. 1.6 and 1.7.

requirements. Placing the clip at or near the amplifier output has the advantage that the low-frequency noise (hum, microphonics, flicker noise) generated in the early stages is attenuated. However, if the signals are allowed to pile up to a level approaching the dynamic signal range anywhere in the amplifier preceding the clip, then statistical fluctuations in the counting rate can drive the amplifier out of its linear range [1,3]. Signals appearing at the output well below amplifier-saturation amplitude can be considerably distorted if they occur in a statistical burst and the clip is too near the output. In a practical amplifier the location of the clipping circuit represents a compromise between the requirements of low noise and low pile-up.

In a high-gain amplifier designed to handle small input signals from pulse-ionization chambers, the clipping time constant is usually placed near the middle of the amplifier. In a lower-gain amplifier designed for scintillation counters, the clip may be near the input. In some cases the differentiation is accomplished by using a suitably small counter anode resistor or amplifier input grid-leak resistor. The clipping time constant is then determined by the product of the effective input-circuit resistance (anode resistor and grid-leak resistor in parallel) and the total input capacitance (counter plus amplifier). This arrangement has the advantage that the input resistance can have a conveniently low value; also, it permits the use of input circuitry with a small dynamic amplitude range without danger of pile-up overloading. However, it has a noise disadvantage which becomes quite important in the case of high-gain amplifiers and makes its use impractical with high-resolution pulse-ionization chambers. The resistor or Johnson noise is shown, in Art. 2.6, to vary inversely with the square root of the effective input resistance. For this reason, the input resistance in ionization-chamber amplifiers is made very large, often hundreds of megohms. In the case of scintillation-counter amplifiers, however, the Johnson noise, even with the worst possible value of input resistor, is usually found to be small compared to the statistical fluctuations in the signal.

Single-RC differentiation has two important disadvantages. The first, already considered, is that the clip can be in one place only and cannot simultaneously satisfy the requirements of minimum low-frequency noise and low-pile-up distortion. The second disadvantage results from the fact that an RC-coupled amplifier cannot, strictly speaking, deliver unipolar pulses. In other words, direct current does not flow through capacitors. If the signal is coupled through a capacitor to a linear load, the time integral of the positive parts of a long string of pulses must equal the integral of the negative parts. At low-duty ratios in a single-clipped amplifier, each signal is balanced by a small but very long undershoot. Because the undershoot is small, it is difficult to distinguish between the undershoot level and the average reference level. The signal height is then easily measured with respect to an apparently stable baseline reference (Fig. 2.3a). However, at high counting rates the undershoot level departs appreciably from the average output level to keep the positive and negative integrals equal (Fig. 2.3b). If the signal is measured with respect to an average reference base line, it is recorded as being smaller than at low counting rates. This variation in apparent signal height with counting rate is the second disadvantage of single clipping.

It should be mentioned that this second disadvantage can be at least partly ameliorated by using diode d-c restoration between the amplifier and the pulse-height analyzer. However, this is not often used because the diode establishes a base line at the peak negative noise level, effectively doubling the amplifier noise (including hum and microphonics). In addition, the diode nonlinearity at small-signal

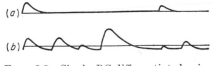

Fig. 2.3 Single-RC-differentiated signals: (a) at low counting rates and (b) at high counting rates.

levels presents a nonlinear load to the amplifier and may cause increased amplifier nonlinearity in the small-signal range.

Double-RC Differentiation. The disadvantages of single-RC differentiation can be overcome by employing two short time constants rather than one in the amplifier circuit. One clip can be placed at or near the input to prevent pile-up overloading. The second clip can be placed well along in the amplifier to eliminate hum and low-frequency noise.

The output signal has the general shape indicated in Fig. 2.1c. The exact shape is, of course, dependent on the relative values of the two short time constants and on their relation to the signal rise time. However, in all cases the signal is bipolar, and if the amplifier is linear, the area included under the positive part is exactly equal to the area under the negative part. For this reason the output-signal location with respect to the average reference base line does not vary with counting rate as it does with single-RC clipping.

However, double-RC differentiating also has some disadvantages. If one compares single- and double-clipped waveforms produced by comparable time constants, one finds that the second derivative of the voltage with respect to time in the neighborhood of the peak is greater with double clipping. That is, with double clipping the signal has a sharper peak. Because sharply peaked signals adversely affect the linearity of many amplifiers and pulse-height analyzers, it may be necessary to use longer RC time constants with double clipping than with single clipping. In addition, even with equal time constants, the presence of the undershoot makes the effective duration of a double-clipped signal greater than that of a single-clipped signal. To prevent pulses from being distorted by the tails of their neighbors, a lower counting-rate limit may have to be imposed with double clipping. This effect is somewhat offset by the fact that base-line displacement is now unimportant, so that in a practical case the upper counting-rate limit at which the spectral distortion is not excessive may be very similar.

It is possible to achieve some of the advantages of double-RC clipping without lengthening the pulse beyond that obtained with single-RC clipping, if the resistor in the second clip is paralleled by a d-c restoring

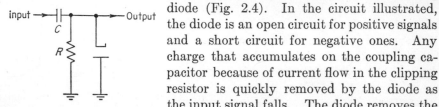

diode (Fig. 2.4). In the circuit illustrated, the diode is an open circuit for positive signals and a short circuit for negative ones. Any charge that accumulates on the coupling capacitor because of current flow in the clipping resistor is quickly removed by the diode as the input signal falls. The diode removes the undershoot so that it is not necessary to wait for it to decay. When this technique is employed, the second clip is usually at the amplifier output, and direct

Fig. 2.4 RC circuit with restoring diode.

coupling between the second clip and the pulse-height analyzer is customarily used to keep the base-line location independent of counting rate. Although the signal appears to end abruptly (Fig. 2.1d), it lasts (as far as signal-pile-up distortion is concerned) until diode conduction becomes negligible. This occurs when the corresponding single-clipped signal has decayed to a negligible value. Of course, as with single clipping, the d-c restoring diode restores the base line to the peak negative noise level rather than to the average signal level. When employing d-c restoration with double clipping, it is essential that the diode be in parallel with the clipping resistor immediately following the second clipping capacitor. If d-c restoration is attempted at a later point in the circuit, the diode will restore the base line to the peak-signal undershoot level and spurious pulses (Fig. 2.1e) will be generated.

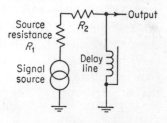

Fig. 2.5 Delay-line differentiating circuit. R_2 is chosen so that $R_1 + R_2$ is equal to the delay-line impedance.

Delay-line Differentiation. A delay line can be used in at least two different ways to convert a step function into a square wave of controlled duration. One way is to impress the signal on a short-circuited delay line from a source whose impedance matches the characteristic impedance of the delay line (Fig. 2.5). After a time interval equal to twice the propagation time of the line, the signal returns from the short-circuited end to cancel the signal at the input end. The accuracy of the cancellation depends upon the accuracy of the impedance match and the phase distortion and attenuation in the delay line. With care in the choice of terminating network to compensate for the inevitable lumped capacitance at the driving end, and to compensate, at least partially, for the phase distortion, the residual ringing signals observed with commercially available helically wound delay cables have been successfully reduced to a few per cent of the signal size. The pedestal or "rear porch" that

results from attenuation in the line (Fig. 2.6a) cannot be compensated for by the termination network. The height of the pedestal depends upon the resistance of the line and results from the fact that the reflected signal is attenuated by two trips through the line and is somewhat smaller than the input signal. The pedestal can be effectively eliminated by passing the signal through an appropriate RC differentiating circuit. The resultant signal (Fig. 2.6b) has no rear porch, but the signal top is no longer perfectly flat.

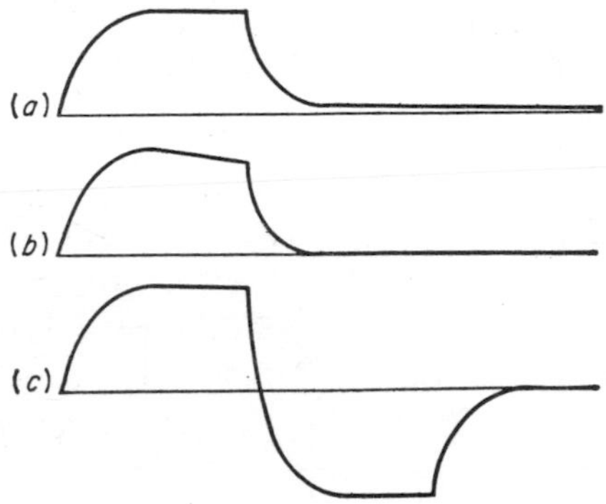

Another way of eliminating the rear porch is to subtract a suitable fraction of the unclipped signal from the clipped signal with a difference amplifier [4]. This is somewhat more complicated, but it has the advantage that the resultant signal retains its flat top.

An alternative technique for converting a step function into a square wave involves the use of a delay line terminated in its characteristic impedance at the receiving end and, preferably but not necessarily, at the sending end. The delayed signal is subtracted from the input signal in a difference amplifier. The input signal may be slightly attenuated at the difference-amplifier input to compensate for the attenuation of the delayed signal in the delay line (Fig. 2.7). This is another way of eliminating the rear porch without resorting to additional differentiation so that the output signal will retain its flat top. This arrangement has the further advantage that the delay line may be terminated at both ends, so that much poorer matches can be tolerated without producing excessive ringing. Of course, this technique involves the use of an additional active element, a difference amplifier, which must have good common mode rejection over a reasonable dynamic range if the output signal is to have no rear porch.

FIG. 2.6 Single-delay-line-differentiated signal: (a) showing "rear porch" due to delay-line attenuation and (b) with rear porch removed by RC differentiation. (c) Double-delay-line-differentiated signal.

The principal argument for using single-delay-line clipping over single-RC clipping is that, for a given degree of flatness in the neighborhood of the pulse peak, the delay-line-clipped signal may be considerably shorter. Where the pulse-height analyzer used requires a flat-topped pulse for good linearity, delay-line clipping is to be preferred unless the counting rates are low, in which case signals clipped with relatively long RC time constants can be used.

The arguments against the use of delay-line clipping are based on the extra complexity of the circuitry and the small residual ringing signals

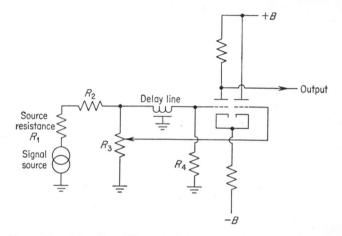

FIG. 2.7 Alternative delay-line differentiating circuit. The delay line is terminated at the receiving end by R_4 and at the sending end by the parallel combination of $(R_1 + R_2)$ and R_3. The tap on R_3 is adjusted to compensate for attenuation in the line.

due to the ever-present delay-line imperfections. An additional drawback may be a slight disadvantage with respect to signal-to-noise ratio. A delay-line-clipped signal is, in effect, the result of subtracting from the signal a delayed image of itself. Thus, in the clipping process the noise preceding the signal is "subtracted" from the noise superimposed on the signal. But since these two noise components are uncorrelated, they combine as the square root of the sum of the squares, regardless of whether they are "added" or "subtracted." If we assume that the noise is uniformly distributed in time, the mean value of the noise is multiplied by $\sqrt{2}$ when delay-line clipping is used.[1] In other respects

---

[1] The signal-to-noise ratio can often be improved by increasing the amplifier rise time with a suitable integrating time constant. If this time constant is comparable to the delay-line period, this simple analysis no longer applies. Under some circumstances it is possible to achieve a better signal-to-noise ratio with delay-line clipping than with RC clipping. For a more complete analysis see Ref. 9, pp. 72ff.

single-delay-line clipping and single-RC clipping give similar results. In both cases, the location of the base line is counting-rate dependent, and it is difficult to control pile-up overloading and low-frequency noise simultaneously.

Double-delay-line Differentiation. Applying delay-line clipping at two places in the amplifier results in a bipolar signal (see Fig. 2.6c) in which the positive and negative areas are equal [3,5]. The base-line location is independent of counting rate, and both pile-up overloading and low-frequency noise can be minimized.

Double-delay-line clipping has a slight additional advantage over double-RC clipping with respect to signal area balance in the overloaded condition. In a double-RC-clipped amplifier, the area balance fails when the amplifier is driven out of its linear range, with the result that the base-line location is no longer entirely independent of counting rate. A double-delay-line-clipped amplifier, on the other hand, can be designed so that the output stage limits for equal positive and negative excursions. This tends to maintain the area balance even in the overloaded condition, provided that the signal rise time is short compared to the length of the clipping lines. If the signal rise time is not short, however, the long tail on the trailing edge of the second half of the signal becomes emphasized in the overloaded condition and the area balance fails.

TABLE 2.1

Clipping	Pulse duration	Base-line dependence on counting rate	Pile-up over-loading	Low-frequency noise	Relative midband noise
Single RC..........	Medium	Varies	Difficult to prevent both		1
Double RC.........	Long	Independent	Low	Low	1
Single delay line....	Short	Varies	Difficult to prevent both		$\sqrt{2}$
Double delay line...	Medium	Independent	Low	Low	$\sqrt{6}$

Like double-RC clipping, double-delay-line clipping has some disadvantages. For a given degree of signal flatness, the double-delay-line-clipped signal is twice as long as the corresponding single-clipped signal. In addition, there is a noise disadvantage which is somewhat more severe than that associated with single-delay-line clipping, because the second clipping operation superimposes on the signal an additional noise component. This time, however, the additional noise component is partially correlated with the noise already present in the signal and is in phase with it, so that half of the additional noise adds linearly and half combines as the square root of the sum of the squares. As a result, with double-delay-line clipping the noise is increased by an additional factor of $\sqrt{3}$ with respect to that obtained with single-delay-line clipping and by an over-all factor of $\sqrt{6}$ with respect to RC clipping.

Table 2.1 summarizes the relative performances of the four clipping systems discussed with respect to effective pulse duration, dependence of base-line position on counting rate, distortion due to pile-up overloading, and amount of low-frequency and midband noise.

2.2 Amplification

In addition to its pulse-shaping function, the linear amplifier is called upon to increase the detector signal level to a value suitable for pulse-height analysis. Most pulse-height analyzers are voltage-sensitive devices, whereas radiation detectors produce impulses of charge. The gain of a linear amplifier connecting the two should, therefore, properly be expressed as a transfer elastance (reciprocal capacitance). Transistorized pulse-height analyzers are being built which are current-sensitive rather than voltage-sensitive. A linear amplifier connecting a detector to such an analyzer accepts coulombs and puts out amperes and therefore has a transfer characteristic which should be expressed in units of reciprocal time (sec^{-1}). However, the characteristics of linear amplifiers are almost never expressed in these forms. In deference to common usage, we shall express the gain of an amplifier as a dimensionless ratio and consider the conversion of charge to voltage, or charge to current, as a separate property of the amplifier input circuit.

Those characteristics of linear amplifiers that determine their suitability in pulse spectrometers are gain, speed of response, linearity, equivalent input noise, gain stability, maximum output-signal amplitude, and overload tolerance. The relative importance of these characteristics depends, of course, upon the application. In an alpha-particle spectrometer using a Frisch grid ionization chamber, low amplifier noise and high gain stability are of primary importance if the system is to achieve high resolution. Overload tolerance is relatively unimportant because alpha particles produced in radioactive decay have a restricted energy range, and unwanted signals from other radiations (e.g., beta and gamma rays) are usually much smaller than the alpha pulses. In a gamma-ray-scintillation spectrometer, on the other hand, the signals are usually large compared to amplifier noise, and the inherent resolution of the detector is not very high, so that amplifier noise is relatively unimportant. However, the range of signal amplitudes may be very large, particularly with large scintillating crystals. If low-energy gamma rays are to be studied in the presence of much higher energy radiation, the amplifier must be designed so that large signals will not give rise to spurious secondary signals, or block the amplifier, or displace its base line for long periods. It is probably possible to design an amplifier with sufficient flexibility for it to be used in all types of pulse spectrometers. Such an amplifier would have high gain and a wide-range attenuator to accommodate it to both large and small input signals, plus low noise, excellent stability and linearity, high maximum output (100 to 200 volts), ability to withstand large overload factors (of the order of 1,000) without paralysis, high inherent speed with a rise time control to reduce the noise bandwidth when used with slow detectors, and a number of possible clipping configurations. Needless to say, an amplifier of this type would be costly and more complicated than necessary for many applications. An alternative is to design a special-purpose amplifier for each application. This is satisfactory for a laboratory engaged in one or a few types of routine measurements over a long period of time. A more practical alternative for a research laboratory is a general-purpose high-output-level, nonparalyzing, low-gain amplifier associated with a set of preamplifiers designed for the various applications of interest. A high-gain, low-noise preamplifier for ionization chambers and proportional counters and a cathode-follower preamplifier for scintillation counters are sufficient for most alpha-, beta-, and gamma-ray pulse-height spectrometers.

2.3 Input Circuits

The function of a linear amplifier input circuit is to transform the detector charge into a voltage or current signal for further amplification. A voltage signal proportional to the detector charge is obtained by integrating the detector current on a small capacitor. The capacitor is made as small as possible in order to make the voltage signal large compared to amplifier noise and to reduce the amount of subsequent amplification required. This implies that the first amplifier stage must be as close to the detector as possible in order to minimize the stray capacitance associated with the connecting wiring. It is often inconvenient to put the whole linear amplifier near the detector, because experimental conditions frequently dictate that the detector be in a crowded or inaccessible location. Usual practice is to build the first amplifier stage as a small preamplifier mounted close to the detector and connected to the main amplifier with a suitably long coaxial cable. The interconnecting cable may be terminated at either or both ends in its characteristic impedance, or it may be left unmatched. In general, if the signal propagation time in the cable is small compared with the rise time of the detector-amplifier combination, it is not necessary to terminate the cable. It may then be considered as a lumped capacitance. So that the cable capacitance will not reduce the speed of response of the system, it is usual to make the circuit impedance at one or both ends of the cable sufficiently low so that the resultant RC time constant is short compared with the system rise time.   If the interconnecting cable is quite long, so that the propagation time is comparable to the system rise time, it is normal practice to terminate the cable in its characteristic impedance at at least one end to prevent reflections from producing spurious rings or, in the case of very long cables, satellite pulses following the main pulses.   In any case, the impedance of the interconnecting circuit is relatively low, and the preamplifier must be capable of driving this low impedance over the full range of input signals, without allowing pile-up distortion due to statistical bursts.[1]

Cathode Followers.   Frequently, a simple cathode-follower circuit (Fig. 2.8) is a suitable preamplifier.   The detector charge Q is integrated on the small input capacitance C associated with the detector and the

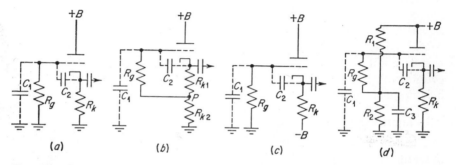

Fig. 2.8   Cathode-follower preamplifier circuits.   (a) and (b) are relatively unstable. (a) is limited to a small dynamic signal range.   (c) and (d) are preferred configurations.

cathode-follower grid circuit, producing a signal pulse $V = Q/C$.   If a high-performance tube is used, the output impedance of the cathode follower (equal to the reciprocal of the tube transconductance) is sufficiently low to drive the interconnecting cable without serious loss in signal amplitude.   For example, if the tube has a transconductance of 10,000 μmhos, the cathode-follower output impedance is 100 ohms and the circuit will drive a 100-ohm-terminated cable with a signal attenuation of only a factor of 2.

The input capacitance of a cathode-follower preamplifier is made up of two components C_1 and C_2 (Fig. 2.8). C_1 is a composite of the detector output electrode capacitance to ground plus the grid-to-plate capacitance of the cathode follower plus stray wiring and socket capacitances to ground. C_2 is the grid-to-cathode capacitance of the cathode follower.   The division of signal charge between C_1 and C_2 depends upon the cathode-follower gain.   The low-frequency gain of a triode cathode

[1] See Art. 2.1 above.

follower is easily shown to be

$$G = \frac{\mu R_L}{(1 + \mu)R_L + r_p} \qquad (2.1)$$

where μ is the amplification factor of the tube, r_p is its dynamic plate resistance, and R_L is the net cathode load resistance. If μ is large compared to 1, the expression can be rewritten

$$G \approx \frac{R_L}{R_L + 1/g_m} = \frac{g_m R_L}{g_m R_L + 1} \qquad (2.2)$$

where g_m is the tube transconductance.

Let us consider the total detector charge Q to be made up of two parts, Q_1 and Q_2, where Q_1 is the charge on C_1 and Q_2 is the charge on C_2. The cathode-follower input voltage V_1 is then Q_1/C_1 and the output voltage $V_o = GV_1$. The voltage across C_2 is $V_2 = V_1 - V_o = (1 - G)V_1$. Therefore

$$Q_2 = C_2 V_2 = C_2(1 - G)V_1 = \frac{C_2(1 - G)Q_1}{C_1} \qquad (2.3)$$

and the ratio of the two charge components is

$$\frac{Q_2}{Q_1} = \frac{(1 - G)C_2}{C_1} \qquad (2.4)$$

Combining Eqs. (2.2) and (2.4) we get

$$\frac{Q_2}{Q_1} = \frac{C_2}{C_1(g_m R_L + 1)} \qquad (2.5)$$

In practical preamplifiers, C_1 and C_2 are usually comparable in value so that, if $g_m R_L$ is large compared to 1 (and the gain, therefore, very nearly equal to 1), Q_2 is negligible compared with Q_1. However, if the interstage impedance is low, $g_m R_L$ is not large compared to 1 and both the gain and the effective input-signal amplitude, V_1, are dependent upon g_m. Therefore, if the charge-to-voltage conversion factor of the preamplifier is to be stable, it is necessary to keep the transconductance of the cathode-follower tube constant.

Figure 2.8a is a simple but rather unsatisfactory cathode-follower preamplifier circuit. With a high-mu tube and reasonable plate supply voltage the quiescent self-bias voltage drop across the cathode resistor R_k will not be more than a few volts. The maximum negative output signal cannot exceed the bias voltage because the cathode current cannot reverse its direction. This bias voltage, therefore, represents an upper limit to the permissible voltage excursion at the input before pile-up distortion occurs, and the practical limit is even smaller because the cathode follower becomes quite nonlinear near cutoff. Furthermore, the voltage across the cathode resistor is not very large compared to grid-cathode contact potential variations that result from small changes in filament voltage. Filament voltage changes are, therefore, accompanied by appreciable cathode current changes. The transconductance of vacuum tubes varies with the cathode current. Therefore, the gain and effective input-signal size are both sensitive to filament voltage changes.

The cathode follower of Fig. 2.8b is less likely to cause pile-up distortion. If R_{k2} is large compared with R_{k1}, the cathode follower can deliver quite large negative signals before it cuts off. However, circuit b is no better than circuit a with respect to gain stability, because only R_{k1} is effective in stabilizing the cathode current against filament voltage changes.

Cathode followers c and d are to be preferred to a and b. In addition to having a large dynamic signal range (because of the large voltage drop in R_k) they also have superior gain stability, because contact potential changes are small compared to the drop in the large cathode biasing resistor. Circuit c is used when positive and negative power supply voltages are available while circuit d is used when there is no negative supply. In circuit d, bypass capacitor C_3 keeps noise, associated with statistical fluctuations in the voltage-divider current, out of the signal circuit.

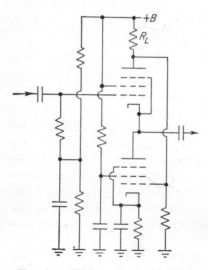

FIG. 2.9 White cathode follower.

The effective charge integrating capacitance in all four cathode-follower circuits is equal to $C_1 + C_2(1 - G)$. The integrating time constant is determined by this capacitance and the effective input resistance. In circuits a, c, and d the input resistance is the parallel combination of the counter anode resistor (not shown) and the grid-leak resistor R_g. In circuit b, because both ends of R_g move with the signal, its effective value is increased by the factor $1/(1 - G')$, where G' is the gain of the cathode follower from the input grid to point P.

Figure 2.9 shows the White cathode-follower circuit [6], which has the advantages of lower output resistance than the circuits of Fig. 2.8, combined with the ability to deliver large negative signals to low-impedance loads.   The output resistance is easily shown to be $1/g_{m_1}g_{m_2}R_L$ and, with ordinary receiving tubes, can be as low as 10 to 20 ohms.   The circuit differs from other cathode followers in that it can deliver a signal current of negative polarity which is larger than the quiescent cathode current. . As the current falls in the upper tube, a positive signal appears across R_L which causes the lower tube to conduct heavily, thus making a large additional load current available.

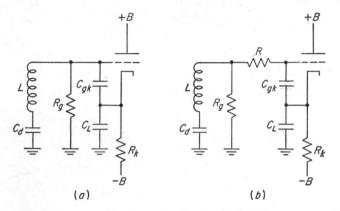

FIG. 2.10   High-frequency equivalent circuit of cathode-follower preamplifier.   (*a*) is likely to oscillate.   (*b*) does not oscillate because of damping resistor R.

All cathode-follower circuits (and the White cathode follower in particular) tend toward instability when driven from a high-impedance source and connected to a capacitive load.   Figure 2.10*a* shows a cathode follower with the stray reactances that contribute to this instability. C_L is the load capacitance, C_{gk} is the grid-to-cathode capacitance of the tube, C_d is the detector plus wiring capacitance, and L is the inductance associated with the lead connecting the detector to the grid.   When drawn this way, the circuit is seen to bear a striking resemblance to the series-tuned Colpitts or Clapp oscillator circuit [7] which oscillates at the resonant frequency of the tank circuit determined by inductance L and the series equivalent of C_d, C_L, and C_{gk}.   These oscillations are usually prevented by including a small resistor R (Fig. 2.10*b*) in series with the grid, which reduces the Q of the tank circuit.   A resistance of about 100 ohms is usually enough to stabilize ordinary cathode-follower circuits, but a White cathode follower, because of its higher gain, may require 1,000 ohms or more.

Integrators.   An alternative input circuit described by Kelly [5] is in the form of an operational integrator like those used in analog computers. The circuit (Fig. 2.11) employs an amplifier pentode and a cathode follower which applies negative feedback via a small capacitor C_f to the input grid. The signal charge Q divides into two parts, Q_i and Q_f. Q_f is the signal charge component that appears across the feedback capacitor C_f, and Q_i is the component that remains on the net input capacitance C_i.

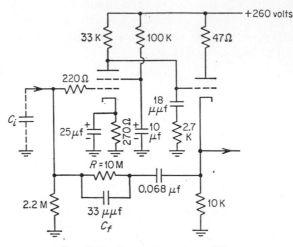

FIG. 2.11 Integrator preamplifier.

If V_i and V_o represent the amplifier input and output voltages, respectively, then $V_i = Q_i/C_i$ and $V_o = -GV_i$, where G is the amplifier gain. The voltage across the feedback capacitor C_f is $V_i - V_o$, so that

$$Q_f = C_f(V_i - V_o) = C_f V_i(1 + G) \qquad (2.6)$$

and

$$Q_i = C_i V_i \qquad (2.7)$$

from which

$$\frac{Q_f}{Q_i} = \frac{C_f}{C_i}(1 + G) \qquad (2.8)$$

Thus, it is seen that, if C_f and C_i are comparable and G is large, Q_f is large compared with Q_i and nearly all of the input charge appears on C_f. Furthermore, if G is large, V_o is large compared to V_i and the output voltage is very nearly equal to the voltage across the feedback capacitor, so that

$$V_o \approx \frac{Q_f}{C_f} \approx \frac{Q}{C_f} \qquad (2.9)$$

Provided that G is large, the input-circuit charge-to-voltage conversion factor is independent of the tube parameters and the relatively uncertain stray input capacitance and depends only on the feedback capacitance, which is easily made quite stable. The resistor R across the feedback capacitor allows it to discharge between signals, so that the output signal decays exponentially with a time constant RC_f.

A similar circuit configuration designed by Goulding [8] (Fig. 2.12) is an excellent preamplifier for transistorized linear amplifiers.[1] The circuit of Fig. 2.12 is a charge integrator like Fig. 2.11, and the same arguments can be used to show that nearly all of the input charge appears

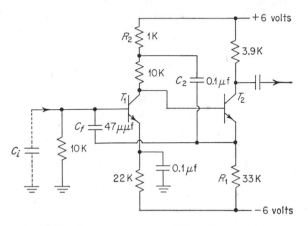

FIG. 2.12   Integrator preamplifier using transistors.

on the feedback capacitor C_f and that the voltage at the emitter of T_2 is approximately Q/C_f [see Eq. (2.9)]. This voltage can be used as the preamplifier output to drive the next amplifier stage, provided that it is a high-input-impedance, voltage-sensitive stage. More commonly, however, the next stage is a low-input-impedance, current-sensitive stage, so the preamplifier output is usually taken from the collector of T_2. The collector current of T_2 is very nearly (neglecting base current) equal to the emitter voltage divided by the emitter circuit resistance. In Goulding's circuit there is a "bootstrap" connection between the emitter of T_2 and the collector load resistor of T_1 via capacitor C_2 which increases the effective collector load resistance of T_1 and, therefore, increases the feedback-loop internal gain. The effective resistance in the emitter circuit of T_2 is, therefore, the parallel combination of R_2 and R_1, but because R_2 is very much the smaller of the two, it is very nearly equal to R_2. The output current is, therefore,

$$i_o \approx \frac{Q}{R_2 C_f} \tag{2.10}$$

[1] Emitter followers (the transistor analog of cathode followers) have been used for input circuits, but they are not as satisfactory as cathode followers because of the low and nonlinear base input resistance of transistors and because of the relatively large base-emitter diffusion capacitance.

2.4   Feedback Loops

All linear amplifiers intended for quantitative spectroscopy are made up of one or more negative feedback loops. Negative feedback increases the amplifier gain stability and linearity by reducing the dependence of gain on the transconductance of the tubes or transistors. Suppose that an amplifier without feedback has a voltage gain K (see Fig. 2.13) and that a fraction β of the output signal V_o is fed back to the input,

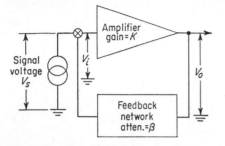

opposite in phase to the input signal V_s, so that the net signal voltage at the amplifier input V_i may be written

$$V_i = V_s - \beta V_o \qquad (2.11)$$

Since $V_o = KV_i$, Eq. (2.11) can be rewritten

Fig. 2.13   Block diagram of a negative feedback loop.

$$\frac{V_o}{K} = V_s - \beta V_o \qquad (2.12)$$

from which
$$KV_s = V_o(1 + \beta K) \qquad (2.13)$$

The gain with feedback G is then

$$G = \frac{V_o}{V_s} = \frac{K}{1 + \beta K} \qquad (2.14)$$

If the gain without feedback K is sufficiently large to make the product βK large compared to 1, then the gain with feedback may be written approximately

$$G \approx \frac{1}{\beta} \qquad (2.15)$$

Although K is dependent upon the transconductance of the active amplifier elements, the feedback factor β is determined by passive linear components. If the amplifier has a large reserve gain (βK product), the gain with feedback is seen to depend only on the linear and stable feedback factor β and is independent of the relatively unstable and often nonlinear transconductance values.

In addition to improving amplifier gain stability and linearity, negative feedback increases the amplifier bandwidth because G remains nearly constant at all frequencies at which βK is large compared to 1, even though, at high and low frequencies, K may be much less than it is in the midband region. These advantages of negative feedback are, of course, not without cost. They are purchased at the expense of decreased amplifier gain. Furthermore, the advantages of increased stability, linearity, and bandwidth are not simultaneously realized. At the extremes of the frequency passband, the reserve gain is not large compared to 1, so that the stability and linearity for signals having either high- or low-frequency components are not significantly improved by negative feedback. The ideal linear amplifier, therefore, has adequate bandwidth for the input-signal frequency spectrum before negative feedback is applied. The application of negative feedback to such an amplifier can very substantially improve both the gain stability and the linearity.

A negative feedback loop may contain a single stage of amplification or it may contain many stages. It is, in general, easier to achieve large

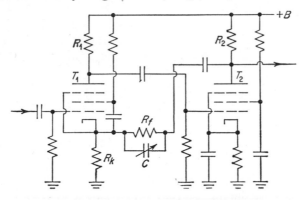

Fig. 2.14   Two-tube feedback loop.

values of reserve gain in loops composed of many stages than in loops containing only one or a few stages. One might, therefore, expect that the most stable design for a linear amplifier which must achieve a specified gain with a specified number of active elements would be a single feedback loop containing all of the active elements. Unfortunately, however, feedback loops that contain a large number of active elements invariably oscillate unless severe artificial bandwidth restrictions are imposed.[1] Most linear amplifier feedback loops are, therefore, built with two or three tubes or transistors, although some contain more.

Figure 2.14 is a practical two-tube feedback loop. The net amplifier input signal V_i is the signal V_s minus a fraction of the output signal fed

[1] If the sum of the phase lags around the loop produced by stray capacitance equals 180° at a frequency at which the loop gain equals or exceeds 1, the loop will oscillate. If the number of tubes in the loop is large, each phase shift can be small and can be associated with only a small loss in loop gain when the sum of the phase lags is 180°. With only a few tubes in the loop, the loss in gain associated with the large phase shifts necessary to add to 180° usually reduces the loop gain to less than 1, so that oscillation cannot occur.

back to the cathode of T_1 via the feedback voltage divider R_f and R_k. The feedback factor β is $R_k/(R_k + R_f)$. The calculation of the gain without feedback K proceeds in the usual way for pentode amplifiers, except that allowance must be made for the cathode degeneration[1] in T_1 due to the resistance of the feedback divider and for the loading effect of the divider at the plate of T_2. The feedback divider resistance presented to the cathode of T_1 is the parallel combination of R_k and $(R_f + R_2)$. If the loop is designed for reasonably high gain, R_k alone is a good approximation for the degenerating resistance. The effective load resistance in the anode circuit of T_2 is R_2 in parallel with $(R_k + R_f)$. Again, if the gain is reasonably high, R_k may be neglected with respect to R_f, so that the effective anode load resistance may be written $R_2R_f/(R_2 + R_f)$. In linear amplifiers for nuclear applications the dynamic plate resistance of pentodes may always be neglected with respect to the much lower anode load resistances that are used to achieve reasonable bandwidth.[2] The gain without feedback may, therefore, be written

$$K = \frac{g_{m_1}R_1}{1 + g_{m_1}R_k} \frac{g_{m_2}R_2R_f}{R_2 + R_f} \tag{2.16}$$

From this the βK product can be evaluated. If it is large compared to 1, the gain with feedback is given by Eq. (2.15). If it is not large compared to 1, the gain with feedback is more accurately obtained from Eq. (2.14).

In the midband frequency range, the signal fed back to the cathode of T_1 is in phase with the input signal V_s, so that the net input signal V_i is their algebraic difference. However, at high frequencies the feedback signal suffers a phase lag due to stray capacitance to ground at the two pentode plates and at the cathode of T_1, so that to determine V_i one must calculate the vector difference between V_s and the feedback signal. At some frequency, the phase lag in the feedback signal is 180° and the feedback is regenerative rather than degenerative. If, at this frequency, the complex βK product has a value equal to or greater than 1, the circuit will oscillate. Even if the βK product is less than 1, the gain at this frequency may be noticeably enhanced so that the transient response of the feedback loop to a step input voltage will include a damped oscilla-

[1] Cathode degeneration is the reduction in gain of an amplifier stage due to the presence of an unbypassed cathode resistor. Signal current flowing in the cathode resistor produces an IR drop which must be subtracted from the input signal to obtain the effective grid-cathode signal.

[2] The upper cutoff frequency of an amplifier stage that does not have inductive peaking is equal to $1/(2\pi RC)$, where C is the total stray capacitance from anode to ground, including the input capacitance of the next stage, and R is the anode load resistor. Since C cannot be reduced indefinitely, wideband amplifiers must employ small anode resistors.

tion (Fig. 2.15). These oscillatory tendencies are usually controlled by a small trimmer capacitor C in parallel with the feedback resistor (Fig. 2.14). This capacitor introduces a phase advance to the feedback at high frequencies to compensate for the phase lags at the plates.

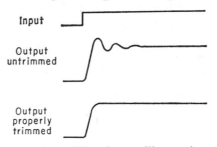

The capacitor is usually adjusted empirically to that value which results in a minimum output-signal rise time without overshoot (Fig. 2.15).

In the two-tube feedback loop of Fig. 2.14, if the gain without feedback is to be large, it is necessary that R_k be small and R_f be large [see Eq. (2.16)]. This implies a small value of the feedback factor. It follows, therefore, that in this circuit it is difficult to achieve a large

Fig. 2.15 Waveforms illustrating proper and improper adjustment of trimmer capacitor in a negative feedback loop.

reserve gain (βK). The three-tube circuit of Fig. 2.16 allows more freedom in design. The cathode follower T_3 can drive a low-resistance feedback divider, which introduces very little cathode degeneration at T_1, without loading the plate circuit of T_2. This circuit also has lower

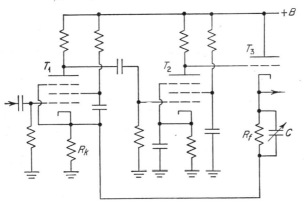

Fig. 2.16   Three-tube negative feedback loop.

output impedance than the two-tube loop of Fig. 2.14 and is, therefore, capable of driving larger values of stray capacitance without serious loss in speed of response. If the feedback-divider resistances are judiciously chosen, it may be possible to neglect cathode degeneration at T_1 with a divider resistance still sufficiently large that the gain of the cathode follower is close to 1. The gain without feedback is then

$$K = g_{m_1} R_1 g_{m_2} R_2 \qquad (2.17)$$

The trimmer capacitor across the feedback resistor performs the same function as the one in the two-tube loop and is adjusted in the same way.

Figure 2.17 shows a two-transistor feedback loop, designed by Goulding [8], to follow the input integrator circuit of Fig. 2.12. It is a current-sensitive circuit which employs current feedback from the emitter of T_2 to the base of T_1 via R_f. If we neglect the base current in T_2 so that the output current is considered to be very nearly equal to the emitter current of T_2, the current feedback factor is that fraction of the emitter current that flows in R_f. The net resistance in the emitter circuit of T_2 is the parallel combination of R_3, R_f, and R_1 (because of the "bootstrap" connection to the collector circuit of T_1). For the values shown in the circuit this parallel combination is approximately equal to R_1, so that the current feedback factor may be written

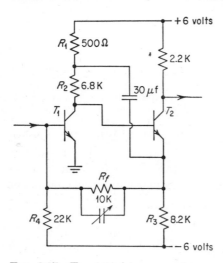

$$\beta \approx \frac{R_1}{R_f} \qquad (2.18)$$

FIG. 2.17 Two-transistor current-amplifying feedback loop.

The bootstrap connection serves to increase the effective value of the collector load resistance at T_1 so that nearly all of the signal current from T_1 flows in the base circuit of T_2. The unfedback current gain K is, therefore, the product of the current transfer ratios of the two transistors. As with the vacuum-tube circuits, if the βK product is large compared to 1, the gain with feedback is $1/\beta$. The trimmer capacitor performs the same function as in the tube circuits.

2.5 Overload

The largest signal from a nuclear detector may frequently be more than a hundred times as large as the smallest signal of interest, and, occasionally, with large scintillation counters the ratio may be more than a thousand. If the amplitude distribution of the small signals is to be studied, the larger signals must not be allowed to interfere with the measurement. The large signals will, of course, drive the amplifier to saturation, but if the amplifier recovers quickly from the overload pulses, the measurement of the small pulses will be undistorted. If, however, the large pulses lead to extensive amplifier paralysis followed by a slow recovery to the quiescent level, smaller pulses occurring during the recovery interval will not be measured correctly and those occurring during the paralysis interval will be lost altogether.

The principal cause of overload paralysis and slow recovery is grid conduction during the positive part of the overload signals. In Fig. 2.18, grid current in T_2 rapidly charges the interstage coupling capacitor via the low impedance of the forward-biased grid-cathode diode and the plate load resistor R_L. After the signal decays, the coupling capacitor must discharge through the grid-leak resistor R_g, and this may be many times larger than the charging resistance. The discharge interval, during which the amplifier reference base line is displaced from its quiescent value, may be very much longer than the duration of the overload pulse.

Linear amplifiers in current use employ a number of techniques to prevent these overload difficulties. One simple solution is to use very small anode load resistors so that the largest possible signal produced at the anode when the tube is driven to cutoff is smaller than the grid bias of the succeeding stage. Unfortunately, this is a severe design restriction because, with such small anode load resistors, it is difficult to obtain much gain per stage. An alternative arrangement is to make the anode load resistors very large and the grid-leak resistors much smaller. If the grid-leak resistor is negligibly small compared with the anode load resistor, the resistance of the coupling capacitor charging circuit is essentially that of the anode load resistor and the charging resistance does not change significantly when the grid conducts. The stage gain is, of course, determined by the effective anode load, which is

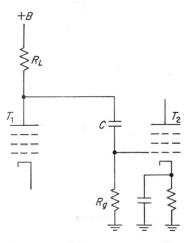

FIG. 2.18　RC interstage coupling network.

the parallel combination of R_L and R_g. This effective resistance can have a reasonable value by proper choice of R_g. A disadvantage of this arrangement is that a very high plate supply voltage is required if the plate current is to be reasonably large. Also, the high power dissipation in the large load resistors can make the amplifier run hot, increasing the drift and decreasing the life of the amplifier components.

Another technique for solving the overload problem involves the use of catching diodes at the anodes to limit the positive voltage swing to values less than the grid bias of the succeeding stages. The anode load resistors can then be large enough for reasonable stage gains without danger of grid-current charging of the coupling capacitors.   Figure 2.19 shows a circuit of this kind in which a cathode follower T_1 provides a low-impedance catching voltage for the limiting diodes.   In this circuit two diodes are used.   One limits the positive voltage excursions, and the other limits the negative signals.   If only the positive signals were limited, the signals, under overload conditions, could be grossly asymmetrical and, at high counting rates, might have a large average value which would alter the bias of the following stage.   The cathode-follower cathode potential automatically adjusts itself to a value a few volts

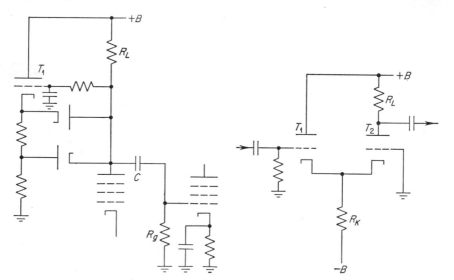

FIG. 2.19 Circuit for limiting anode voltage swing to prevent grid-current paralysis in coupling network.

FIG. 2.20 "Long-tailed-pair" amplifier.

positive with respect to the anode.   This arrangement is to be preferred to one using a fixed catching power supply because it would be difficult to control the anode current with sufficient precision to keep the quiescent anode potential within a few volts of the catching power supply potential.

Still another popular technique for avoiding overload difficulties makes use of "long-tailed-pair" amplifier stages (LTP) instead of pentodes. An LTP amplifier can be thought of as a cathode follower driving a grounded grid amplifier (Fig. 2.20).   The large common cathode resistor R_k (R_k is the "long tail" of the LTP) goes to a moderately high negative power supply voltage (of the order of 100 volts) and determines the total cathode current, which divides approximately evenly between the two tubes.   A negative input signal reduces the current in T_1 so that the common cathode potential drops and the current in T_2 increases. R_k is generally sufficiently large so that the current change in T_2 is almost exactly the same as the current change in T_1. The signal current in T_2 produces an amplified negative output signal at the plate of T_2. Unlike most other amplifier stages, the LTP does not produce signal phase inversion. If the negative input signal is very large, T_1 cuts off and all of its current transfers to T_2, producing a limited negative output signal. If the input signal is positive, current transfers from T_2 to T_1, producing an amplified positive output signal. A very large positive input signal causes all of the current in T_2 to transfer to T_1, after which T_1 becomes an unloaded cathode follower with a large cathode resistor. Such a cathode follower has a gain of nearly unity. As the grid goes positive, the cathode goes along with it, and very large positive signals are required before the grid is driven positive with respect to the cathode. It is easy to design

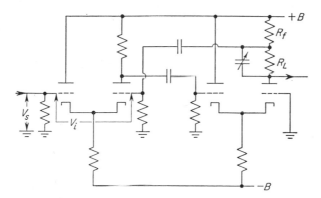

FIG. 2.21 Negative feedback loop using two LTP amplifiers.

an LTP stage such that the largest positive signal that T_2 can deliver (corresponding to the transfer of all the current in T_2 to T_1) is not large enough to cause grid current to flow in a similar LTP stage following it.

LTP amplifiers readily lend themselves to inclusion in negative feedback loops. Figure 2.21 shows such a loop in which negative feedback is applied to the otherwise idle right-hand grid of the first pair. This pair can then be thought of as a difference amplifier in which the signal at the plate of T_2 is proportional to the difference between the signals at G_1 and G_2 and is relatively insensitive to common mode signals (i.e., equal signals of the same polarity at both grids). Common mode rejection results from the fact that equal signals on both grids do not cause current to transfer between the two tubes, and if R_k is large, the total cathode current changes very little with potential of the two grids. The net feedback-loop input signal V_i can therefore be considered as the difference between the signal V_s and the signal fed back to G_2. If the loop reserve gain is large, V_i is small and the feedback signal is very nearly equal to V_s. The output signal is then $V_s(R_L + R_f)/R_f$. The trimmer capacitor across R_L performs the usual function.

LTP amplifiers are usually built with triodes rather than pentodes. Because the left-hand tube has no anode resistor, the grid-to-plate capacitance does not suffer Miller effect multiplication.[1] It is not necessary, therefore, to screen the grid from the plate in order to achieve good high-frequency performance.

2.6   Noise

The random addition of amplifier noise to the detector signals increases the uncertainty in the measurement of the amplitude of these signals and therefore decreases the resolution of the spectrometer. Its importance depends upon the relative size of the signal with respect to the noise (signal-to-noise ratio) and the uncertainties in the signal amplitude due to other causes (principally the statistical uncertainty in the number of ion pairs produced in the detector, and in the detector amplification, if any). It is not our intention to pursue the subject of noise in great detail because this has been done very well elsewhere.[2] We shall merely list the principal components of the composite noise signal together with the amplifier parameters that determine their size.

Resistor or Johnson Noise. The thermal motion of electrons gives rise to the generation of a noise voltage E in all resistors, which is governed by the relation

$$E^2 = 4kTR\,\Delta f \tag{2.19}$$

where k is Boltzmann's constant (1.381×10^{-23} joule per °K), T is the absolute temperature in degrees Kelvin, R is the resistance in ohms, and Δf defines the frequency bandwidth in which the noise is measured. In a linear amplifier connected to a nuclear detector, the dominant source of Johnson noise is the effective input resistance determined by the parallel combination of the detector load resistor and the amplifier grid-leak resistor. Pulse-shaping considerations dictate that this effective input resistance be always large compared to the reactance of the input capaci-

---

[1] If an amplifier stage has a gain G, the voltage across the grid-to-plate capacitance is equal to the input signal multiplied by $(1 + G)$. The charge that must be supplied to this capacitor by the driving circuit is, therefore, $(1 + G)$ times as great as the charge that would flow into an equal capacitance to ground. From the point of view of the driving circuit, the plate-to-grid capacitance is multiplied by $(1 + G)$ and this multiplication is generally referred to as the Miller effect.

[2] The sources of noise in linear amplifiers and their effect on the performance of nuclear pulse spectrometers are discussed very thoroughly in Ref. 9 and more briefly in Ref. 1.

tance C in the frequency range passed by the amplifier. The voltage-divider action of this RC network causes the net noise voltage at the amplifier input E_i to be proportional to E/R. Since E is proportional to $\sqrt{R}$, E_i is proportional to $1/\sqrt{R}$, so that Johnson noise can be reduced to any extent desired by increasing the effective input resistance.

Significant Johnson noise can be generated in grid parasitic suppressing resistors and unbypassed cathode resistors. With reasonably small values of these resistors, however, the associated noise is usually negligible.

Shot Noise. Statistical fluctuations in the cathode current of the amplifier input tube give rise to a noise component in the plate signal called shot noise. When the smoothing effect of the space-charge cloud surrounding the cathode is taken into account, it is found that the effective shot noise, referred to the input grid, is inversely proportional to the transconductance of the input tube. Shot noise is, therefore, minimized by using a high-transconductance tube at the amplifier input.

Partition Noise. If the amplifier input tube is a pentode, the cathode current divides between the plate and the screen, and the statistical fluctuations in this division give rise to partition noise. In most pentodes partition noise is several times as large as shot noise. For this reason, when low noise is important, the amplifier input tube is usually a triode (or a triode-connected pentode).

Grid-current Noise. Linear amplifier tubes are always operated with the grid negative with respect to the cathode, so that the grid current is relatively small. Nevertheless, statistical fluctuations in this small grid current may produce a significant amount of noise. The net grid current is made up of components from several sources: (1) cathode electrons emitted with sufficient energy to overcome the grid bias; (2) positive-ion current due to residual gas in the tube; (3) electrons emitted by the grid due to heating by radiation from the cathode; (4) photoelectrons emitted by the grid due to light from the cathode or other sources; (5) photoelectrons emitted by the grid due to bombardment by soft X rays emitted by the plate because of its bombardment by cathode electrons.

The first component is opposite in polarity to the other four, so that it is possible, by suitably adjusting the grid potential, to make the net grid current zero. Unfortunately, however, the opposing grid-current components contribute independently to grid-current noise so that, although the net grid current is zero, the grid-current noise is not.

Component 1 can be reduced by increasing the grid bias. Components 2 and 5 can be reduced by decreasing the operating plate voltage because this lessens the probability of ionizing residual gas and decreases the energy of the plate X rays. Unfortunately, both of these adjustments reduce the tube transconductance and, therefore, increase the shot noise, so that the final choice of operating point must represent a compromise between the conflicting requirements of low grid current and high trans-conductance.   Grid-current components 3 and 4 are usually unimportant in tubes in which the grids have a high work function.   Tubes with gold-plated grids are usually the best choice.

Shot noise and partition noise are uniformly distributed over the frequency spectrum.   In linear amplifiers the currents due to Johnson noise and grid-current noise flow in the predominantly capacitive input circuit.   Because the reactance of the input circuit decreases linearly with frequency, the input voltage resulting from Johnson noise and grid-current noise also decreases linearly with frequency.

Flicker Effect.   An additional noise component, the cause of which is not well understood, is often observed in amplifier circuits.   The power associated with this noise component is seen to vary inversely with frequency, and the voltage therefore varies inversely with the square root of the frequency.   For want of a better name, it is called flicker noise.   Flicker noise is usually unimportant at frequencies above a few kilocycles.   A judicious choice and location of amplifier clipping time constants can usually make flicker noise negligible.

Hum and Microphonics.   Hum and microphonics are disturbing signals at specific frequencies.   Hum is observed at power-line frequency and at its harmonics and results from poorly filtered power supplies or pickup from the filament supply.   It can be reduced by improving the power supply filtering, by twisting and shielding the filament supply lines, and by using tubes in which the grid is well shielded from the filament. Because it is primarily a low-frequency disturbance, it can also be reduced by proper location of the clipping circuits.

Microphonics result from the resonant vibration of tube elements, and occasionally other circuit components, caused by mechanical or acoustical disturbances.   They can be reduced by shock-mounting the offending elements or the entire amplifier.   Microphonics are unimportant above the audio range, so that they, too, can be controlled by proper location of clipping circuits.

Transistor Noise.   Transistors have noise sources analogous to those in vacuum tubes, but their relative importance is quite different.   While in vacuum-tube circuits the grid current is nearly always very small compared with the plate current, in transistor circuits the base current is not nearly so small compared with the collector current.   In transistorized linear amplifiers, therefore, base-current noise dominates all others.   It varies with frequency much the same as does grid-current noise in vacuum-tube amplifiers.   It can be reduced by operating the input transistor at a low value of base current, provided that this does not decrease the transconductance excessively.

REFERENCES

1. Elmore, W., and M. Sands: "Electronics," pp. 124ff., McGraw-Hill Book Company, Inc., New York, 1949.
2. Jordan, W., and P. Bell: A General Purpose Linear Amplifier, *Rev. Sci. Instr.*, vol. 18, p. 703, 1947.
3. Fairstein, E.: Non-blocking Double-line Linear Pulse Amplifier, *Rev. Sci. Instr.*, vol. 27, p. 476, 1956.
4. Koch, H., and R. Johnston (eds.): Multichannel Pulse Height Analyzers, *Natl. Acad. Sci.–Natl. Research Council Publ.* 467, pp. 21ff., 1957. Remarks by E. Fairstein.
5. Kelly, G.: A New Amplifier for Pulse Spectrometry, IRE National Convention Record, Part 9, p. 63, 1957.
6. Moody, N., W. Battell, W. Howell, and R. Taplin: A Comprehensive Counting System for Nuclear Physics Research, *Rev. Sci. Instr.*, vol. 22, p. 551, 1951.
7. Clapp, J.: An Inductance-Capacitance Oscillator of Unusual Frequency Stability, *Proc. IRE*, vol. 36, p. 356, 1948.
8. Goulding, F.: Transistorized Radiation Monitors, *IRE Trans. on Nuclear Sci.*, vol. NS-5, p. 38, 1958.
9. Gillespie, A.: "Signal, Noise, and Resolution in Nuclear Counter Amplifiers," McGraw-Hill Book Company, Inc., New York, 1953.

CHAPTER 3

SINGLE-CHANNEL PULSE-HEIGHT ANALYZERS

The output signals from a linear amplifier connected to a proportional detector have an amplitude distribution related to the energy spectrum of the radiation incident upon the detector. The energy spectrum can be inferred by measuring the amplitude distribution with a pulse-height

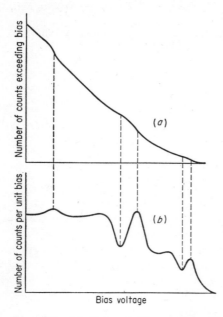

FIG. 3.1 (*a*) Integral bias curve; (*b*) differential bias curve obtained by point-by-point differentiation of the integral bias curve.

analyzer. This can be done in a number of ways with electronic circuits that vary considerably in size and complexity.

3.1 Integral Discriminators

The simplest pulse-height analyzer consists of an integral discriminator and an electronic counter or scaler.[1] An integral discriminator is a circuit that rejects all signals with an amplitude less than the bias setting and passes to the scaler all signals with an amplitude greater than the bias. A pulse-height distribution can be measured with an integral discriminator by recording the counting rates observed at a number of bias settings. The number of observations and the voltage intervals between them are chosen to yield the desired resolution. If the counting rate is plotted against the bias voltage, one obtains the "integral bias curve" of the pulse-height distribution (Fig. 3.1*a*).

[1] Scaling circuits have been very adequately discussed in the literature [1–3], so it will not be necessary to consider them here.

Figure 3.1*b* shows the frequency distribution of pulse amplitudes or "differential bias curve" obtained by point-by-point differentiation of the integral bias curve. This differentiation can be done graphically by measuring the slope of the integral bias curve at a large number of points. Better accuracy is obtained, however, with considerably less effort by plotting as the differential bias curve the differences between successive counting-rate observations divided by the corresponding bias voltage interval.

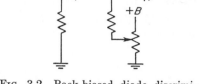

Pulse-amplitude discriminator circuits of several types have been widely used.   Probably the simplest is the back-biased diode (Fig. 3.2). That portion of an input signal

FIG. 3.2   Back-biased diode discriminator.

which exceeds the bias is passed by the low forward resistance of the diode to the succeeding circuit, while signals whose peak amplitude is less than the bias are blocked.   Figure 3.3 shows a typical set of input and output waveforms for an ideal diode discriminator in which the diode is assumed to have no capacitance between plate and cathode, zero forward resistance, infinite reverse resistance, and a very sharp transition between forward and reverse conditions.

Even with an ideal diode the simple diode discriminator has some limitations.   The output signals are not all the same size but vary from zero to a maximum equal to the difference between the largest input signal and the diode reverse bias. Some sort of pulse-standardizing circuit therefore must be interposed between the diode and the scaler.[1] Also, the load imposed on the linear amplifier is nonlinear and varies with the diode bias, so that the effective zero-signal base line may vary with both duty cycle and bias.   But the principal difficulties with diode discriminators result from the fact that

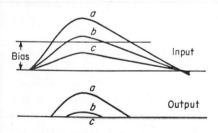

FIG. 3.3   Three typical input signals to the back-biased diode discriminator of Fig. 3.2 and the corresponding output signals.

ideal diodes do not exist.   If the input signal has a fast-rising leading edge, an appreciable displacement current may flow in the diode capacitance, so that signals smaller than the diode bias can trigger the scaler. Capacitance effects may be less troublesome with some semiconductor

[1] The scaler itself is usually an unsuitable pulse-standardizing circuit because its triggering threshold is often dependent upon the count stored at any instant.

diodes than with vacuum diodes, but then there are comparable difficulties associated with the very much lower reverse resistance of most semi-conductor diodes. Also, the transition between forward and reverse conduction with real diodes is not infinitely sharp but extends over a range of several tenths of a volt, and even more important, the transition voltage is not absolutely constant but varies with cathode temperature in vacuum diodes and with junction temperature in semiconductor diodes. In vacuum diodes with oxide-coated cathodes the transition voltage varies about 50 mv with a 10 per cent change in filament voltage. In germanium diodes the transition voltage varies about 2.5 mv per °C.

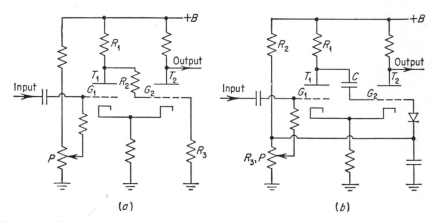

Fig. 3.4   (a) Direct-coupled Schmitt trigger circuit; (b) capacitively coupled Schmitt trigger circuit.

A very widely used amplitude discriminator is the Schmitt trigger circuit [4], two forms of which are shown in Fig. 3.4. Figure 3.4a is the classical direct-coupled Schmitt trigger, and Fig. 3.4b is a capacitively coupled version whose performance is very similar, provided that the input-signal duration is short compared to the coupling time constant determined by coupling capacitor C and the diode reverse resistance.[1] The capacitively coupled circuit has the advantage that its bias is determined by only one voltage divider rather than two, so that the bias is less sensitive to drift in the resistor values. The circuit can exist in two states, depending on the potential of the input grid. We shall define the OFF state as the one in which the grid (G_1) of T_1 is negative with respect to the grid (G_2) of T_2, so that T_1 is cut off and T_2 is conducting, and the ON state as the reverse condition where the grid of T_1 is positive,

---

[1] The d-c restoring diode in Fig. 3.4b reduces duty-cycle effects. At the end of each signal it rapidly removes the charge accumulated on the coupling capacitor C when the circuit was in its triggered state.

T_1 is conducting, and T_2 is cut off. Let us assume that the circuit is initially in the OFF state. G_2 is at a potential V_2 determined by resistors R_1, R_2, and R_3 (Fig. 3.4a) or just R_2 and R_3 (Fig. 3.4b), and the two cathodes K are at a slightly more positive potential, the difference being the grid bias of T_2, V_b. Now let an input signal raise the potential of G_1. When it gets to within a voltage V_c of the cathodes, T_1 begins to conduct. The potential of the plate of T_1 then starts to fall, carrying with it the potential of G_2. This causes the cathode potential to drop, decreasing the bias on T_1 and increasing its current, which makes its plate drop still further. The process is regenerative and continues until T_2 is cut off and all of the cathode current flows in T_1.* The common cathode potential is now slightly negative with respect to its initial value but positive with respect to G_1 by approximately V_b, if the two tubes have similar characteristics and the drop in R_1 is not very large. G_2 has fallen

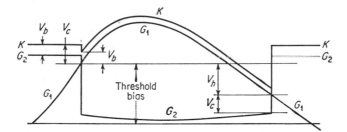

FIG. 3.5   Typical voltage waveforms at the grids (G_1 and G_2) and the cathodes (K) of a Schmitt trigger circuit.

in potential by an amount determined by the cathode current, R_1, and the coupling network and, if the parameters are suitable for triggering action, is now negative with respect to the cathodes by an amount which exceeds the cutoff voltage V_c by a voltage V_h. With T_2 cut off, T_1 now acts like a cathode follower and the two cathodes rise and fall with the input signal on G_1. However, when G_1 drops below the triggering potential by V_h, the bias on T_2 becomes V_c and T_2 starts to conduct. The plate current in T_1 decreases as cathode current flows in T_2. This causes the plate of T_1 to rise in potential, driving G_2 positive, and the circuit regeneratively switches to its initial OFF state.

Figure 3.5 shows a typical set of grid and cathode waveforms for a Schmitt trigger circuit. The quantities of greatest significance are the triggering threshold voltage, which depends on the quiescent voltage of

---

* V_c may be thought of as the cutoff bias voltage for T_1. More rigorously, however, the regenerative switching action begins at a bias voltage slightly less than the cutoff value, at which the transconductance of T_1 is sufficiently large to lead to a regenerative loop gain of unity.

G_1 and is determined by the setting of potentiometer P (Fig. 3.4), and the hysteresis or backlash voltage V_h. The hysteresis is important because it determines the practical minimum value for the triggering bias. If the bias is set to a value less than the hysteresis voltage, an input signal may trigger the circuit from OFF to ON but then may never fall to a sufficiently negative value to trigger the circuit back OFF. In the case of the d-c-coupled circuit (Fig. 3.4a), the circuit will then remain in the ON state indefinitely. The a-c-coupled circuit (Fig. 3.4b) cannot stay in the ON state indefinitely but will ultimately recover after a time, long compared with the pulse duration, determined by the coupling time constant.

The output signal is usually taken from the plate of T_2. Because this electrode does not participate in the triggering action, external loading cannot affect the circuit performance. Output signals can, of course, be taken from other places, such as the plate of T_1 or the cathodes, if the polarity or waveform is more suitable for a particular application.

The Schmitt trigger has several advantages over the biased diode as an integral discriminator. It produces an output signal of standard amplitude for all input signals that exceed the triggering threshold, so that it may be used to drive a scaling circuit directly. Also, it presents a light and constant load to the linear amplifier over a reasonably large range of input-signal sizes because T_1, after triggering, acts like a cathode follower and will tolerate a substantial positive grid swing without drawing grid current. Furthermore, its threshold is less sensitive to cathode temperature variations. This is due to the balanced nature of the circuit. Suppose that the filament voltage is reduced so that G_1 must approach closer to the common cathode potential in order to make T_1 conduct and start the triggering action. The same decrease in filament voltage makes T_2 operate at a slightly smaller bias so that the cathode potential drops. If the two tubes have identical characteristics, this drop in cathode potential is enough to exactly compensate for the decrease in cutoff bias of T_1. Of course, in a practical circuit the tube characteristics are not identical and the compensation is not perfect, but a stability improvement of an order of magnitude is not unusual.

In theory the hysteresis of a Schmitt trigger circuit can have any value greater than zero; practical vacuum-tube Schmitt triggers, however, are rarely built with less than a volt or two of hysteresis. Smaller values would be associated with low regenerative loop gain and sluggish triggering. A more sensitive integral discriminator can be made without sacrificing stability by preceding a fixed-bias Schmitt trigger with a balanced difference amplifier having adjustable bias. Figure 3.6 shows two such discriminator circuits. In Fig. 3.6a, T_1 and T_2 constitute the difference amplifier and T_3 and T_4 are an a-c-coupled Schmitt trigger like that of Fig. 3.4b.   The diode between the plates of T_1 and T_2 is normally conducting and does not allow a signal to be passed to the Schmitt trigger until the plate currents in T_1 and T_2 are equal (assuming that R_1 equals R_2), so that the threshold varies linearly with the bias control even down to bias values at which both tubes are conducting.   In Fig. 3.6b, the

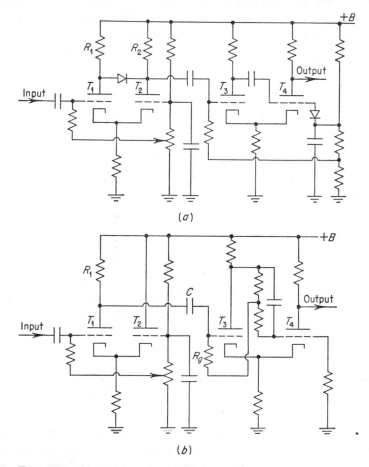

(a)

(b)

Fig. 3.6   Two ways of increasing the sensitivity of Schmitt trigger circuits by preceding them with biased difference amplifiers.

Schmitt trigger circuit is somewhat different from those already discussed in that, although it is direct-coupled, the two grids derive their potentials from the same voltage divider.   Feedback from the plate of T_3 to its own grid is degenerative.   The circuit is regenerative in spite of this because the grid-leak resistor R_g at the grid of T_3 is large compared with R_1, the plate resistor of T_1, and the coupling capacitor C is large, so that a negligible fraction of the plate swing of T_3 appears at its grid. This circuit differs from the others in another respect in that it is quiescently biased in what we previously referred to as the ON state and is triggered to the OFF state by a negative signal at the grid of T_3.

The circuits of Figs. 3.4 and 3.6 have been drawn with triodes for the sake of clarity, but when fast triggering is desired or when it is desired to minimize the capacitive feedback to the driving circuit via plate-to-grid capacitance in T_1, pentodes are generally used. A further refinement is shown in Fig. 3.7. If the circuits of Figs. 3.4 and 3.6 are operated with

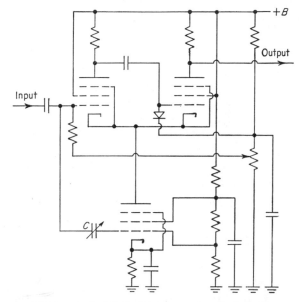

FIG. 3.7 A capacitively coupled Schmitt trigger circuit, including a mechanism for eliminating the feed-through signal that results from displacement current flowing in the grid-cathode capacitance of the input tube.

large values of threshold bias and the input signals have fast-rising leading edges, then signals which are smaller than the bias can produce output signals because the displacement current flowing in the grid-cathode capacitance of T_1 can reduce or even cut off the current in T_2. If the common cathode resistor is replaced by a vacuum tube (Fig. 3.7), a trimmer capacitor C can be adjusted so that a signal current flows in this tube which is equal and opposite to the grid-cathode displacement current, thus eliminating the feed-through problem.

The trend toward the use of transistors in nuclear counting systems has led to the development of transistor discriminators, many of which are rather similar to their vacuum-tube counterparts. However, the relatively low and variable base input impedance of transistors (as contrasted with the high impedance of vacuum-tube grid circuits) can lead to non-linear loading and duty-cycle problems when the circuits are voltage-driven.   Figure 3.8 shows a current-biased and current-driven transistor discriminator which has performance characteristics similar to those of vacuum-tube Schmitt triggers.   It utilizes a pair of emitter-coupled transistors to achieve temperature compensation, and positive feedback from the collector of T_2 to the base of T_1 for regenerative switching. Potentiometer P and resistor R_b can supply either positive or negative current bias for either polarity of input signal.   Diode D_1 protects T_1 against the possibility of damaging excess base-emitter cutoff bias, and D_2 keeps T_1 out of saturation.   Both diodes serve to keep the circuit input impedance low so that it can be driven from current sources of only moderate output impedance with-

out excessive nonlinearity.   If re-sistor R_1 is included, the circuit becomes a voltage-sensitive dis-criminator with a very nearly con-stant input impedance equal to R_1.

The discriminator circuits de-scribed are highly useful elements in more complex systems but are used very little by themselves as pulse-height analyzers.   This is the result of a severe statistical weakness in the use of integral discriminators. Since the radioactive disintegra-tions observed almost always occur randomly distributed in time, any observation in a finite time interval

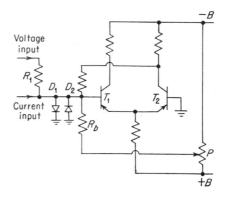

Fig. 3.8 A transistor discriminator. The circuit can be triggered by either current or voltage input signals and can be biased for signals of either polarity.

is only an approximate indication of the true average counting rate.   The usual index of the uncertainty in a counting-rate observation is the standard deviation of a large number of such observations from the mean value.   The standard deviation σ is defined as

$$\sigma = \sqrt{\frac{\sum_{n=1}^{K} (\delta x_n)^2}{K - 1}} \qquad (3.1)$$

where K is the number of observations and x_n is the deviation of the nth observation from the mean.   It can be shown [5] that, for random events obeying a Poisson distribution, the standard deviation in an observed count N is very nearly equal to $\sqrt{N}$.   If N_i and N_j represent two adjacent points on the integral bias curve with standard deviations $\sigma_i = \sqrt{N_i}$ and $\sigma_j = \sqrt{N_j}$, respectively, then the corresponding point on the differential bias curve D_{ij} may be represented by the fractional standard deviation

$$\frac{\sigma_{ij}}{D_{ij}} = \frac{\sqrt{N_i + N_j}}{N_i - N_j} \tag{3.2}$$

Over a substantial portion of the differential bias curve, where the ordinates represent the small differences between nearly equal large numbers, the fractional uncertainty may be very high.   Table 3.1 illustrates this

TABLE 3.1

N_i	N_j	D_{ij}	σ_{ij}	σ_{ij}/D_{ij}
2,000	1,000	1,000	55	5.5%
10,000	9,000	1,000	138	13.8%
100,000	99,000	1,000	446	44.6%

difficulty with a few numerical examples.   It follows that, if a reasonably high statistical accuracy is required in the differential bias curve, the individual points on the integral bias curve must be determined to extremely high precision.   This implies that the individual counting-rate observations must be very long.

3.2   Differential Discriminators

The statistical difficulty with integral discriminators can be eliminated by the use of differential discriminators (single-channel pulse-height analyzers).   A differential discriminator consists of two discriminator circuits with a small, usually adjustable, difference in their triggering thresholds so that signals in a small voltage range ΔV exceed one threshold but not the other.   Signals exceeding the thresholds may be counted simultaneously with two scaling circuits for the same time interval.   Signals exceeding the lower threshold N_L can be divided into two parts: those in the voltage interval ΔV and those above the upper threshold. The latter part is, of course, identical with the number of signals obtained from the upper discriminator N_U because both observations are made simultaneously and identical events are involved.   The number of events D in the voltage interval ΔV, as determined by subtracting the upper and lower measurements, is therefore known to an accuracy characterized by a standard deviation σ_D equal to the square root of the small difference D rather than to the square root of the sum of the discriminator counts as with a single discriminator.   Table 3.2 shows some numerical examples which, compared with those in Table 3.1, illustrate the considerable statistical advantage of the differential discriminator.

TABLE 3.2

N_U	N_L	D	σ_D	σ_D/D
2,000	1,000	1,000	32	3.2%
10,000	9,000	1,000	32	3.2%
100,000	99,000	1,000	32	3.2%

While the pulse-height analyzer as described can be a useful instrument, it is more complicated than necessary and is therefore almost never used in this form. All commercial analyzers and most laboratory instruments include an anticoincidence circuit, which cancels all signals above the upper threshold, so that only signals that fall in the voltage range ΔV are passed to the scaler. In this way only one scaling circuit is necessary, and that one can be slower and have a smaller capacity than either of the other two, since it is only concerned with the relatively small differential count D rather than with the large N_U and N_L counts. Also, the experimenter is saved the tedium of recording two numbers and subtracting.

3.3 Anticoincidence Circuits

The anticoincidence circuits in all single-channel analyzers perform the same logical function, but may differ considerably in form from circuit to circuit. The circuits receive input signals from the upper and lower discriminators and produce an output signal if the signal from the lower discriminator is not accompanied by one from the upper discriminator. The signals from the two discriminators do not normally occur at exactly the same time. Since the input signal has a finite rise time, it crosses the lower threshold somewhat before it crosses the upper threshold. The anticoincidence circuit must not be sensitive to the first part of the lower-discriminator signal because, at that time, it is not yet determined whether the input signal will also cross the upper threshold. One common technique is to derive the input to the anticoincidence circuit from the trailing edge of the lower-discriminator waveform. If the signal exceeds the upper threshold, the upper discriminator triggers after, and recovers before, the lower discriminator (Fig. 3.9). The anticoincidence circuit must, therefore, include a memory circuit so that information from the upper discriminator will be available at the time the lower discriminator recovers.

One circuit that performs these functions[1] is shown in Fig. 3.10. The leading edge of the lower-discriminator signal charges capacitor C_1 positively through diode D_1, but because of the low forward resistance of D_1,

---

[1] This circuit, due to W. A. Higinbotham of the Brookhaven National Laboratory, is used in the Baird-Atomic model 510 single-channel pulse-height analyzer.

it produces only a very small signal at G_1. The trailing edge of the lower-discriminator signal produces a negative step at G_1 which recovers with a time constant R_1C_1. If the upper discriminator has not been triggered, there is no signal at G_2 and a negative output appears at the output of the

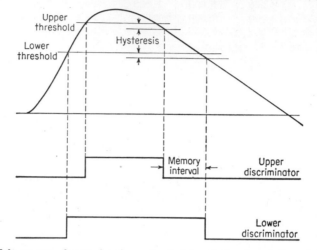

FIG. 3.9   Voltage waveforms showing a typical input signal and the relative timing of output signals from the two discriminators of a single-channel pulse-height analyzer. The time interval between the recovery of the upper discriminator and the recovery of the lower discriminator (denoted "memory interval") must be allowed for in the design of anticoincidence circuits.

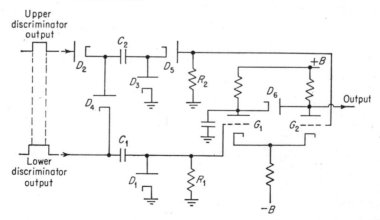

FIG. 3.10   An anticoincidence circuit for a single-channel pulse-height analyzer.

difference amplifier. If the upper discriminator is triggered, the leading edge of its output waveform charges C_2 through diodes D_2 and D_3. When the upper discriminator recovers, however, C_2 remains charged because D_2 opens. The charge remaining on C_2 provides the essential memory over the interval between the recovery of the two discriminators.   When the lower discriminator recovers, diode D_4 closes, sending a negative signal to G_2 via C_2 and D_5 at the same time as the negative signal arrives at G_1. The two signals cancel in the difference amplifier, producing no output. Diode D_6, between the plates of the difference amplifier, clamps out the small positive signal produced when C_1 charges through the small but finite forward resistance of D_1 as well as the small positive common mode output of the difference amplifier that occurs when negative signals are

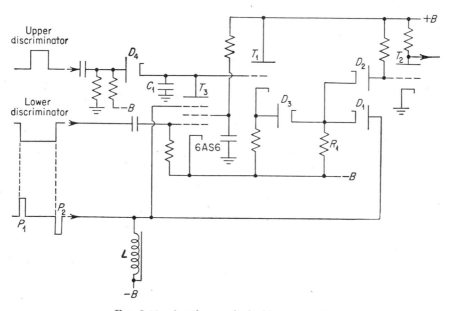

Fig. 3.11   Another anticoincidence circuit.

simultaneously present at G_1 and G_2. D_5 prevents the small positive signal caused by charging C_2 in D_3 from appearing at G_2 and producing an output signal.

Another anticoincidence circuit that has been widely used[1] is shown in Fig. 3.11.   The positive output from the lower discriminator is differentiated by the short-circuited delay line L into two short pulses, one positive, P_1, and the other negative, P_2. P_1, which occurs when the lower discriminator triggers, passes through diode D_1 but is blocked by D_2 and does not produce an output signal. D_3 is quiescently nonconducting because of the negative d-c voltage at the grid of T_1.   If the upper discriminator is not triggered, the negative pulse P_2, produced when the lower discriminator recovers, cuts off D_1, allowing the current in R_1 to flow in D_2.

[1] This circuit, due to J. E. Francis, Jr., of the Oak Ridge National Laboratory, was first published in an excellent review article by A. B. van Rennes [6].

This produces a negative pulse at the grid of T_2 and a positive pulse at the output. If the upper discriminator is triggered, it charges capacitor C_1 positively through D_4. Dual-control tube T_3 (type 6AS6) has been cut off at its control grid by a negative signal from the lower discriminator, so that C_1 cannot discharge. This provides the memory over the interval between the recovery of the upper discriminator and the recovery of the lower discriminator. When the lower discriminator recovers, T_3 is turned on at its control grid but is kept nonconducting by P_2 at the suppressor grid. C_1 therefore remains charged until P_2 ends. The positive voltage at the grid (and, therefore, at the cathode) of cathode follower T_1 turns on diode D_3, which then carries the current in R_1. When P_2 cuts off D_1, no current is transferred to D_2 and no output is produced. At the end of

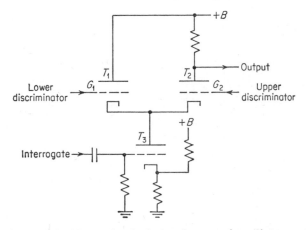

FIG. 3.12   An anticoincidence circuit that makes use of an "interrogate" signal.

pulse P_2, T_3 once more conducts, discharging C_1, and the circuit is ready for the next signal.

Although the anticoincidence circuit must not be pulsed until after the input signal has passed its peak, it is not necessary to derive the pulsing signal from the recovery of the lower discriminator. A somewhat simpler anticoincidence circuit results if an anticoincidence "interrogate" signal is available before either discriminator recovers. A circuit of this type is shown in Fig. 3.12. The discriminators associated with this circuit are not Schmitt triggers but one-shot multivibrators (univibrators) triggered by biased difference amplifiers. The univibrators are set to have a natural period somewhat greater than the rise time of the input signals. An additional discriminator with a small fixed bias generates a standard positive pulse early in the rise of each input pulse. This pulse is delayed by a little more than the input-signal rise time and is used as the interrogate pulse. (The inclusion of this extra discriminator makes this system more complicated than those just described, unless the discriminator is necessary for some other purpose. The system from which this circuit is derived used the extra discriminator to drive an associated coincidence circuit.) Tubes T_1 and T_2 have their grids connected to the lower and upper discriminators, respectively, at points which are quiescently at a positive voltage of about 100 volts. The d-c conditions in the discriminators are adjusted so that, quiescently, G_1 is about 10 volts positive with respect to G_2. T_3 is biased to cutoff. If an interrogate signal appears when neither discriminator has been triggered, T_3 is pulsed on and its plate current is supplied through T_1, producing no output. If the lower discriminator is triggered, G_1 drops in potential about 20 volts. The interrogate signal now finds G_2 positive with respect to G_1 so that plate current for T_3 flows in T_2, producing an output signal. If both upper and lower discriminators have been triggered, G_1 and G_2 both drop about 20 volts, leaving G_1 positive with respect to G_2 once more. The interrogate pulse flows in T_1 and no output is produced.

3.4 Resolution and Accuracy

Frequently the pulse-height distributions to be studied with single-channel pulse-height analyzers have complex shapes and contain significant fine structure. If the pulse-height analyzer is not to degrade the system resolution, it must be operated with a differential bias voltage ΔV (often referred to as "window width") which is small compared to the natural line width of the detector-amplifier combination. In order to cover the entire spectrum without gaps, a large number of measurements must be made at a series of threshold bias values (base-line settings) differing by no more than the selected window width. If the accumulated data are to represent accurately the true pulse-height spectrum, it is necessary that, for each measurement, the effective base-line voltage and window width both be known accurately. Errors in the base-line-voltage calibration appear as errors in the spectral energy scale, and errors in the window-width calibration produce errors in the intensity scale.

It is usually relatively easy to achieve acceptable accuracy (of the order of 0.1 per cent) in the base-line calibration by using multiturn precision potentiometers to set the bias, but comparable accuracy in the window-width calibration is much more difficult to achieve. Suppose that a particular spectrum covers a range of 0 to 100 volts and is to be scanned with a 1-volt window width. If each discriminator has a bias calibration accurate to 0.1 volt (0.1 per cent of full scale), the uncertainty in the window width may have a maximum value of 0.2 volt (20 per cent), if the errors happen to add, and a root mean-square value of 0.14 volt (14 per cent). To avoid such large errors base-line bias for the two discriminators is almost always derived from a single potentiometer, the differential bias

being determined by another control.   Figure 3.13 shows a pair of difference amplifiers with their input grids connected to the same base-line bias
potentiometer, while the differential window-width bias is applied to the
other grid of the upper difference amplifier.   The effective bias on the
upper difference amplifier is the sum of the two bias settings, while that
on the lower difference amplifier is determined by the base-line bias
potentiometer alone.

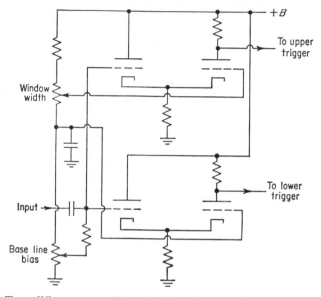

FIG. 3.13   Two difference amplifiers deriving base-line bias from the same bias
potentiometer.   Additional bias is imposed on the upper difference amplifier by the
"window-width" potentiometer.

Biasing both discriminators with the same base-line potentiometer
eliminates channel-width errors resulting from potentiometer imperfections.   However, the discriminators have imperfections of their own
which also contribute to channel-width errors.   No discriminator has ever
been built with absolute threshold stability.[1]   The thresholds in vacuum-
tube circuits vary with filament voltage and, in semiconductor circuits,
with junction temperature, and the use of balanced circuits only reduces,
but does not eliminate, these variations.   Regulation of filament voltage

---

[1] The Kandiah discriminator [7] and the discriminator designed by Barabuschi
et al. [8] have thresholds which are determined by the very stable relationship between
the current and the dynamic resistance in a conducting diode and, therefore, achieve
very much better stability than the discriminators so far described.   However,
neither of these circuits can be operated with a bias of more than a few volts.   The
ratio of bias instability to maximum full-scale bias is not significantly better in these
circuits than in the more conventional circuits.   They are, however, useful at much
lower signal levels.

(or ambient temperature for semiconductor circuits) can do a great deal to improve threshold stability, but residual threshold drifts due to tube or transistor aging can only be eliminated by periodic recalibration. While these drifts have a small effect on the base-line calibration, their effect on the window width is, of course, much more pronounced.

3.5 Window Amplifiers

Variations in effective window width can be reduced by about an order of magnitude by employing a "window amplifier" before the two discriminators. A window amplifier is a biased amplifier which has zero gain for signals below its threshold and a well-stabilized gain (usually about 5 or 10) for signals above its threshold. It is followed by two discriminators, the lower discriminator having a small fixed bias and the upper discriminator having an additional adjustable bias which, when divided by the amplifier gain, determines the window width. For example, if the window amplifier has a gain of 10, then a 10-volt differential bias between the two discriminators results in an effective window width of 1 volt. If the differential bias were to vary by a tenth of a volt, the window

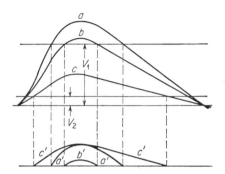

Fig. 3.14 A typical set of input- and output-voltage waveforms for a window amplifier. If the bias voltage is V_1, input signals a and b lead to output signals a' and b'. If the bias is V_2, input c produces output c'. For illustrative purposes c is shown to exceed V_2 by the same amount as a exceeds V_1.

width would change by only 1 per cent, whereas without a window amplifier, the change would be 10 per cent.

Of course, the window-width stability can be no better than the gain stability of the window amplifier. While it is usually not difficult to design a low-gain amplifier with a gain stable to better than 1 per cent by using negative feedback, window amplifiers present a different and especially difficult problem. In a linear amplifier a certain amount of signal distortion is permissible, provided that signals of different size are similarly distorted, so that linearity is preserved. This is not true of window amplifiers, because signals of different amplitudes have different shapes and, therefore, have Fourier integrals that extend over different portions of the radio spectrum. Signals that just exceed the threshold bias are narrower than larger signals. Also, the relationship between signal amplitude and width is dependent upon the bias setting. These effects are illustrated in Fig. 3.14. Signals a and b exceed the threshold V_1 by different amounts and so present to the window amplifier signals a' and b', which are seen to be quite different in shape.   Also, signal c, which exceeds another possible threshold V_2 by the same amount as signal a exceeds V_1, presents a signal c' to the window amplifier which is considerably wider than signal a'.

If the window-amplifier bandwidth is limited so that it does not amplify signals a' and c' by the same amount, then the effective window width will vary with base-line setting.   The extent of this variation can be determined and corrected for by calibrating the analyzer, but it is, of course, preferable that such calibration not be necessary.   Insufficient window-amplifier bandwidth will also cause the gain to be different for

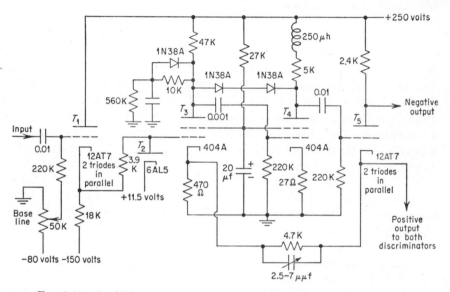

FIG. 3.15   A wideband window amplifier stabilized by negative feedback.

signals a' and b' so that, if the window-width calibration is to be stable, the window amplifier not only must have stable gain but also must have stable bandwidth.

Designers of video amplifiers do not ordinarily have to be concerned with bandwidth stability because the bandwidth is determined by load resistors and circuit capacitances which vary but little.   However, in negative feedback amplifiers the situation is different because the bandwidth also depends on the reserve gain (βK), which varies with the trans-conductance of the amplifier tubes or transistors.   The ideal window amplifier, therefore, would have a bandwidth commensurate with the range of the input-signal frequency components even without negative feedback, negative feedback being used only to improve gain stability. Unfortunately, with present-day tubes and transistors this is very difficult to achieve.   Window amplifiers in most single-channel analyzers have barely enough bandwidth to make the window width independent of base-line setting, even with negative feedback, so that the gain stability achieved is often disappointing.

Figure 3.15 is a circuit diagram of one of the most satisfactory window amplifiers in current use [6]. It makes use of very high performance vacuum tubes (the 404A has a gain-bandwidth product of 200 megacycles) and has 57 db of reserve gain to make its gain of about 10 quite stable. The diodes between the plates of T_3 and T_4 keep the amplifier gain near zero until all tubes are conducting and are in a high-transconductance condition. As the input signal passes the threshold level, the diodes cut off, allowing the amplifier gain to increase suddenly. The gain is then determined largely by the feedback network because, with all tubes in a high-gain condition, the internal loop gain is large.

This window amplifier produces two output signals: a positive signal that goes to both discriminator circuits and a proportional negative signal. The negative signal goes to the common cathodes of the upper discriminator through a small trimmer capacitor and compensates for the displacement current in the grid-cathode capacitance of the discriminator tube. An alternative arrangement that performs the same function was described in Art. 3.1 and illustrated in Fig. 3.7.

3.6 Pulse-increment Analyzers

An interesting alternative solution to the single-channel-analyzer problem has been proposed by Gatti and Piva [9]. It makes use of what we

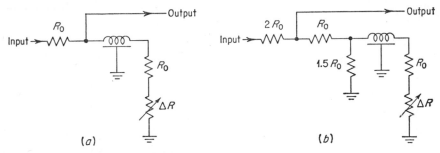

FIG. 3.16 Two circuits for adding an increment to an input signal at a specific time. The increments produced by the mismatch resistance ΔR, added to the delay-line terminating resistance R_0, are proportional to the input-signal amplitudes. Both circuits work the same way, but in circuit (b) stray capacitance loaded across the output has a smaller perturbing effect on the delay-line terminating impedance.

shall call the "pulse-increment" technique to realize high window-width stability without using a window amplifier. The high stability in this case results from the use of only one discriminator circuit to define both edges of the channel, so that any drift in the discriminator threshold affects both edges equally and leaves the window width unaffected.

Two somewhat different pulse-increment techniques have been described in the literature [9–11]. The first makes use of an imperfectly matched delay line (Fig. 3.16) to add a small fractional increment to the input signals after a delay interval equal to twice the propagation time of the line. The input signals may have any of a variety of shapes, but the discussion is simplified by considering the input signals to have the square shape associated with single-delay-line differentiation (Fig. 3.17a). If this signal is impressed on the circuit of Fig. 3.16a, in which the propagation time of the delay line τ is equal to a quarter of the input-pulse duration, the output pulse has the shape of Fig. 3.17b, rising to an initial value V_1 equal to half the input pulse. The incremental portion of the output pulse ΔV is easily shown to be $V\,\Delta R/(4R_0 + 2\,\Delta R)$, where V is the amplitude of the input pulse, R_0 is the characteristic resistance of the delay line, and ΔR is the added mismatch resistance which can be used to control the amplitude of the pulse increment. If the signal of Fig. 3.17b is connected to a discriminator with a threshold bias V_b, then all signals greater than $(V_b - \Delta V)$ will trigger the discriminator, but only those between $(V_b - \Delta V)$ and V_b will trigger it in the time interval between t_1 and

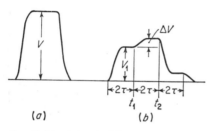

FIG. 3.17 A typical input and output signal for the circuits of Fig. 3.16. τ is the delay-line-signal propagation time.

t_2. If only those signals that trigger the discriminator in this time interval are counted, the circuit is a single-channel analyzer with a stable window width equal to ΔV.

The circuit of Fig. 3.16b behaves very nearly the same as that of 3.16a, but it has the advantage that the delay line is somewhat decoupled from the input capacitance of the discriminator circuit so that this capacitance does not degrade the match at the delay-line input. In this case $V_1 = \frac{4}{9}V$ and $\Delta V = V\,\Delta R/(18R + 9\,\Delta R)$.

In the circuits of Fig. 3.16a and b and, in fact, in all linear pulse-reshaping circuits, ΔV is proportional to V, so that the effective window width is proportional to the base-line setting. This is different from the other single-channel analyzers so far discussed in which, within certain limits, the window width is independent of the base-line setting. However, this is not necessarily a disadvantage, and there are those who argue that it is, rather, an advantage because it provides constant fractional instrument resolution which makes it possible to scan a wide range of signal amplitudes without losing spectral detail in the low-energy region. Nevertheless, most experimenters are accustomed to, and express a preference for, pulse-height analyzers with constant, rather than variable, channel width.

A second pulse-increment type of pulse-height analyzer [10,11] provides constant channel width at the expense of a somewhat more complicated electronic circuit. Although developed originally for a multichannel pulse-height analyzer, the technique is equally applicable to a single-channel instrument. Input signals of arbitrary shape are converted to flat-topped signals of controlled duration by a pulse-lengthening or pulse-stretching circuit.[1] After the signal has reached its peak value, a standard incremental pulse is added to it (Fig. 3.18). The composite signal goes to a single adjustable discriminator. If the discriminator is triggered while the incremental pulse is present (as determined by connecting the differentiated discriminator output and the pulse-increment generator to a coincidence circuit), the signal is considered to be in the

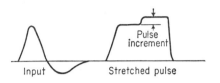

channel. If the discriminator is triggered before the arrival of the pulse increment, the signal is above the channel and is discarded because the differentiated leading edge of the discriminator output does not coincide with the pulse increment. The amplitude of the pulse increment, of course, determines the window width. Since the same pulse increment is added to all signals, the window width is the same at all base-line settings and has high stability, limited only by the stability of the pulse-increment generator.

FIG. 3.18 Input- and output-voltage waveforms for a pulse-increment circuit that makes use of a pulse stretcher and a pulse-increment generator.

REFERENCES

1. Higinbotham, W., J. Gallagher, and M. Sands: The Model 200 Pulse Counter, *Rev. Sci. Instr.*, vol. 18, p. 706, 1947.
2. Collinge, B.: Scaling and Coincidence Circuits, *Nuclear Power*, vol. 3, p. 595, 1958.
3. Clark, E.: Direct Coupled Transistor Logic Complementing Flip-flop Circuits, *Electronic Design*, vol. 5, part I, June 15, 1957; part II, July 1, 1957.
4. Schmitt, O.: A Thermionic Trigger, *J. Sci. Instr.*, vol. 15, p. 24, 1938.
5. Beers, Y.: "Introduction to the Theory of Error," Addison-Wesley Publishing Company, Reading, Mass., 1953.
6. Van Rennes, A.: Pulse Amplitude Analysis in Nuclear Research: part II, *Nucleonics*, vol. 10, no. 8, p. 22, August, 1952.
7. Kandiah, K.: A Sensitive Pulse Amplitude Discriminator, *Proc. IEE*, vol. 101, part II, no. 81, p. 239, 1954.
8. Barabuschi, S., C. Cottini, and E. Gatti: High Sensitivity and Accuracy Pulse Trigger Circuit, *Nuovo cimento*, ser. 10, vol. 11, no. 5, 1955.
9. Gatti, E., and F. Piva: A New Single Channel Elementary Amplitude Discriminator, *Nuovo cimento*, vol. 10, p. 984, 1953.
10. Gatti, E.: A Stable High Speed Multichannel Pulse Analyzer, *Nuovo cimento*, vol. 11, p. 153, 1954.
11. Colombo, S., C. Cottini, and E. Gatti: Improvements on a Multichannel Pulse Analyzer, *Nuovo cimento*, vol. 5, p. 748, 1957.

[1] Several pulse stretchers will be considered in detail in Chap. 4.

CHAPTER 4

MULTICHANNEL PULSE-HEIGHT ANALYZERS I

Although single-channel pulse-height analyzers are entirely adequate for a large number of measurements, there are many experiments that justify an investment in more elaborate equipment. When an energy spectrum is studied with a single-channel analyzer, only those signals that fall in the channel are recorded, while a much larger number of signals that are not included in the channel are discarded. Such wastefulness is tolerable only if the signals are plentiful. It is hardly necessary to say that this is not always the case. In some experiments many thousands of signals are available each second; in others there may be only a few signals per day, and the experimenter must extract as much information as he can from these few signals. In low-counting-rate experiments it is, therefore, often worthwhile to employ a number of single-channel analyzers biased to accept different portions of the spectrum or, better still, a single instrument with a large number of pulse-height channels.

The length of time that must be devoted to a single counting-rate observation is determined by the counting rate and the required statistical accuracy. Occasionally pulse-height measurements must be made with radioactive materials that have half-lives comparable to this counting time. If the measurement is made with a single-channel pulse-height analyzer, each observation must be corrected for the age of the source. Furthermore, as the source decays, each observation must be longer and longer to achieve the same statistical accuracy. But if a counting interval is increased to compensate for the source decay, the source will be still weaker during the next interval. Ultimately, the counting time dictated by statistical considerations will be equal to the source half-life. To achieve the same statistical accuracy in the next observation the counting interval would have to be infinitely long. It follows, therefore, that some pulse-height spectra cannot be measured accurately with a single-channel instrument even though careful corrections are made for source decay. Here again the use of a multichannel pulse-height analyzer is indicated.

In general, whenever the intensity or character of the radiation to be measured varies during the counting interval, multichannel analysis has important and, frequently, essential advantages.   But even in experiments in which the counting rates are high and constant, the use of multichannel pulse-height analyzers may be indicated on economic grounds. Because of the high cost of construction and operation of particle accelerators and nuclear reactors, experimental time with such facilities is very expensive.   Multichannel pulse-height analyzers and other complex electronic data-handling devices can pay for themselves many times over by reducing the time required to do experiments with these facilities.

Multichannel analyzers of many different kinds are in use in laboratories all over the world.   It is not our intention to try to discuss all of these devices in detail.   We shall, rather, divide these instruments into several different categories, discuss each category in general, and then illustrate these discussions with a study of specific circuits.

All multichannel pulse-height analyzers contain some or all of the following elements: (1) a quantizing and digitizing device (analog-to-digital converter) that associates each input signal with a specific amplitude channel; (2) a memory or data storage device that keeps track of the number of signals that fall in each of the amplitude channels; (3) a data display device that provides the experimenter with an indication of the information stored in the memory; (4) auxiliary output devices such as data printers, curve plotters, paper-tape or card punches, magnetic-tape output systems, etc.

The remainder of this chapter will be devoted to a study of analog-to-digital conversion systems.   Chapter 5 will be concerned with data storage systems.   Display and output systems will be discussed in association with the specific storage systems to which they are most closely related.

4.1 Multidiscriminator Converters

The first multichannel pulse-height analyzers made use of direct extensions of single-channel techniques.   Just as two discriminators can be used to define one pulse-height channel, $n + 1$ discriminators can be used to define n channels.   Each of the discriminators, except the first and the last, defines the upper edge of one channel and the lower edge of the next channel.   The discriminators are numbered in order of increasing bias, the bias increments between successive discriminators serving to determine the channel widths.   The sequence of discriminator biases may follow an unlimited number of patterns, provided only that they increase monotonically (the concept of negative channel width has no meaning), but in the most common arrangement the biases are adjusted to provide channels that are as nearly equal as possible.   Each discriminator can be associated with a scaler or other counting device that tallies all the events that exceed its bias, but as in the case of single-channel analyzers (see Art. 3.2), it is much more common to employ anticoincidence circuits so that a discriminator sends a signal to the associated counting device only if the pulse that triggers it does not also trigger the next higher discriminator. Any of the anticoincidence circuits used in single-channel analyzers (Art. 3.3) can be used in multichannel analyzers. However, when the analyzer has more than just a few channels, anticoincidence circuits that make use of interrogate signals are preferable because each anticoincidence circuit can then be a very simple one. The interrogate signal can be derived either from the discriminator that determines the lower edge of the first channel or from an auxiliary discriminator more sensitive than the others.

Multidiscriminator pulse-height analyzers may have any number of channels, although very few have under 10, while the largest in current use has 120 channels. When the number of channels is large, for reasons of economy and reliability it is important to employ simple discriminator circuits with as few circuit components as possible. The effective bias of a simple discriminator circuit will not, in general, be independent of the input-signal shape. The signal shape depends somewhat on the detector used, and if a window amplifier is employed, it will vary considerably with the window-amplifier bias (see Art. 3.5 and Fig. 3.14). In order to avoid the necessity of recalibrating the channel widths whenever the detector or the window-amplifier bias is changed, the discriminators are frequently preceded by a pulse pretreatment unit. The pretreatment unit serves to standardize the shapes of the signals presented to the discriminators and to provide them with flat tops so that they can be measured accurately even with slow-acting circuits. The simple pulse-"stretching" circuit of Fig. 4.1 might be used to perform these functions. Capacitor C is charged to the peak value of a positive input signal by cathode follower T_1 and diode D. Some time before the signal reaches peak amplitude, discharge tube T_2 is cut off by a signal from a sensitive discriminator (possibly the same discriminator that generates the interrogate pulse for the anticoincidence circuits). As the input signal falls, the diode opens and capacitor C remains charged to the peak signal amplitude. This signal is coupled to the discriminators by cathode follower T_3. After enough time has elapsed for the discriminators to settle (about a microsecond or two), T_2 is turned on and C is discharged to its quiescent condition.

The simple pulse stretcher of Fig. 4.1 does not perform very well. Its principal weakness results from the nonideal characteristics of the diode D. If it is a vacuum-tube diode, its most troublesome characteristic is its plate-to-cathode capacitance, which is not negligibly small compared with C. As the input signal falls, a fraction of the fall is coupled to the grid of T_3 by the voltage-divider action of the diode capacitance and C. The finite charging current capability of the diode and T_1 requires that C be small (20 $\mu\mu$f is reasonable). The capacitance associated with a vacuum diode and its socket is about 5 $\mu\mu$f so that, as the input signal decays, the stretcher output can be expected to drop about 20 per cent from its peak value. If a point-contact semiconductor diode is used, the capacitive effect is less important because the diode capacitance is only about 1 $\mu\mu$f. However, the finite diode reverse resistance and the appreciable reverse-resistance recovery time[1] allow charge to leak off the storage capacitor C and lead to an output signal that is not very flat.

Figure 4.2 is a somewhat more sophisticated pulse-stretching circuit [1] that is used in some commercial multidiscriminator pulse-height analyzers. It uses two extra diodes and a cathode follower to reduce the

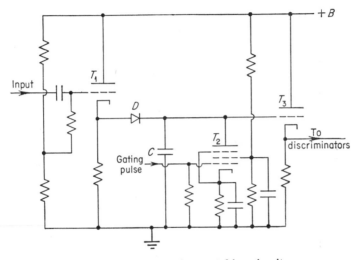

Fig. 4.1 Simple pulse-stretching circuit.

difficulties associated with charging-diode imperfections. T_5 is the output cathode follower of a feedback window amplifier like that of Fig. 3.15. Storage capacitor C (shown near the anode of T_9) is normally held at a potential close to that of the cathode of T_5 by a current of about 2 ma that flows through D_1 and D_2 in series and into the plate of T_{11}. A negative gating pulse, derived from the leading edge of the input signal, cuts off T_{11}, causing its current to transfer to T_{10}. This opens the discharge circuit for the storage capacitor without altering the cathode current of T_5, because the plate of T_{10} is also connected to the cathode of T_5. A few tenths of a microsecond later, the input signal, which has passed through

---

[1] Because of the finite lifetime of minority carriers in a semiconductor diode, the conductivity of the diode in the reverse direction remains high for a short time after it has passed a current in the forward direction. The reverse resistance does not achieve its full value until the carriers have been swept across the depletion layer or have recombined.

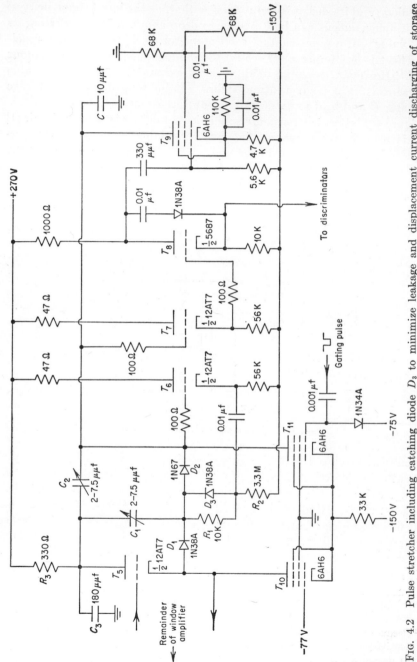

FIG. 4.2 Pulse stretcher including catching diode D_3 to minimize leakage and displacement current discharging of storage capacitor.

a delay line and the window amplifier, arrives at T_5 and charges the storage capacitor positively through diodes D_1 and D_2 in series.   Diode D_3 is normally nonconducting, being reverse-biased by about 0.5 volt by the voltage divider R_1R_2.   Nearly all of the positive signal on the storage capacitor is applied to the anode of D_3 via cathode follower T_6, whose gain is approximately 0.98.   As the signal rises, both terminals of D_3 move almost together so that, at the signal peak, the reverse voltage across D_3 is the initial 0.5 volt plus about 2 per cent of the signal height.   As the input signal falls, the anode of D_1 returns to its quiescent value and the cathode tends to follow via its reverse resistance and minority carrier conduction during the reverse-resistance recovery time.   However, the cathode of D_1 is not allowed to drop more than about a volt because D_3 starts to conduct. When the input signal has decayed, therefore, nearly all of the voltage difference between the cathode of T_5 and the storage capacitor appears across the reverse resistance of D_1 and only about a volt appears across the reverse resistance of D_2.   The leakage current in D_2 is, therefore, very small, and the charge on C remains fairly constant for several microseconds.

Trimmer capacitors C_1 and C_2 introduce some refinements in the circuit performance. C_3 is connected to the plate resistor R_3 of T_5, so that the time constant of the anode circuit approximately matches that of the cathode circuit.   The current flowing in T_5 therefore produces signals at the plate and cathode that have the same shape but are opposite in polarity. C_1 can then be adjusted so that its displacement current almost exactly balances that flowing in the plate-to-cathode capacitance of D_1. C_2 compensates for that fraction of the displacement current in D_2 that is proportional to the input signal and is due to the gain of cathode follower T_6 being less than unity.   Compensation for the displacement current in D_2 need not be perfect because the reverse voltage that appears across it is very small.

The stretched signal is coupled from the storage capacitor to the discriminators by two cascaded cathode followers T_7 and T_8 which drive the high input capacitance of the discriminators without appreciably loading the storage capacitor. T_6 is not used for this purpose because any loss in gain due to loading would lead to an increased reverse voltage across D_2. After about a microsecond or two, when the discriminators have had time to settle, the gating pulse is removed from T_{11}, allowing its plate current to discharge the storage capacitor.   The discharge of the storage capacitor should be as rapid as possible.   If another, smaller, signal were to produce a gating pulse before the discharge were complete, the discharge might be interrupted when the voltage on the storage capacitor was greater than the amplitude of the second signal and the second signal would be measured incorrectly. T_9 is included, therefore, to speed up the discharge. Because of the large capacitive load at the cathode of T_8, when the voltage starts to fall at its grid the cathode cannot keep up and the resultant grid-cathode signal reduces the plate current and produces a positive pulse at its plate. T_9, which is normally nonconducting, is turned on by this signal and discharges the storage capacitor rapidly. When the output returns to its quiescent value, the positive signal at the plate of T_8 disappears and T_9 cuts off once more.

The relatively short time required to translate pulse height into channel number is the principal virtue of multidiscriminator converters. With conventional, slow, discriminator circuits the total conversion time need be only a few microseconds, and faster circuits have been built that operate in less than a microsecond.[1] Nevertheless, multidiscriminator pulse-height analyzers have not been used extensively because of two important disadvantages. First, since each channel has a discriminator circuit and an anticoincidence circuit, instruments with a large number of channels have a large number of circuit elements. This leads to high initial cost and low reliability. Secondly, it is difficult to adjust the channels to be equal in width, and because of inevitable drifts (see Art. 3.4), it is difficult to keep them in adjustment. As with single-channel analyzers, a small change in the bias of a discriminator produces a relatively large fractional change in the width of the two channels for which the discriminator bias marks a boundary.

The importance of channel-width stability in a multichannel pulse-height analyzer is not always appreciated. The number of events recorded in each channel depends upon the spectral intensity at each pulse-height level and on the width of the channel. If all channels are precisely equal or, alternatively, if the width of each channel has been determined by calibration, the true pulse-height distribution can be determined from the number of events tallied in each channel by dividing each number by the corresponding channel width. Any uncertainty, however, in a channel width results in a corresponding uncertainty, over and above the statistical error, in the spectral intensity at that pulse height. The pulse-height spectra obtained when the channel widths are in error show spurious peaks and valleys corresponding to wide and narrow channels, respectively. These artifacts may be misinterpreted as significant lines in the spectra, or, alternatively, their presence may obscure the recognition of real low-intensity spectral lines.

Accurate calibration of channel widths in a multidiscriminator analyzer presents problems of more than trivial difficulty. Consider, as an example, an analyzer in which the channel widths are 1 per cent of the full-scale pulse-height range, and suppose that it is desired to know the channel widths to an accuracy of 1 per cent. It is then necessary to measure the

[1] Eldorado Electronics, Berkeley, Calif., manufactures a multidiscriminator pulse-height analyzer that is said to have a resolving time of less than 0.5 μsec.

effective bias of each discriminator to an accuracy of 0.01 per cent of full scale. A calibrating pulse generator with such high precision and with sufficient resolution in its pulse-height control is difficult to obtain. The most precise pulse generators currently available make use of a relay with mercury-wetted contacts (to avoid contact bounce and assure low contact resistance) to produce a voltage impulse equal to a precise reference voltage. A precision laboratory potentiometer could be used to supply an adequate reference voltage for a mercury relay pulse generator, but an alternative procedure is more convenient for routine channel-width calibration. The mercury relay, operating at an accurately controlled repetition rate (usually at power-line frequency), is supplied with a linearly increasing reference voltage from a slow, highly linear sweep circuit. The pulses, increasing slowly in amplitude, are applied to the pulse-height analyzer, in which they are tallied in successively higher channels. Because the pulse amplitudes increase linearly in time and the pulse-repetition frequency is constant, the number of pulses tallied in each channel is a measure of the channel width. The precision of the measurement depends upon the sweep linearity and the number of pulses tallied in each channel, because there is an uncertainty of one count depending on the phase of the pulse generator at the time the sweep passes the channel edges. Highly linear sweep circuits are not difficult to make. If the sweep speed is adjusted to provide at least 100 events per channel, the channel widths can be calibrated to an accuracy of 1 per cent. Earlier calibrators of this type used synchronous motor-driven multiturn potentiometers to provide the linearly increasing reference voltage. The precision of these calibrators, however, was limited by the finite resolution of the potentiometers used, due to the finite number of convolutions in the resistance wire of the potentiometers. The electronically generated sweep has, of course, almost unlimited resolution.

The problems associated with channel-width uncertainty in multidiscriminator converters can be eliminated by employing the pulse-increment technique described in Art. 3.6. Each discriminator bias determines a channel location, but all the channel widths are determined by the amplitude of the pulses from the pulse-increment generator. The channel widths, therefore, are all precisely equal, even though there may be a small (usually unimportant) uncertainty in the channel locations due to drifts in the discriminator thresholds. The bias differences between successive discriminators can be adjusted to be approximately equal to the amplitude of the pulse increments so that successive channel edges will be adjacent. Unfortunately, this cannot be done perfectly, so that, with the pulse-increment technique, there must always be gaps or overlaps or both at the channel edges. This means that some events, falling between channels, will not be counted, or others, falling in overlap intervals, will

be counted twice.   However, with careful adjustment, the gaps and overlaps can be made quite small, and any residual errors can be removed by
calibration.

4.2   Pulse-height-to-time Converters

Measurements of time intervals can be made to very high precision.
The interval to be measured is divided into a number of exactly equal
subintervals by a periodically ticking clock or by an electronic oscillator,
and the length of the interval is determined by counting the subintervals.
Time intervals can be sorted into quantized lengths and tallied in channels
whose widths are as precisely equal as the intervals between clock ticks or
oscillator cycles.   Furthermore, there need be no gaps or overlaps

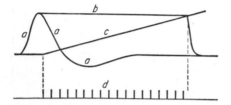

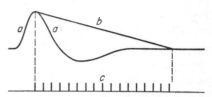

FIG. 4.3   Typical waveforms in pulse-
height-to-time converter.   Input signal
(a) is converted to flat-topped signal (b)
in pulse stretcher and compared with
linear sweep (c).   Clock pulses (d) are
turned on when sweep starts and turned
off when sweep achieves equality with
stretched signal.

FIG. 4.4   Typical waveforms in discharge
type of pulse-height-to-time converter.
Input signal (a) charges capacitor, which
is then discharged linearly, producing
waveform (b).   Gated oscillator (c) is
turned on at beginning of discharge and
turned off when discharge is complete.

between channels, because all intervals encompass a unique number of
integral subintervals.

These characteristics of time measurements can be exploited in measuring pulse-height distributions by converting each impulse into a proportional time interval.[1]   Two essentially equivalent techniques for accom-
plishing this conversion are illustrated in Figs. 4.3 and 4.4.   In Fig. 4.3,
an input signal a is converted to a flat-topped signal of the same amplitude
b by a pulse-stretching circuit.   When the signal has achieved peak amplitude, a linear sweep c is initiated and, at the same time, a clock oscillator
is turned on, generating time marks d.   The stretched signal b and the
linear sweep c are connected to a comparison circuit which turns off the

---

[1] Pulse-height-to-time conversion was first used by Wilkinson [2] in a relatively slow
pulse-height analyzer in which the amplitude of each input signal was recorded on a
strip chart in a digital code.   It has since been widely applied to pulse-height analyzers
using various storage mechanisms.

clock oscillator and resets the stretcher to zero when the sweep attains the amplitude of the stretched signal.   The number of oscillator cycles tallied by a suitable scaling circuit is a quantized, digital measure of the input-signal amplitude.

In the alternative conversion technique of Fig. 4.4, a capacitor is charged to the peak value of the input signal a by a circuit quite similar to a pulse stretcher.   However, instead of leaving the capacitor charged to the signal peak, it is discharged with a constant current so that the capacitor voltage decays linearly to zero.   The clock oscillator is turned on when the discharge begins and is turned off when a comparison circuit indicates that the capacitor has discharged to its quiescent value.   As before, the number of oscillator cycles tallied is a measure of the input-signal amplitude.

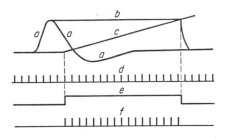

Fig. 4.5   Waveforms in sweep type of converter using a continuously running clock oscillator. Input (a) is stretched to flat-topped signal (b) and compared with linear sweep (c). Sweep and gate waveform (e) are started in synchronism with continuously running clock (d) and continue until sweep equals stretched signal. Clock pulses occurring during gate interval (f) are counted in scaler.

It is difficult to choose between the sweep and the discharge systems of pulse-height-to-time conversion.   Both are capable of the same accuracy and speed and require electronic circuits of comparable complexity.   Both systems are in use in laboratory-built and commercial pulse-height analyzers.

In some converters the clock oscillator is pulsed on and off, as shown in Figs. 4.3 and 4.4.   In others the clock oscillator is allowed to run continuously and a gate circuit passes clock pulses to the scaler during the measuring interval.   The clock may then be a crystal-controlled oscillator (crystal oscillators are more difficult to pulse on and off than most other types) with very high frequency stability.   In this case it is usual to synchronize the start of the comparison sweep (see Fig. 4.5), or the linear discharge, with the clock oscillator to eliminate the uncertainty of as much as one oscillator cycle that would result if the sweep were permitted to begin at a time unrelated to the oscillator phase.   In view of the increased circuit complexity required to synchronize the sweep with the oscillator, the advisability of a continuously running crystal oscillator is questionable.   This is particularly true because instability of the clock oscillator is usually a much less important source of error than instability in the sweep and comparison circuits.

In another, logically equivalent, pulse-height-to-time converter a storage capacitor, charged to the peak signal amplitude, is discharged by quantized charge steps rather than by a constant current (Fig. 4.6).   The number of discharge steps required to return the capacitor to its quiescent potential is a measure of the input-signal amplitude.   The advantages of this system are that the step-repetition frequency is unimportant and that the discharge always ends un-ambiguously at the end of a step, so that the scaler need never contend with part of an oscillator cycle.

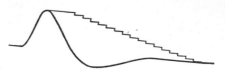

FIG. 4.6   Waveforms in step discharge pulse-height-to-time converter.

Pulse-stretching Circuits.   Pulse-stretching circuits consist of a mechanism for charging a storage capacitor to the peak value of an input signal and leaving it charged for some time after the input signal has decayed. The significant performance characteristics of pulse stretchers are linearity, speed, and amount of residual slope (ideally none) of the stretched signal.   The charging circuit may contain an inherently linear element, such as a cathode follower, or it may include a negative feedback circuit to control the capacitor charging.   Simple cathode-follower and diode stretchers, like those discussed in Art. 4.1, can be fairly linear if only small charging currents are required, but charging currents which are so large that they cannot be delivered at negative bias cause the cathode follower to operate in the positive-grid region in which it presents a nonlinear load to its driving circuit.   These circuits, therefore, are satisfactory for charging small storage capacitors moderately rapidly or for charging large capacitors slowly.

The size of the storage capacitor is determined by the required duration of the stretched signal, the permissible residual slope, and the amount of leakage current.   The important sources of leakage current[1] are the finite reverse resistance of semiconductor charging diodes and grid-current and heater-to-cathode leakage in vacuum tubes connected to the storage capacitor.   Vacuum charging diodes can be used to eliminate the reverse-resistance problem, and grid currents can usually be made quite small, so the most troublesome source of leakage current is usually heater-to-cathode leakage.   It might be supposed that heater-to-cathode leakage could be avoided by stretching negative signals so that the charging diode would present its anode to the storage capacitor.   Unfortunately, however, at the end of the stretching interval the storage capacitor must be discharged

[1] Normally, leakage in the storage capacitor is negligibly small compared with the leakage in other paths.   However, some of the residual slope in a pulse stretcher is caused by partial penetration of the capacitor dielectric by the stored charge (dielectric "soakage").   This can be minimized by a proper choice of storage capacitor. Polystyrene-insulated capacitors exhibit very little "soakage," and mica capacitors are usually satisfactory.

positively, and heater-to-cathode leakage in the discharging tube is equally troublesome.

A common technique for minimizing heater-to-cathode leakage is to "bootstrap" the heater of the offending cathode by connecting it to the stretcher output cathode follower. In this way the heater-to-cathode voltage remains small and constant regardless of the amplitude of the stretched pulse. It is advisable, then, to supply power to the bootstrapped heater from a specially constructed filament transformer, with its secondary well separated from the primary and the core, so that the stray capacitance associated with the transformer is small.

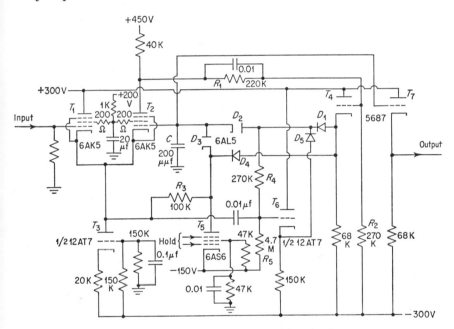

FIG. 4.7   Feedback pulse-stretching circuit.

When leakage considerations dictate that the storage capacitor must be large but the input signals are short in duration (so that the capacitor must be charged quickly), it is helpful to make use of negative feedback. Negative feedback stretchers contain a difference amplifier that compares the voltage on the storage capacitor with the input signal. The output signal from the difference amplifier controls a charging circuit, causing it to deliver just the right amount of charge to the storage capacitor to make the capacitor voltage equal the signal voltage. The charging circuit is made unidirectional by the inclusion of a diode or other nonlinear element so that, once charged, the storage capacitor does not discharge until a separate discharging circuit is turned on.

Figure 4.7 shows a feedback stretcher, reported by Schumann [3], that is employed in a number of commercial multichannel pulse-height analyzers. T_1 and T_2 constitute the difference amplifier that compares the input signal with the voltage across the storage capacitor C. T_3, in the cathode circuit of the difference amplifier, has a large cathode resistor and a fixed grid voltage so that its plate current is substantially independent of its plate voltage. It serves to keep the sum of the cathode currents in T_1 and T_2 independent of the input-signal size, thus improving the common mode rejection of the difference amplifier and increasing the stretcher linearity. The difference-amplifier output, taken from the plate of T_2, is direct-coupled, via voltage divider R_1R_2, cathode follower T_4, and diodes D_1 and D_2, to the storage capacitor and the grid of T_2. This constitutes a direct-coupled negative feedback loop with a feedback factor of unity and, therefore, a gain very nearly equal to 1. Quiescently, current flows in the plate circuit of T_5, some of which flows through diodes D_1, D_2, and D_3 in series, so that these diodes are conducting and the feedback loop is closed. D_4, which is in parallel with the series combination of D_1, D_2, and D_3, carries most of the plate current of T_5, so that the voltage drop in the diodes is small.[1] The remainder of the plate current of T_5 flows in resistor R_3 to the difference-amplifier cathode which, because of self-bias in the difference-amplifier tubes, is a few volts positive with respect to the grid of T_2.

Early in the rise of an input signal which is to be stretched, T_5 is cut off by a "hold" signal derived from an auxiliary discriminator circuit. With almost no current flowing in R_3, the cathode of D_3 is very nearly at the potential of the difference-amplifier cathodes and D_3 is reverse-biased by a few volts. The very small residual plate current that flows in T_5, if its cutoff is imperfect, produces a voltage drop in R_3 that is smaller than the self-bias of T_2 so that, even if T_5 does not cut off sharply, D_3 is completely cut off and no path exists for the discharge of the storage capacitor.

A positive input signal at the grid of T_1 causes current to shift from T_2 to T_1. The plate of T_2 goes positive, carrying with it cathode follower T_4, which charges the storage capacitor positively via diodes D_1 and D_2 and brings the grid of T_2 to very nearly the same potential as the grid of T_1. When the difference between the voltages at the grids of T_1 and T_2 is just sufficient to produce a plate signal at T_2 equal to its grid signal, the feedback loop is in balance and charging of the storage capacitor ceases. The low-frequency gain of the difference amplifier is about 60, so that the voltage on the storage capacitor is about 1.7 per cent less than the input signal if the input signal is sufficiently long to allow the loop to come to equilibrium.

---

[1] D_4 is not essential to the performance of the pulse stretcher. It merely reduces the size of the small positive-voltage step that appears at the storage capacitor when T_5 is cut off.

As the input signal reaches its peak positive value and starts to fall, the plate of T_2 drives cathode follower T_4 in the negative direction. However, this does not discharge the storage capacitor, because diodes D_1 and D_2 open. The storage capacitor is, therefore, left charged at very nearly the peak value of the input signal.

Reverse leakage and capacitive effects in the charging diodes are minimized by a mechanism similar to that used in Fig. 4.2. Diode D_5 is normally reverse-biased by a few volts via voltage divider R_4R_5 and cathode follower T_6. As the input signal rises, this reverse bias is maintained because the positive signal at the difference-amplifier cathodes (very nearly equal to the signal on the storage capacitor) is coupled to the grid of T_6. However, when the input signal falls, the anode of D_5, remains at its most positive value so that, as the grid and cathode of T_4 go negative, the small reverse current that flows in D_1 is caught by D_5 which conducts and prevents the appearance of a large negative voltage across D_2. D_2 is a vacuum diode, so negligible reverse current flows in it and the action of D_5 prevents the flow of an appreciable displacement current in the plate-to-cathode capacitance of D_2. The only significant leakage current, therefore, is due to heater-to-cathode leakage in D_2, and this can be reduced, if necessary, by bootstrapping the filament transformer secondary. Cathode follower T_7 couples the stretcher output voltage to the rest of the pulse-height-to-time converter.

Figure 4.8 is another pulse-stretching circuit [4] of the feedback type that includes a mechanism for avoiding the heater-to-cathode leakage problem. It also features high internal loop gain and high capacitor charging current, so that a large capacitor can be charged in a short time with very little nonlinearity. These features result from the unique properties of the secondary emission amplifier tube (EFP60)* that is used to charge the storage capacitor. The EFP60 contains a secondary emission electrode (dynode) in addition to the usual electrodes of an ordinary pentode amplifier tube. Grid-controlled electrons from the cathode impinge upon the secondary emission dynode and eject secondary electrons. The secondary electrons are collected on the anode, which is maintained at a more positive potential than the dynode. If the cathode electrons strike the dynode with sufficient energy (about 25 electron-volts or more), each primary electron produces, on the average, more than one secondary electron. At normal operating voltages (100 to 200 volts from cathode to dynode and 300 to 400 volts from cathode to anode) the secondary emission multiplication ratio is about 5, so that the net dynode current is four times as large as the current incident upon it and is opposite in polarity to the incident current. A positive signal at the control

* The EFP60 is manufactured by Philips, Eindhoven, Holland, and is distributed in the United States by Amperex Electronic Corp., Hicksville, N.Y.

grid, therefore, causes the dynode potential to go positive, and because the EFP60 is capable of delivering large cathode currents at negative bias, dynode currents of more than 100 ma are available. Thus, the EFP60 dynode can charge a storage capacitor rapidly in the positive direction. No hot cathodes need be connected to the storage capacitor, so the heater-to-cathode leakage problem does not exist.

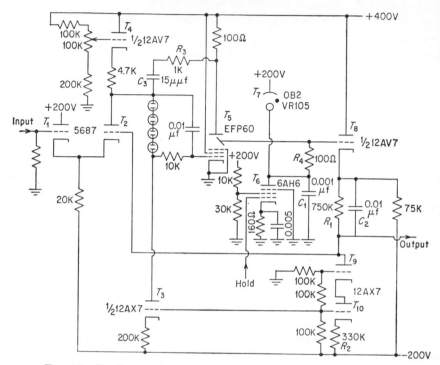

Fig. 4.8 Feedback pulse stretcher with secondary emission amplifier.

Tubes T_1 and T_2 constitute a difference amplifier which compares the voltage on the storage capacitor C_1, via cathode follower T_8, with the input signal. The difference-amplifier output, taken from the plate of T_2, controls the grid potential of the EFP60 T_5 and determines the amount of charging current delivered to the storage capacitor. Quiescently, discharge tube T_6 has a plate current of about 10 ma which tends to discharge the storage capacitor. Negative feedback automatically adjusts the charging current from the EFP60 dynode to exactly equal the discharging current when the difference-amplifier grids are at about the same potential. If the difference-amplifier grid potentials are different, the EFP60 dynode current increases or decreases, as necessary, to restore the balance. The potentiometer at the grid of T_4 adjusts the potential of the top of the anode load resistor of T_2 so that, when the feedback loop is in balance, the currents in T_1 and T_2 are about equal.

Since the output signals from a pulse-stretching circuit may last considerably longer than the input signals, the stretcher duty ratio may be high even at moderate input counting rates.   In order to ensure that the zero level is independent of counting rate, the stretcher loop is direct-coupled.   This necessitates the use of voltage-dropping coupling elements in order that the input and output d-c levels be about the same.   The anode of T_2 is connected to the grid of T_5 by a string of constant-voltage neon tubes.   This network provides a low-impedance drive for the EFP60 grid so that, even if it draws some grid current during charging of the storage capacitor, the d-c conditions are only slightly affected. T_3 maintains a constant current in the neon bulbs so that the voltage drop across them (about 200 volts) remains quite constant.   Resistor R_1, bypassed by a 0.01-$\mu\mu$f capacitor C_2, constitutes another voltage-dropping coupling element. T_9 and T_{10} cause a current to flow in R_1 which is virtually independent of the cathode potential of T_8.   The series arrangement of T_9 and T_{10} has a dynamic resistance equal to the cathode resistor R_2 multiplied by the product of the amplification factors of the two tubes. The tubes used have an amplification factor of about 100 each, so that the dynamic resistance of the circuit is about 3,300 megohms.   This is very large compared to R_1, so the voltage across the parallel combination of R_1 and C_2 does not change appreciably even if the duration of the stretched signal is comparable to the time constant R_1C_2.

When the circuit is turned on, the voltage between dynode and cathode of the EFP60 is, in general, less than 25 volts, and at this low voltage the secondary emission ratio is less than 1.   The net dynode current is then opposite in polarity to the normal operating current, and the sense of the feedback around the loop is positive rather than negative.   The dynode would tend toward cathode potential rather than toward its normal operating value.   However, if the dynode potential is too low, voltage-regulator tube T_7 strikes and raises the dynode potential to a value at which the secondary emission ratio is greater than 1.   The negative feedback loop takes over from this point, raising the dynode to its normal operating potential and extinguishing T_7. T_7 then remains nonconducting.

In normal operation discharge tube T_6 is cut off by an auxiliary "hold" signal before the input signal arrives.   The EFP60 dynode current then starts to charge the storage capacitor positively.   However, a slight rise in the potential of the storage capacitor causes the difference amplifier to cut off the EFP60 so that charging ceases with the EFP60 just at cutoff. A positive input signal unbalances the difference amplifier, which turns the EFP60 on once more.   The storage capacitor then charges to the peak value of the input signal, at which time the difference amplifier turns the EFP60 off again. As the input signal falls, the EFP60 is driven still further in the cutoff direction while the storage capacitor remains charged. The grid of the EFP60 is well screened from its dynode so that displacement currents to the storage capacitor are negligible.

Because the stretcher loop contains a number of high-gain elements, it has a tendency to oscillate at a high frequency. Local negative feedback via R_3 and C_3 prevents sustained oscillation. However, in every feedback loop there is a finite time delay between the application of an input signal and the arrival of the feedback signal which may lead to transient overshoot or ringing with fast-rising input signals. If the feedback is late in a stretcher circuit, the storage capacitor may overcharge. But because a stretcher feedback loop is unidirectional, once the storage capacitor is overcharged, negative feedback is unable to correct the condition. In this circuit the storage capacitor is prevented from overcharging by the small resistor R_4 in series with it. The voltage drop in R_4 is proportional to the rate of charge of the storage capacitor. By including this voltage drop in the signal fed back to the difference amplifier, the difference amplifier is able to control the charging rate so that the storage capacitor does not overcharge.

Linear Sweep Circuits. The linearity of a converter of the sweep type can be no better than that of the sweep waveform to which the stretched signal is compared. A number of highly linear sweep circuits, developed originally for radar applications, are available for generating suitable sweep waveforms [5,6]. Most of these circuits include a capacitor and a mechanism for supplying it with a nearly constant charging current. Figure 4.9 is a primitive linear sweep circuit. If the capacitor C is initially discharged when the switch is closed, the full battery voltage E appears across resistor R and a charging current E/R flows into the capacitor. The voltage across C increases with time, but so long as the capacitor voltage is negligibly small compared with the battery voltage, the charging current remains substantially constant and the voltage across C increases linearly. Of course, as the capacitor continues to charge, the voltage drop across R decreases and the charging current falls off.[1] The slope of the sweep waveform is determined by the residual voltage across R so that, by the time the sweep voltage is 1 per cent of the battery voltage, the slope has fallen 1 per cent from its initial value. If, therefore, large-amplitude linear sweeps are desired, the battery voltage must be exceedingly high.

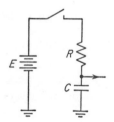

FIG. 4.9 Simple linear sweep circuit.

[1] The voltage across the capacitor, expressed as a function of time, is

$$E_c = E[1 - \exp{(-t/RC)}]$$

The Miller integrator circuit of Fig. 4.10 employs negative feedback to maintain a substantially constant voltage across the charging resistor even though the capacitor voltage approaches the power supply voltage. If the charging current flowing in R raises the grid potential by Δe, the plate potential must fall by $k\,\Delta e$, where k is the voltage gain of the amplifier. If k is large, the net voltage across the capacitor $(1 + k)\,\Delta e$ and the output voltage $k\,\Delta e$ are very much larger than Δe. On the other hand, the change in voltage across the charging resistor is merely the change in grid potential Δe so that, for a given amount of nonlinearity, the Miller integrator can deliver an output signal k times as large as that of the circuit of Fig. 4.9.

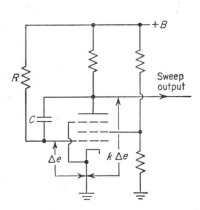

FIG. 4.10 Miller integrator sweep circuit.

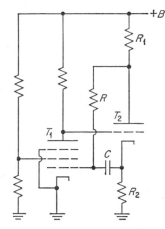

FIG. 4.11 Miller integrator sweep circuit with compensating resistor R_1 for improving sweep linearity.

Figure 4.11 shows a variation on the Miller integrator which can be adjusted for even better linearity and, in addition, has the low output impedance of a cathode follower. If the resistor ratio R_2/R_1 is adjusted to be equal to the pentode voltage gain, then as the capacitor charges, the voltage change at the plate of T_2 is equal to the voltage change at the grid of T_1. Therefore, the voltage across the charging resistor R does not change as the capacitor charges, so the charging current remains constant. The sweep linearity is almost perfect, being limited only by the fact that the amplifier gain is not exactly constant over the full sweep range so that it cannot match the resistance ratio R_2/R_1 perfectly.

The "bootstrap" sweep circuit (Fig. 4.12) is a topological variation of the Miller integrator that delivers positive rather than negative sweep waveforms. The only significant differences between the two circuits are in the locations of power supplies and ground connections. Capacitor

C_1 is very large and, in association with the d-c restoring diode D, can be considered as a battery connecting the cathode of T_1 to the top of the charging resistor R.   As capacitor C charges positively, it raises the potential of the grid of T_1, which carries its cathode and the top of the charging resistor along with it.   The change in the voltage across the charging resistor is very small and results from the fact that the gain of T_1, as a cathode follower, is slightly less than 1.   The screen of T_1 is bootstrapped along with the top of the charging resistor.   This increases the cathode-follower gain to a value determined by the pentode, rather than the triode, amplification factor of T_1.

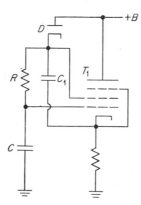

FIG. 4.12   "Bootstrap" sweep circuit.

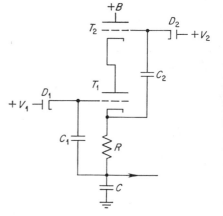

FIG. 4.13   Double-bootstrap sweep circuit.

Figure 4.13 is a variation on the bootstrap circuit that employs a dual triode in place of a pentode.   Capacitors C_1 and C_2 are very large and, with their d-c restoring diodes, act like coupling batteries.   Cathode follower T_1 bootstraps the top of charging resistor R to keep the voltage across it constant as C charges.   Cathode follower T_2 bootstraps the anode of T_1, increasing its effective amplification factor to the product of the amplification factors of T_1 and T_2.   By using a high-mu dual triode a linearizing gain of as much as 10,000 can be achieved.

Discharge Converters.   Pulse-height-to-time converters in which the storage capacitor is discharged linearly will be illustrated by two circuits from practical pulse-height analyzers.   Figure 4.14 is a circuit, designed by Byington and Johnstone [7] at the Los Alamos Scientific Laboratory, that includes, in addition to the discharge converter, an ingenious temporary storage device that reduces data losses caused by finite conversion and storage time.   All input signals pass through a pulse-stretching circuit, which constitutes the temporary storage device.   If the discharge

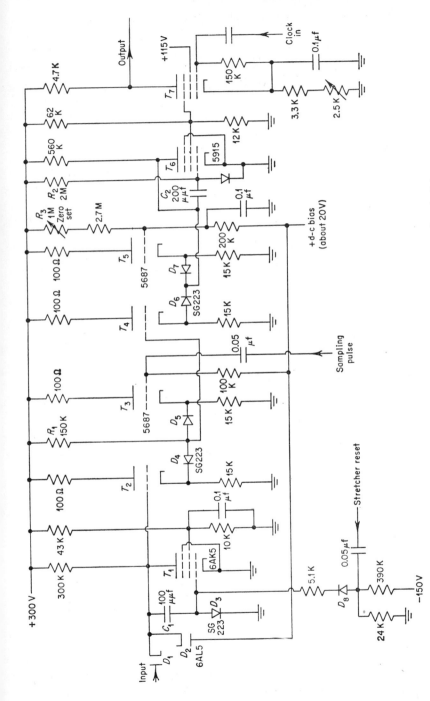

FIG. 4.14 Discharge converter with temporary storage pulse stretcher.

and memory circuits are not already occupied by a preceding signal, the input signal is immediately transferred to the discharge circuit for measurement. However, if the discharge or memory circuits are occupied, the signal is retained in the pulse stretcher until the measurement of the preceding signal is complete, after which it is transferred to the discharge circuit. In this way, even though two signals follow each other closely in time, both can be measured, whereas without a temporary storage circuit the second signal must be discarded if it occurs before the measurement of the first is complete. Of course, with only one temporary storage circuit, if three signals occur close together, only the first and second can be measured and the third must be discarded. This, however, is statistically much less likely than the occurrence of a pair of pulses, so that, at moderate counting rates, the temporary storage circuit eliminates most of the counting losses.

The input signal from a cathode follower (not shown in Fig. 4.14) charges storage capacitor C_1 via diodes D_1 and D_3. Diode D_8 is normally reverse-biased so that, as the input signal falls and D_1 and D_3 open, C_1 is left without a discharge path and remains charged to the peak value of the input signal. C_1 and pentode T_1 may be considered as a Miller sweep circuit in which the charging resistor is the combined reverse leakage resistance of D_3 and D_8. This leakage resistance is very large so that the storage capacitor does not discharge appreciably during the temporary storage interval. The stretched signal appears as a positive voltage at the grid and cathode of cathode follower T_2 and at the cathode of D_4. The grid of T_3 is normally at the potential of the stretcher output when the stretcher is uncharged (about $+20$ volts), so that, with a positive signal at T_2, D_5 conducts, D_4 is cut off, and no signal appears at the grid of T_4. If the discharge and memory circuits are not occupied, a positive sampling signal, which is larger than the largest measurable input signal, is applied to the grid of T_3. This cuts off D_5 and allows the current in R_1 to close D_4, coupling the stretcher output signal to T_4.

T_6, C_2, and discharging resistor R_2 constitute the discharge circuit. T_6 is quiescently at zero bias, its plate being caught by D_7 and cathode follower T_5 at a potential which can be adjusted by R_3 to be equal to the zero-signal level from the stretcher. Because T_6 is at zero bias, its screen potential is low. The screen of T_6 is connected to the second control grid of gated beam tube T_7, cutting off its plate current. Therefore, the 1-megacycle signals from the crystal-controlled clock oscillator at its first control grid do not appear at the plate. The sampling pulse at T_3 passes the stretcher output to T_4, which charges C_2 via D_6. At the end of the sampling pulse the grid of T_4 returns to its quiescent potential and D_6 cuts off. The large plate current in T_6, which is still at zero bias, is now switched to the plate load resistor. The plate potential therefore drops slightly, driving the grid negative through capacitor C_2 to a negative equilibrium bias of a few volts which is compatible with the new plate potential, the plate load resistor, and the power supply potential. The drop in grid potential decreases the screen current as well as the plate current, so the screen potential rises, turning on T_7 at its second control grid and allowing clock signals to appear at its plate. T_6 now behaves like a Miller sweep circuit, the current in R_2 discharging C_2 linearly. When the plate of T_6 falls to its initial potential, it is once more caught by diode D_7. With feedback from the plate paralyzed, the current in R_2 raises the grid to zero bias; the increase in screen current cuts off T_7 at its second control grid, and the clock pulses are interrupted. The train of output clock pulses extends in time from the end of the sampling pulse, when the discharge starts, until the discharge is complete. The end of the sampling pulse is synchronized with the clock to permit the discharge to begin at a standard phase of the clock oscillator. The end of the sampling pulse is also used to trigger the reset generator, which applies a positive pulse to the grid of T_1 via D_8 to discharge the stretcher immediately after its contents have been transferred to the discharge circuit.

Figure 4.15 is a transistorized pulse-height-to-time converter of the discharge type. Included in the circuit diagram is a linear gate circuit. A linear gate is an essential element of all pulse-height-to-time converters. Its function is to admit an input signal to the converter and then to exclude all other input signals that arrive while the first signal is being measured. This prevents the later signals from introducing errors into the measurement in progress. It follows, of course, that not every input signal is measured. At low input counting rates relatively few signals need be discarded, but at high input counting rates the number of signals discarded, because of the finite duration of the measuring interval, may constitute an appreciable fraction of the input signals. However, the linear gate and the circuits that control it are designed to accept signals without prejudice with respect to their amplitudes, so that those signals which are recorded constitute a representative sample of the signals presented to the input. The spectral distribution of pulse amplitudes is, therefore, undistorted, even though some of the input signals are not measured.

In most pulse-height-to-time converters the linear gate circuit is a separate and distinct circuit element, but in the circuit of Fig. 4.15, the linear gate shares some components with the discharge circuit, so the two must be considered together. Transistors T_1 and T_2 constitute a negative feedback loop whose voltage gain, determined by the ratio R_2/R_1, is 0.1. Positive input signals, in the range of 0 to 100 volts, appear at the emitter of T_2 as negative signals in the range of 0 to 10 volts. R_3 is adjusted so that, with no input signal present, the emitter of T_3 is at ground potential.

Normally, the circuit is in a blocked condition, with T_4 and T_5 conducting and in saturation so that, even though an input signal cuts off T_1, no signal appears at the base of T_6. Shortly before the arrival of a signal to be measured, T_4 and T_5 are cut off by a positive signal at the base of T_4 and by a negative signal at the base of T_7. The base of T_6 remains at ground

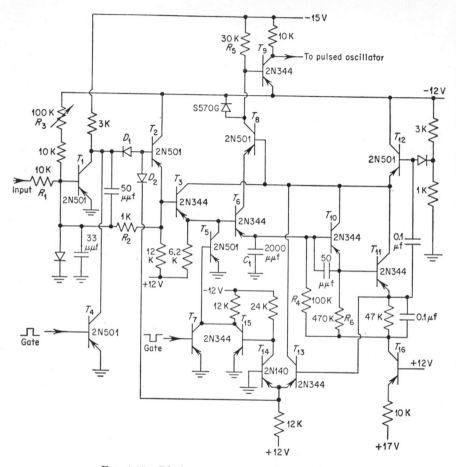

FIG. 4.15   Discharge converter using transistors.

(if R_3 has been properly adjusted) until the input signal arrives and drives it negative. T_6 is an emitter follower responsible for charging the storage capacitor C_1 to the peak value of the signal applied to its base. Normally, a current of 0.12 ma in discharge resistor R_4 flows through T_6 and T_8, cutting off T_9. T_9 then presents a negative voltage to the pulsed oscillator (not shown) which prevents it from oscillating. A negative signal at the base of T_6 causes it to charge C_1 to the signal peak. As the signal starts to decay, the base of T_6 is driven positive, but C_1 holds its emitter at the peak signal voltage. This cuts T_6 off so that R_5 drives T_9 to saturation, allowing the pulsed oscillator to start. At the same time, the current in R_4 starts to discharge C_1. Cascaded emitter followers T_{10} and T_{11} bootstrap the bottom end of R_4 so that the voltage across R_4, and therefore, the discharge current, remain constant, leading to a linear discharge of C_1. The base current in T_{10} constitutes a small part of the discharge current which is maintained constant by a bootstrap mechanism. T_{11} bootstraps the bottom of emitter resistor R_6, in addition to discharge resistor R_4, and T_{12} bootstraps the collector of T_{10}, so that all during the discharge T_{10} operates at very nearly constant emitter current and collector voltage. Its base current, therefore, remains quite constant. It merely increases the discharge rate slightly without impairing its linearity. T_{12} also bootstraps the collectors of T_3, T_{11}, and T_{13}, permitting the use of low-voltage transistors to handle signals larger than their collector voltage ratings.

If the discharge is to be linear, it is necessary that the reverse base-emitter leakage current in T_6 be negligible or, at least, constant. Therefore, during the discharge the reverse base-emitter voltage must be kept small and, preferably, constant. Diode D_2 and emitter followers T_{10}, T_{11}, and T_{13} keep the base of T_2 from going more than a fraction of a volt positive with respect to the emitter of T_6. The base voltage of T_6 is determined by emitter followers T_2 and T_3 and remains about 1 volt positive with respect to the emitter during the discharge. Because the reverse base-emitter voltage of T_6 is small and constant, the leakage current is, likewise, small and constant. Diode D_1 serves to disconnect the base of T_2 from the collector of T_1 during the discharge so that it can be successfully caught by D_2.

Shortly after the input signal passes its peak and starts to decay, a signal from T_9 causes the removal of the gating signals from the bases of T_4 and T_7. The collector of T_1 is then once more clamped to ground potential so that subsequent input signals cannot reach T_6 during the discharge. However, while the emitter of T_6 is substantially negative, T_5 must not be allowed to be turned on because this would impose a large reverse base-emitter bias on T_6. This is prevented by the negative signal at the emitter of T_{13} which turns off T_{14}, allowing T_{15} to saturate and hold T_5 cut off even though T_7 is no longer conducting. When C_1 is nearly discharged, T_{13} transfers current to T_{14} which cuts off T_{15} and turns on T_5, thus clamping the base of T_6 securely to ground potential just before the end of the discharge. As the discharge continues, T_6 starts to conduct once more, supplying current to R_5, cutting off T_9, and stopping the clock oscillator.

The circuit includes several features which make its performance substantially independent of ambient temperature. The zero-signal potential at the base of T_6 (with T_4 and T_5 not conducting) is somewhat dependent upon the base-emitter voltage drops in T_1 and T_3. However, variations with temperature in the base-emitter voltages of these two transistors affect the potential at the base of T_6 in the opposite sense. Of course, the emitter potential of T_6 varies with temperature, but this has the same effect on both the start and the end of the discharge and therefore has no net effect. The voltage across the discharge resistor R_4 depends on the potential of the emitter of T_6. There is, however, a compensating temperature-dependent variation in the potential of the bottom of R_4, so the slope of the discharge is not temperature-dependent. This results from the fact that T_{16} is initially in saturation so that its collector and emitter potentials are essentially the same. The base of T_{16} is fixed at the $+12$-volt power supply potential while its emitter potential is free to change with temperature by about the same amount as the emitter of T_6. Because T_{16} is in saturation, its collector potential changes with the emitter potential, thus maintaining the voltage across R_4 constant in spite of temperature changes.

4.3 Beam-deflection Converters

Standard cathode-ray tubes and specially constructed beam-deflection devices have been applied, in a number of ways, to the problems of pulse-amplitude quantization and analog-to-digital conversion. All of the systems make use of a specially fabricated target or shadow mask, mounted inside the tube or, in those systems that use conventional cathode-ray tubes, mounted on the front surface of the tube. Apertures in the target or shadow mask serve to define the channel edges.

The deflection sensitivity of a beam-deflection tube depends on the tube geometry and the accelerating potentials. The geometry of a well-constructed tube is extremely stable and well-regulated power supplies are commonplace. Beam-deflection converters, therefore, can have very stable channel boundaries, so that channel widths need not be recalibrated periodically. Also, since electron guns can be built with very linear deflection characteristics, over-all converter linearity can be very good.

One type of beam-deflection converter tube has a number of adjacent insulated electrodes located at the target end of the tube. An input signal applied to the deflection plates determines which of the target electrodes is struck by the electron beam. The electron beam, normally biased off, is turned on at the peak of the input signal, so that the number of the target electrode struck by the beam is a measure of the input-signal peak height. Each target electrode is connected to a suitable tallying device.

The principal limitations of this type of converter result from the finite size of the focused electron beam, from the variation in spot size with position (deflection defocusing), and from the variation in spot shape with position (astigmatism).   A modern electrostatically focused and deflected electron gun can focus a beam of several microamperes to a spot a few mils in diameter at accelerating voltages compatible with reasonable deflection sensitivity and linearity over 2 to 3 in. of target.   If a high-quality electron gun is built into a tube with 10 target electrodes, the spot size may be no more than a few per cent of a channel width and relatively stable channel-edge definition may be achieved.   If, however, many more than ten target electrodes are used, the spot size may be a substantial fraction of a channel width.   The charge signal at a target electrode depends, of course, upon the fraction of the beam intercepted by the target.   If the spot is not small compared to the target, many input signals may give rise to target signals of less than maximum size.   The effective channel width is then determined, at least partly, by the minimum amplitude of target signal acceptable to the associated tallying device.   The channel width is no longer completely determined by geometrical factors alone but now depends somewhat upon the sensitivity of the discriminator in the tallying circuit.   This means, in effect, that to achieve good channel-width stability each target must be connected to a moderately stable discriminator.   The contribution of the beam-deflection tube to the converter is, then, little more than to increase its cost.   Furthermore, since the effective spot size cannot be made exactly equal to the space between adjacent target electrodes, the converter must have either gaps or overlaps between channels or, because of astigmatism, perhaps both.   As a result of these difficulties, this type of converter has attracted little attention.

Another type of beam-deflection converter can be made with a shadow mask of uniformly spaced opaque stripes placed over the face of a standard cathode-ray tube [8].   The input signal, applied to one set of deflection plates, is allowed to rise to its peak value with the beam turned off. The beam is then turned on while the input signal decays to zero. A photomultiplier tube viewing the face of the cathode-ray tube sees a series of light flashes as the spot crosses the opaque stripes of the shadow mask.   The pulses from the photomultiplier are counted in a scaler, the number being proportional to the input-pulse height.   The maximum allowable signal-decay rate is determined by the speed of the scaler.   The over-all conversion time can be minimized if the signal decays linearly at this maximum rate.   A run-down circuit like that of a discharge converter (see Art. 4.2) is suitable for producing an appropriate signal shape.

The only advantage that this type of converter can claim over the previously considered pulse-height-to-time converters is that the signal decay need not be highly linear, since the conversion linearity is deter-

mined by the geometry of the shadow mask and the deflection characteristics of the cathode-ray tube.   This, however, is not a real advantage
because highly linear sweeps are easy to make, whereas the linearity and
uniformity of even a perfect shadow mask are nullified, at least in part, by
the nonuniform multiple reflection and scattering of light between the
front and the back surfaces of the cathode-ray-tube face.   The system is
more complex than the other height-to-time converters, has no real
advantages, and is, therefore, little used.

A much more promising beam-deflection system has been developed
by Porter and Borkowski [9] of the Oak Ridge National Laboratory.
This system makes use of a specially built beam-deflection tube containing a target grid with one hundred equally spaced apertures and a signal
plate directly behind it to catch the beam when it passes through an
aperture.   An input signal, applied to a set of deflection plates, deflects
the beam to a point where some, all, or none of the beam current is collected by the signal plate.   The signal-plate current is compared, at the
input of an amplifier, with a fixed reference current which is adjusted to
be approximately equal to one-half of the deflection-tube beam current.
The output of the amplifier is mixed with the input signal at the deflection
plates in such a way that, if the signal-plate current exceeds the reference
current, the beam is deflected downward, and if the signal-plate current is
smaller than the reference current, the beam is deflected upward.   If the
signal-plate current is larger than the reference current, the beam moves
downward until half the beam current is intercepted by the upper edge of
a target grid strip.   If more than half of the beam current is intercepted
by the target grid, the signal-plate current is less than the reference current, so the amplifier drives the beam upward until the beam straddles the
upper edge of a target grid strip where half the beam is intercepted and
half goes to the signal plate.   Therefore, no matter where the input signal
directs the beam, feedback from the comparison amplifier redirects the
beam to the nearest upper edge of a target grid strip.   Even though the
input signals may have a continuous set of values, when equilibrium conditions are established the deflection-plate voltage can only be one of a discrete, quantized set of values determined by the quantizing-tube geometry.   The equilibrium deflection-plate voltage is the nearest quantized
approximation to the input-signal amplitude.

While the beam-deflection quantizer might be used in association with a
number of tallying devices, its characteristics are best exploited by associating it with a beam-deflection electrostatic memory.   Storage locations
in such a memory are addressed by a set of discrete voltages on deflection
plates.   If the deflection plates of the memory tube are connected in
parallel with the deflection plates of the quantizing tube, the storage channel appropriate to the input signal is automatically selected.   Details of

the electrostatic memory and the information storage process will be discussed in the next chapter (Art. 5.4).

4.4 Miscellaneous Converters

Several other types of pulse-height-to-time converters have been built or proposed, and others will undoubtedly be developed in the future. The number of possible configurations is enormous, and an attempt at a complete discussion would be beyond the scope of this volume. We shall, therefore, limit ourselves to a brief consideration of four other converter configurations.

A scheme proposed by Alberisi et al. [10] makes use of a single discriminator and a set of delay lines to sort input signals into a number of amplitude channels. The input signals are inserted at the junctions of a number of delay lines, connected in series, via a set of attenuators in such a way that an input pulse produces a train of pulses increasing in amplitude at the output end of the series of delay lines. In a converter with n channels there are $n - 1$ delay lines and n attenuators adjusted so that the amplitudes of successive pulses in the output-pulse train correspond to the sequence A/n, $A/(n - 1)$, . . . , $A/1$, where A is proportional to the input-pulse amplitude. The train of pulses is applied to a single discriminator with a fixed bias adjusted to be equal to $1/n$ times the largest pulse amplitude to be measured. The time at which the discriminator triggers, measured with respect to the time of arrival of the input pulse, is a measure of the input-pulse amplitude. This time can be determined by sending a signal, derived from the input pulse, down another set of delay lines to n coincidence circuits, each also connected to the discriminator output. At one coincidence circuit the delayed input signal and the discriminator output signal arrive simultaneously, the number of the coincidence circuit being determined by the input-pulse height. The pulse-height analyzer is completed by connecting each coincidence circuit to a suitable tallying circuit.

If the attenuators are carefully adjusted to produce a pulse train as indicated above, the amplitude channels will all be equal. Furthermore, because only passive elements are involved, the relative channel widths should be quite stable. The single discriminator used should, of course, be as stable as possible, but since variations in its threshold affect all channel edges proportionally, the stability requirements are not too severe. The circuit is comparable in cost and complexity with multi-discriminator converters and must be adjusted with the same care. It has the advantage of greater channel-width stability and the disadvantage of longer conversion time.

A system that has been extensively applied to the problem of digitizing slowly varying voltages has frequently been suggested as a possibility for nuclear pulse-height measurements. If an input signal is to be measured in the range of 0 to V volts, it is first stretched and then compared with the voltage $V/2$. If the signal is greater than $V/2$, the first stage of an electronic register (consisting, for example, of a set of "flip-flop" circuits) is set to the "1" state. If the signal is less than $V/2$, the first register stage is left in the "0" state. The first register stage is connected to an electronic switch which then removes the voltage $V/2$ if the register remains in the 0 state but sustains it if the register has been triggered to the 1 state. At the same time a voltage $V/4$ is added, so that the input is now being compared with either $V/4$ or $3V/4$, depending on the state of the first register stage. The result of the second comparison determines the setting of the second register stage which in turn determines whether the $V/4$ voltage component will be removed or sustained. A voltage $V/8$ is then added to the resultant voltage and another comparison is made. The process is continued for a number of steps determined by the number of amplitude channels desired. At each step the binary number stored in the resistor represents a closer approximation to the amplitude of the input signal. If n comparisons are made, the number of amplitude intervals defined is 2^n, so that input signals can be sorted into a large number of channels in only a few operations. For example, seven comparisons define 128 channels and ten comparisons define 1024 channels.

It has been argued that this technique makes much more economical use of conversion time than pulse-height-to-time converters in which a comparison is required for each channel. Furthermore, electronic switching techniques are sufficiently well refined to measure voltages in this way to three significant figures. Nevertheless, no satisfactory nuclear pulse-height analyzers have been built using this technique, and it is doubtful that any will be. The major problem is the high precision required in the first few coarse voltage steps in order to achieve equal and stable channel widths. Consider a 128-channel converter in which the first voltage step is 0.1 per cent higher than the intended value $V/2$. If there are no errors in any of the other voltage steps, all channels will be equal except channel 63, which will be 6.4 per cent too wide. A similar error in step $V/4$ makes channels 31 and 95 3.2 per cent too wide. The channel widths are seen to be very sensitive to slight errors in the values of the coarse voltage steps. Very precise and stable resistors must be used in the voltage dividers that generate the coarse voltage steps. Wire-wound resistors are probably not acceptable for a high-speed converter, except at low-resistance values, because it would be difficult to compensate for their inductance. Other resistor types probably could not be held to sufficiently close tolerances to achieve good channel-width stability. Of course, these considerations do not detract from the utility of this conversion scheme in those applications in which channel-width equality and stability are not important.

A variation on the step discharge converter (see Art. 4.2 and Fig. 4.6) that makes use of two sizes of discharge step has been described by MacMahon and Gosolovitch [11]. The "dual-step" converter features a reduction in conversion time, for a 100-channel analyzer, of up to a factor of 5 as compared with other pulse-height-to-time converters using the same clock frequency. After a storage capacitor is charged to the peak value of an input signal, the step discharge is begun with large steps equal to 10 per cent of the full-scale voltage. The number of large steps is counted in the second ("tens") decade of a decimal scale of 100. An amplitude discriminator terminates the coarse discharge when the voltage on the storage capacitor has been reduced to the neighborhood of 10 per cent of full scale. The discharge then proceeds in reduced steps of 1 per cent of full scale until the capacitor has been discharged to zero. These fine discharge steps are counted by the first ("units") decade of the scaler. The number stored in the scaler at the end of the discharge is a digital representation of the input-pulse amplitude. It will be observed that a signal of full-scale amplitude can be measured by 10 coarse steps and 10 fine steps, or a total of 20 steps, as opposed to a conventional converter which would require 100 steps.

In the dual-step converter it is not important that the discriminator which terminates the coarse discharge be biased to exactly 10 per cent of full scale. Any value higher than 10 per cent is acceptable, but a value close to 10 per cent (for example, 13 per cent) is to be preferred. For some values of input signal the number of fine discharge steps may then be greater than 10. When this occurs, an additional count is added in the second decade of the scaler so that the number stored at the end of the discharge represents the input signal without error, regardless of the discriminator bias.

The adjustment of the relative sizes of the coarse and fine discharge steps is quite critical. If they are not exactly in a 10 to 1 ratio, then the widths of channels 9, 19, 29, etc., will be different from the others. This will introduce spurious peaks or valleys in pulse-height spectra, occurring at 10-channel intervals. This pattern is easily recognized and may be corrected by adjusting the relative size of the discharge steps until the discontinuities in a test spectrum disappear.

A converter in which the input-signal amplitude controls the frequency of a frequency-modulated oscillator has been described by Russell and Lefevre [12]. The advantages claimed for the converter are high stability of channel position and width. The input signal, stretched to a length of about 4 μsec, determines the current in a saturating winding on a ferrite-core inductor, which is a frequency-determining element in a free-running LC oscillator. The oscillator output is applied, through isolating amplifiers, to a set of tuned circuits. The tuned circuits, each corresponding to a different amplitude channel, are adjusted to resonate at frequencies spaced approximately uniformly over the oscillator tuning range. The frequency intervals are chosen so that the half-amplitude point on the high-frequency side of the resonance curve of one tuned circuit coincides approximately with the half-amplitude point on the low-frequency side of the resonance curve of the next tuned circuit. Amplitude discriminators, biased to the half-maximum value of the rectified tuned-circuit output signals, define the pulse-height-analyzer channel boundaries.

The center value of each analyzer channel is very precisely defined and stable because the resonant frequency of a tuned circuit depends on stable, passive elements. The channel widths are also rather well determined because the rectified output voltage from the tuned circuits (of the order of 100 volts) is large compared to the uncertainty in the discriminator thresholds. Also, the maximum voltage amplitude is somewhat stabilized by overdriving the amplifiers that drive the tuned circuits so that their output is limited by the relatively stable "bottoming" characteristic of the amplifier tubes.

The oscillator frequency does not vary exactly linearly with input-signal amplitude. However, the nonlinearity is easily compensated for by adjustment of the tuned-circuit resonant frequencies. The individual discriminator biases are adjusted to provide equal channel widths. It is, of course, impossible to make adjacent channel edges coincide exactly, so there are small gaps, overlaps, or both, between channels.

High-Q-tuned circuits do not respond instantly to signal-frequency changes. The response time is proportional to the Q and inversely proportional to the frequency. The tuned circuit Q is determined by the oscillator-frequency deviation range and the number of channels that must be included in this range. For converters with many more than 10 channels, the required Q may be difficult to achieve. Also, the operating frequency must be high in order to keep the conversion time short. The frequency-modulation converter is, therefore, not very well adapted to analyzers with a large number of channels unless an oscillator is employed with a very wide tuning range. A klystron oscillator, tuned by varying its repeller voltage, has been suggested as a possibility. However, it is doubtful that such a costly and complex design is warranted because other, simpler, converters can achieve better channel-width stability. The frequency-modulation converter does have unusually high channel-position stability, but this is usually much less important than channel-width stability.

REFERENCES

1. Kelly, G.: Pulse Amplitude Analyzers for Spectrometry, *Nucleonics*, vol. 10, no. 4, p. 34, April, 1952.
2. Wilkinson, D.: A Stable Ninety-nine Channel Pulse Amplitude Analyzer for Slow Counting, *Proc. Cambridge Phil. Soc.*, vol. 46, part 3, p. 508, 1950.
3. Schumann, R., and J. McMahon: Argonne 256-channel Pulse-height Analyzer, *Rev. Sci. Instr.*, vol. 27, p. 675, 1956.
4. Chase, R.: 100 Channel Quartz Line Pulse Height Analyzer, *Brookhaven Natl. Lab. Rept.* BNL 401 (T-14), May, 1956.
5. Puckle, O.: "Time Bases," Chapman & Hall, Ltd., London, 1955.
6. Chance, B., V. Hughes, E. F. MacNichol, D. Sayre, and F. C. Williams: "Waveforms," MIT Radiation Laboratory Series, no. 19, McGraw-Hill Book Company, Inc., New York, 1948.
7. Byington, P., and C. Johnstone: A 100-channel Pulse Height Analyzer Using Magnetic Core Storage, IRE National Convention Record, Part 10, p. 204, 1955.
8. Fulbright, H., and J. McCarthy: A Thirty-channel Pulse-height Discriminator Based on a Cathode Ray Tube, *Phys. Rev.*, vol. 87, p. 184, 1952.
9. Koch, H., and R. Johnston (eds.): Multichannel Pulse Height Analyzers, *Natl. Acad. Sci.–Natl. Research Council, Publ.* 467, p. 110, 1957.
10. Alberisi, A., C. Bernardini, and I. Quercia: Proposal for an Analog-to-Digital Electronic Converter Suited for Nuclear Pulse Height Analysis, *Nuclear Instruments*, vol. 3, p. 201, 1958.
11. MacMahon, J., and S. Gosolovitch: A 100 Channel Pulse Height Analyzer Utilizing Dual Step Conversion, Proceedings of the International Symposium on Nuclear Electronics, organized by the French Society of Radio Electricians, Paris, 1958.
12. Russell, J., and H. LeFevre: An F-M Multichannel Pulse-height Analyzer, *Nucleonics*, vol. 15, no. 2, p. 76, February, 1957.

CHAPTER 5

MULTICHANNEL PULSE-HEIGHT ANALYZERS II

A pulse-amplitude distribution is determined by counting the number of pulses falling in each of a number of pulse-height channels. In the last chapter we discussed the more popular schemes for associating each input pulse with the appropriate pulse-height channel. In this chapter we shall be concerned with the techniques used for counting and keeping track of the number of pulses that fall in each channel.

5.1 Scalers

A straightforward method for accumulating and storing multi-channel pulse-height data is to associate each pulse-height channel with a separate scaling circuit. The scalers must have a resolving time commensurate with the maximum expected channel counting rates. In general, the scalers need not have as short a resolving time as the converter section of the pulse-height analyzer if the number of channels is large, because it is then relatively unlikely that successive pulses will fall in the same channel. At the same time, allowance must be made for the fact that many pulse-height spectra have prominent peaks in which the counting rate is considerably higher than in other portions of the spectrum. It is not unusual for the counting rate in one or several channels to be as much as ten times the average counting rate in all channels. The resolving time of the scalers should be sufficiently short to prevent excessive counting loss in the highest-counting-rate channel if spectral distortion, in the form of flattened peaks, is to be avoided.

The number of counts accumulated in each channel in the course of an experiment must be large enough to yield the desired statistical accuracy. This imposes a lower limit on the capacity of the individual channel scalers. However, in the vast majority of nuclear spectra the individual channel counting rates vary over a wide range. If a particular total count must be recorded in one of the low-counting-rate channels in order to achieve sufficient statistical accuracy, the total count in the high-counting-rate channels may be many times greater. It is convenient, therefore, to provide considerable reserve count capacity to prevent overflow in the high-count channels.   This may be done by building each scaler with a large number of electronic binary or decimal counting stages, but it is generally more economical to use a mechanical impulse counter preceded by only a few electronic stages.

The principal advantage of a scaler data storage system is that information can be entered rapidly, in less than a microsecond with many simple scaling circuits.   However, it has a number of disadvantages.   If the number of channels is large, the cost and physical size of a scaler memory are considerably greater than those of most of the alternatives.   In addition, the large number of active elements subject to failure makes a large scaler memory relatively unreliable.   Also, although it is certainly not impossible, it is difficult to associate a scaler memory with an automatic data display or an automatic data printer.   The data stored in a scaler memory are usually transcribed by hand.   This is not particularly troublesome when there are only 10 or 20 data channels, but with 100 or more channels manual recording of the data is not only tedious but is likely to be associated with a disconcertingly large number of recording errors.

Most scaler memories are associated with multidiscriminator converters.   This results in pulse-height analyzers with short resolving times because both the converter and the storage sections are fast.   An exception is the 100-channel pulse-height analyzer, designed at the Atomic Energy Research Establishment, in Harwell, England [1], which combines a pulse-height-to-time converter and a scaler memory in an unusual way.   An important problem in any pulse-height analyzer using a pulse-height-to-time converter is the design of the mechanism by which information is transferred from the converter scaler (the "address" scaler) to the memory.

In the particular analyzer above, the problem is solved in an ingenious way that takes advantage of the special characteristics of glow-transfer counter tubes (dekatrons).   Dekatrons are gas-filled decade counting tubes in which a glow discharge is formed between the anode and one of ten cathodes.   The discharge can be transferred from one cathode to the next, thus increasing the stored count by 1, by applying a pair of pulses, in sequence, to two sets of "guide rails" contained in the tube.   If only one set of guide rails is pulsed, the glow does not advance.   Figure 5.1 shows how a set of 100 dekatrons can be connected to a two-decade address scaler so that information can be transferred from the address scaler to the dekatron memory without any intervening equipment.   The count registered in the address scaler serves to select a horizontal line corresponding to its "tens" digit and a vertical line corresponding to its "units" digit.   The horizontal lines are connected to the first set of guide rails in each dekatron and the vertical lines to the second set.   The selected horizontal and vertical lines are pulsed in sequence so that the dekatron at their intersection receives appropriate signals for increasing its count by 1.   None of the other dekatrons receive pulses on both sets of guide rails, so none of the others record a count.   The dekatrons, in effect, perform a coincidence function as well as a counting function. The same sort of performance can be achieved with other types of memory scalers if a coincidence circuit is placed at each of the intersections of the

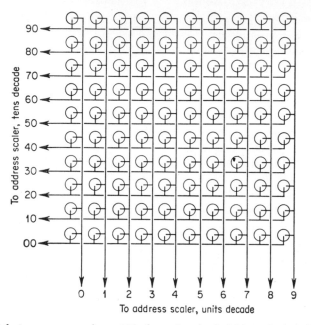

FIG. 5.1   Dekatron memory for a 100-channel pulse-height analyzer, showing connections between the address scaler and the dekatron guide rails.

horizontal and vertical lines and the selected lines are pulsed simultaneously.   The dekatron system, however, saves 100 coincidence circuits.

5.2 Delay-line Memories

As experimenters demanded higher resolution and, therefore, more data channels in their pulse spectrometers, it became clear that the possibilities of alternatives to the costly and unreliable scaler memories should be investigated.   Digital computer memory systems were the obvious alternatives to consider, for many of the computer memory systems store information at a low unit cost, with higher reliability than can be achieved with scalers.

The first multichannel pulse-height analyzer incorporating a computer memory was built in 1951 by Hutchinson and Scarrott [2].   They employed an ultrasonic delay line as the memory element.   In general, any device that is characterized by an appreciable time delay between input and output signals can be used as a memory element.   It is merely necessary to connect the output to the input through an amplifying and reshaping circuit which compensates for the attenuation and distortion in the delay element.   If a signal is introduced into such a system, it continues to circulate indefinitely through the closed memory loop with a period equal to the characteristic delay interval of the delay element.   If the delay interval is long, more than one pulse can be introduced at the input before the first pulse returns.   The number of pulses that can be stored depends on the time length of the delay and on the allowable pulse-packing density, which is determined by the pulse width that the system can pass without excess attenuation and distortion.   As with any pulse circuit, the minimum pulse width that the system can handle is determined by its frequency bandwidth, so the total information capacity of the delay-line memory is determined by its delay-bandwidth product. However, all systems that transmit electrical signals at less than the velocity of light are characterized by delay dispersion that tends to broaden short pulses more and more as the delay is increased.   This corresponds to a reduction in bandwidth, so that the delay-bandwidth product cannot be increased indefinitely by increasing the delay.   Furthermore, the signal attenuation in any delay element increases with the delay, and a practical upper limit to the delay of a single element is that which attenuates the input signal to the point where it is not easily distinguished from the regenerating amplifier noise.

Because of dispersion and attenuation, the information capacity of electromagnetic delay lines is not large.   A typical electromagnetic delay line might have a bandwidth, in short lengths, of 10 megacycles and an attenuation of 1 db per μsec.   The 10-megacycle bandwidth implies a practical limit of about three pulses per microsecond, so a 100-μsec length of delay line could, in the absence of delay dispersion, store 300 pulses. If the input-signal power level is taken as 1 watt, then the signal at the output of the delay line, 10^{-10} watt, can probably be distinguished from the noise[1] of a well-built 10-megacycle amplifier.   However, if the delay were 200 μsec, recognition of the signal above noise would be out of the question.   If, in addition, we take delay dispersion into account, we find that the upper limit on the number of pulses that may be stored in such an electromagnetic delay line is in the neighborhood of 100.

---

[1] The power associated with resistor or Johnson noise at the input of an amplifier may be written $P = 4KT \Delta f$, where K is Boltzmann's constant (1.38×10^{-23} joule per °K), T is the absolute temperature of the input resistance, and Δf is the amplifier bandwidth.   With a 10-megacycle bandwidth, at normal room temperature (300°K), $P = 1.66 \times 10^{-13}$ watt.   The total effective input noise in a practical amplifier might be only slightly greater, say 3×10^{-13} watt, resulting in a signal-to-noise ratio of 25 db.

Acoustic delay lines can be built with much larger capacity. In an acoustic delay line an electrical signal is converted to an acoustic signal by an input transducer. The acoustic signal propagates through the delay medium at the characteristic velocity of sound in that medium and is converted, some time later, to an electrical signal by an output transducer. The delay dispersion in a well-constructed acoustic delay line is sufficiently small to permit the packing of several thousand pulses in a single line. Furthermore, with properly matched input and output transducers the signal attenuation, including insertion losses, generally falls in the range of 40 to 60 db, so that amplifier noise presents no problem. The first practical acoustic delay lines were tanks of mercury with quartz-crystal electromechanical transducers at each end. Later, higher-quality lines were built using fused quartz as the delay medium, with quartz-crystal input and output transducers. The quartz lines were smaller, lighter, and less expensive than the mercury lines. Acoustic lines have also been built using metal wires (nickel or stainless steel) as the delay medium, with magnetostrictive input and output transducers. The magnetostrictive lines are less expensive than the quartz lines and can be easily adjusted in length, but they are limited by the transducers and by delay dispersion to about one-fifth the bandwidth of the quartz lines.

A delay line can be used to store multichannel pulse-height data by dividing its time length into subintervals and associating each subinterval with a pulse-height channel. The first storage subinterval is preceded by a "start" pulse which is, in some way, distinguishable from the other pulses,[1] and the subintervals are identified by their time relationship with respect to the start pulse. Each subinterval can store a pulse pattern which is related to the number of input signals which have been recorded in the corresponding pulse-height channel.

Let us consider, as an example, a delay-line memory capable of storing a start pulse and 2,000 data pulses. Let us suppose that this memory is to be used to store data for a 100-channel pulse-height analyzer. Therefore, in the subinterval associated with each channel there is time for as many as 20 pulses. If each pulse in a subinterval is used to represent one input signal in the corresponding pulse-height channel, the memory will be capable of recording a maximum of 20 signals in each channel, which is hardly enough to be useful.

[1] The start pulse can be larger or wider than or different in polarity from the other pulses. Alternatively, the start pulse can be inserted by a "gate-pulse" generating circuit whose output is somewhat shorter in duration than the full delay interval. Pulses may be inserted into the delay-line memory only during the gate pulse, so that the first pulse returning from memory after the gate interval can be recognized as the start pulse. The start pulse is used to retrigger the gate-pulse generator, which inserts a new start pulse into the delay line, in the same time location relative to the other stored information as the original start pulse.

The channel storage capacity can be very considerably increased by employing coding techniques.   If each of the possible pulse locations in a subinterval is assigned a suitable weighting factor, numbers much larger than 20 can be represented by 20 pulses.   The simplest arrangement is to allow the pulses to represent digits in the binary number system.[1]   A pulse is used to represent a "1," and the absence of a pulse in a particular time location is used to represent a "0."   The bits can be arranged in order of either ascending or descending significance, but as we shall see shortly, it is more convenient to let the first bit in a given

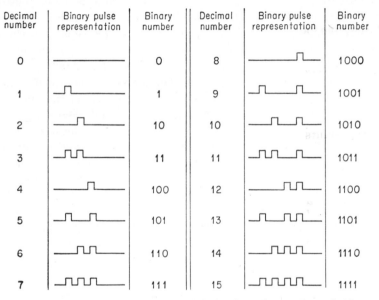

Decimal number	Binary pulse representation	Binary number	Decimal number	Binary pulse representation	Binary number
0		0	8		1000
1		1	9		1001
2		10	10		1010
3		11	11		1011
4		100	12		1100
5		101	13		1101
6		110	14		1110
7		111	15		1111

FIG. 5.2   Binary representation of decimal numbers 0 through 15.

subinterval represent one count, the second bit two counts, the third bit four counts, and so on, in order of increasing significance.   Figure 5.2 shows how the decimal numbers 0 through 15 can be represented by four binary digits and illustrates the appearance of the corresponding pulse trains.   Since, conventionally, time is considered to progress from left to right, while numbers are written with their most significant digit to the left, the pulse trains, with the least-significant bit first, look like mirror images of the corresponding binary numbers.

The largest number that can be represented by n bits is $2^n - 1$.   Therefore, with 20 bits per channel the capacity of each channel is $2^{20} - 1$ or 1,048,575 events.   This is more than adequate for the vast majority of nuclear experiments.

[1] Binary digits are commonly referred to as "bits" in computer literature.

In order to incorporate a delay-line memory into a pulse-height analyzer, it is necessary to provide a mechanism for associating an input signal with the appropriate group of memory bits. In computer terminology this might be expressed as locating the memory address corresponding to the input-pulse height. This is done with the aid of a set of time marks that are synchronized with the memory cycle. In the Hutchinson-Scarrott system the start pulse, as it emerges from the memory line, turns on a clock oscillator whose period corresponds to the desired interval between pulses in memory. The clock oscillator, in turn, drives a frequency divider, the output of which serves to divide the clock pulses into subgroups corresponding to pulse-height channels. For the memory configuration referred to above, the frequency divider separates the clock pulses into 100 groups of 20 pulses each. Two pulse trains, synchronized with the delay-line period, are now available. The 2,000 clock pulses mark the time locations in memory at which bits can be inserted, and 100 pulses from the frequency divider mark the beginning of the pulse-height channels and identify the least-significant bit in each channel.

A pulse-height-to-time converter can be used in at least two ways to locate memory addresses corresponding to input-pulse amplitudes. Cycles of the converter oscillator can be counted by an address scaler, as described in Art. 4.2. Another scaler can make a continuous count of the channel-mark pulses from the frequency divider. After each channel mark, the counts in the two scalers can be compared. The time at which the counts in the two scalers are the same is the proper time for tallying the input pulse in its pulse-height channel in memory.

The Hutchinson-Scarrott system is considerably simpler than this, in that neither the address scaler nor the channel-mark scaler is required. It makes use of an analog, rather than a digital, system for locating memory addresses. The comparison sweep signal in the converter, instead of being triggered by the input signal, runs continuously in synchronism with the delay-line memory cycle. The amplitude of the sweep voltage at any instant is, therefore, commensurate with the number of the pulse-height channel that appears at the end of the memory line at that time. The input signal is stretched in the usual manner and is compared with the sweep voltage. The time of equality is noted, and the next channel-mark signal is used to initiate the tallying of the signal in memory.

The analog addressing system is illustrated in Fig. 5.3. A 10-channel analyzer is represented because too many channel marks would make the drawing confusing. Input signals may arrive at any time with respect to the linear sweep waveform. If, when the input arrives, it is larger than the instantaneous sweep amplitude (input *a*, Fig. 5.3), it is measured some time later in the same sweep cycle. If, however, the signal arrives at a time when the sweep has already attained a greater amplitude (input b), it is measured in the next sweep cycle.   It will be observed that, even though input signals a and b have the same amplitude, different lengths of time are required to complete their measurement.   In general, the time required to measure a signal can have any value from zero to the full memory period.   Assuming that the input signals have no systematic time correlation with the memory cycle, the average time required to measure a signal is one-half the memory cycle time.

Once the appropriate memory address has been located, the tallying of the input signal is completed by increasing the number stored at that address by 1.   The adder that performs this function can be of either parallel or serial type.   A parallel adder operates on all the bits of the numbers to be added simultaneously.   A serial adder operates on the bits

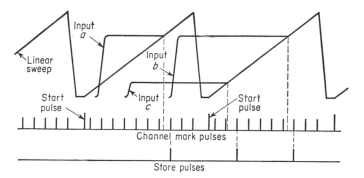

Fig. 5.3   Waveforms illustrating the addressing system in the Hutchinson-Scarrott pulse-height analyzer. a, b, and c represent three possible input signals after they have been lengthened in the pulse stretcher.

in sequence, one at a time, starting with the least-significant bit.   Since a delay-line memory is serial in nature (the bits of the stored numbers emerge from the memory one at a time), a serial adder is the logical choice. Furthermore, the addition of 1 in a serial adder operating in the binary number system involves very simple logical decisions.   A binary number can be increased by 1 in the following manner.

If the first bit (the least-significant bit) is 0, it is changed to 1.   All of the other bits are left unchanged.   If the first bit is 1, it is changed to 0 and the next bit is examined.   If the second bit is 0, it is changed to 1 and all the remaining bits are left unchanged.   If the second bit is 1, it is changed to 0 and the third bit is examined.   The process continues until the first 0 is changed to 1, at which time the addition is complete.

The adder circuit (Fig. 5.4) is part of the regenerating amplifier that connects the output of the memory delay line to its input.   The signals presented to the adder have passed through the memory delay line and an amplifier, both of which have limited bandwidth and delay dispersion.

The signals are therefore somewhat broader than when they were inserted into the memory line. If they were reinserted into memory without alteration, each successive pass through memory would degrade the signal pattern until adjacent signals could not be resolved from each other. The adder circuit is, therefore, gated by clock pulses from the primary oscillator, so that the pulses have a standard shape and location in time when reinserted into the memory. The adder recognizes positive input signals with an amplitude of about 20 volts as 1's and the absence of such signals as 0's. Normally, the grid of T_1 is about 10 volts positive with

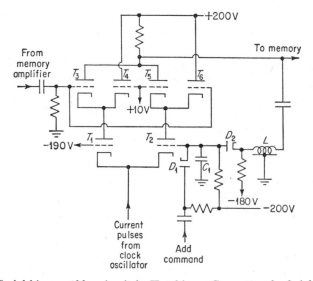

Fig. 5.4   Serial binary adder circuit in Hutchinson-Scarrott pulse-height analyzer.

respect to the grid of T_2, so that a positive input signal, applied simultaneously to the grids of T_3 and T_6, will cause only T_3 to conduct and produce a negative output pulse with an amplitude of about 20 volts. The duration of the output pulse is limited to the duration of the clock pulse at the cathodes of T_1 and T_2, even though the input signal may be somewhat longer. If the negative output pulse is considered to represent a 1, the adder, in its normal state, leaves the contents of memory unaltered and merely regenerates the information stored.

When an input signal is measured in the pulse-height-to-time converter, an "add-command" signal is generated which charges storage capacitor C_1 about 20 volts positive via D_1, just prior to the arrival of the first bit in the channel. This causes current pulses from the clock oscillator to flow in T_2 rather than in T_1. If during a clock pulse the adder input is positive (corresponding to a 1 from the memory amplifier), the clock pulse flows in T_6 and produces no output.   The 1 input is, thus, converted to a 0 output.   If the next bit is a 1, it is treated in the same way.   However, when a 0 arrives from memory, the clock pulse flows in T_5, producing a negative output pulse which enters the memory as a 1.   This same output signal, after a short delay, discharges the storage capacitor via D_2, returning the adder to its normal condition.   Thus, upon receipt of an add-command signal, the adder changes 1's to 0's and 0's to 1's until the first 1 appears at its output, after which it passes signals without alteration.   In this way, it accomplishes the logical requirements for the serial binary addition of 1 to the stored count.   Delay line L is included in order to permit the adder to deliver an output 1 signal of standard duration before the storage capacitor is discharged and the adder reverts to its normal condition.

If a pulse-height analyzer is to be a useful instrument, the information stored in its memory must be made available to the experimenter.   The data may be presented either in digital form or as an analog plot of the accumulated counts as a function of channel number.   In general, both presentations are desirable.   The analog display permits the experimenter to keep track of the progress of the experiment and to recognize significant features in the pulse-height spectrum.   The digital presentation makes possible accurate numerical analysis of the results, such as background and dead-time corrections and the quantitative determination of radiation intensities.

The original Hutchinson-Scarrott pulse-height analyzer presents the stored information as binary digital information on the face of a cathode-ray tube.   The cathode-ray-tube spot is swept in a raster similar to that used in television (but rotated through 90°).   The horizontal sweep is the same sweep waveform that is used in the pulse-height-to-time converter. It is triggered by the start pulse in memory and has a period slightly less than the memory recirculation interval.   The vertical sweep is triggered by the channel marks obtained from the frequency divider.   The clock oscillator pulses are applied to the control grid of the cathode-ray tube so that each memory-bit location is portrayed as a slightly intensified dot on the cathode-ray-tube screen, each vertical row of dots corresponding to the bits of a particular storage channel.   Pulses from the adder, in addition to being returned to memory, are also applied to the cathode-ray-tube grid, so that storage locations that contain a 1 appear brighter on the screen than those which contain a 0.   The numbers stored in each channel can be read, in binary notation, directly from the cathode-ray-tube screen.   In addition, an approximate analog pulse-height distribution can be inferred by inspection of the cathode-ray-tube display.   The location of the highest bright dot in each channel gives a rough indication (within a factor of 2) of the count stored in that channel.   The display is more nearly logarithmic than linear, because each dot represents twice as many counts as the dot beneath it.   The analog display is, of course, quite imperfect, because it is difficult to account, visually, for any but the most significant bit in each channel.   With practice, some appreciation of the significance of lower-order bits can be acquired, but it is still quite difficult to recognize small peaks in which the counting rate is less than twice that in the neighboring channels.

A more satisfactory analog display can be achieved by converting the serial binary numbers into proportional voltages with a circuit like that of Fig. 5.5.   The circuit includes a diode "pump" with a "dipper" capacitor C_1 that transfers a quantity of charge $Q = C_1V$ to the "bucket" capacitor C_2 each time a 1 (signified by a pulse of amplitude V) is presented to its input. C_2 is included in a feedback loop which constitutes a charge integrator (see Art. 2.3).   Resistor R is adjusted so that half the

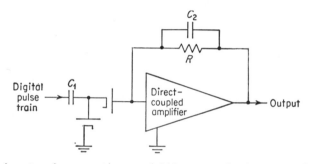

FIG. 5.5   A system for converting a serial binary number into an analog voltage.

charge on C_2 leaks off in the time interval between memory bits.   If the bits are presented to the circuit in order of increasing significance, the capacitor leakage causes each bit to be weighted twice as heavily as the preceding bit.   The net voltage at the integrator output at the time of the last bit in each channel is a linear, analog representation of the count stored in that channel.

While the cathode-ray-tube display in the original Hutchinson-Scarrott pulse-height analyzer presents all the information stored in memory, it does so in rather inconvenient form.   It is by no means a simple matter to translate 100 long binary numbers into decimal numbers and to record them without error.   An automatic data printer is, therefore, a substantial asset to the experimenter.

In order to print the data in decimal form, it is necessary either to translate the stored binary information into decimal notation during the printout process or, alternatively, to arrange for the original storage to be in decimal notation.   Gallagher and McKibben [3] of the Los Alamos Scientific Laboratory have devised a relatively simple modification to the

Hutchinson-Scarrott adder which causes the information to be stored in a binary-coded decimal notation that can be readily translated into standard decimal form for printing.   The bits in each storage channel are subdivided into groups of 4 bits, each group being used to represent a decimal digit.   The system is somewhat less economical of storage space than is the straight binary system.   For example, 20 bits can represent a maximum of 99,999 counts in the binary-coded decimal system (compared with 1,048,575 counts in straight binary notation).

In the Gallagher and McKibben decimal storage system (Fig. 5.6) decimal-digit marks are generated which are time-coincident with every fourth clock pulse.   So long as each fourth-bit location contains a 0, the

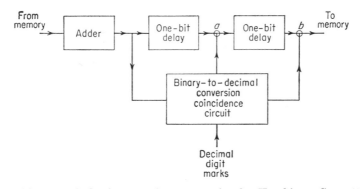

FIG. 5.6   Binary-to-decimal conversion system in the Hutchinson-Scarrott pulse-height analyzer as modified by Gallagher and McKibben [3].

addition proceeds in the usual way, so that, up to the count of 7, the binary and decimal adders perform the same.   However, when a pulse appears in the fourth-bit location, signifying 8 counts, it is recognized by the binary-to-decimal conversion coincidence circuit, which produces an output pulse.   Two short sections of electromagnetic delay line are inserted between the output of the adder and the main memory, each of which has a time length equal to the spacing between bits.   At the same time as the fourth bit emerges from the adder, the third and second bits may be found at mixing points a and b (Fig. 5.6).   The presence of a 1 in the fourth-bit location causes the coincidence circuit to insert 1's in the third- and second-bit locations.   As a result, when 8 counts have been accumulated, the number in memory is 1110 instead of 1000.   Subsequent counts are added according to the rules of serial binary arithmetic, so that the ninth count is represented by 1111, the tenth by 10000, and so on. Whenever there is a 1 in a memory location that is associated with a decimal-digit mark, the coincidence circuit inserts 1's in the two preceding bits, thus giving the group of 4 bits the significance of a decimal digit.

The binary-coded decimal information can be read directly from the cathode-ray-tube screen or it can be printed. It is easier to read the binary-coded decimal numbers than it is to read straight binary numbers, because it is only necessary to be able to recognize the ten combinations of four bits that represent the digits 0 through 9. It is not necessary, for example, to know the decimal equivalent of 2^{14}.

In order to print the information stored in memory, the four-bit groups are presented, one at a time, to a decoder. The decoder translates each four-bit group into the corresponding decimal digit and sends an impulse to the appropriate number solenoid in an electrically operated printer. It is necessary, of course, to select the decimal-digit groups in a standard sequence so that the printed numbers can be associated with the proper storage channels. The memory can be addressed for printout in much the same way that it is addressed for storage. The output of the pulse stretcher is replaced, at the comparison circuit input, by the output of a stepping-switch-controlled d-c voltage divider. The voltage divider is adjusted to present 100 discrete, evenly spaced d-c voltages to the comparison circuit in sequence, each d-c voltage being approximately equal to the mean voltage level of a pulse-height channel. Each d-c voltage level is compared with the sweep waveform, and the channel mark following equality is selected. The decimal-digit marks in each channel are selected in sequence by a switched delay circuit.

In order to generate a standard decimal number the decoder must receive simultaneously all four bits corresponding to a decimal digit, despite the fact that the bits emerge from memory serially. This is accomplished with the aid of three short lengths of electromagnetic delay line, each with a time length equal to the bit spacing in memory, and four coincidence circuits (see Fig. 5.7). The selected decimal-digit mark arrives at all four coincidence circuits simultaneously, at a time when the first of the four bits of the corresponding decimal digit reaches the last coincidence circuit. At the same time the other three bits appear at their respective coincidence circuits. The presence of a 1 at a coincidence circuit input when the decimal-digit mark arrives triggers the coincidence circuit which, in turn, energizes an electromagnetic relay. The contacts of the four relays are arranged in a matrix which directs a source of electrical power to one of ten output leads, corresponding to the decimal digits 0 through 9. The output leads are connected to the control solenoids of an electrically operated printer which records the selected decimal digit. In this way the stored information is printed, digit by digit, in a format controlled by relay and stepping-switch circuits.

Delay-line memories have been used in pulse-height analyzers because they are relatively economical and can be built with adequate storage capacity for most of the applications of pulse spectrometry. They have, however, some drawbacks which have spurred the search for still better memory systems. One drawback is the rather long memory "access time." The access time of a computer memory is the time required to locate a desired memory address and to read, and if necessary restore, its contents. In the case of a delay-line memory, the time required for a single consultation may have any value from zero to the full memory circulation period. In the usual case, where input signals occur at random times, the average access time is half the memory period. The memory period is determined by the bit spacing (usually from 0.2 to 2.0 μsec) and the number of bits and is commonly in the neighborhood of 1,000 μsec. The maximum data tallying rate is limited, therefore, to an average of

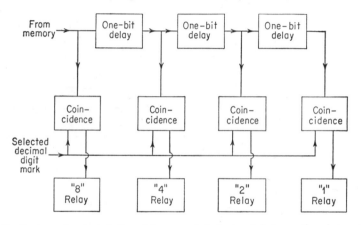

Fig. 5.7 System for translating binary-coded decimal information into standard decimal notation, preparatory to printout, in Gallagher and McKibben pulse-height analyzer.

about 2,000 events per second. Even at moderate counting rates an appreciable number of input signals must be rejected because the analyzer is occupied with other signals. With a properly designed analog-to-digital converter, of course, this does not lead to spectral distortion, except in the case of time-correlated input events, because the analyzer selects input signals for analysis at random. Still, the accurate determination of radiation intensities is made difficult by the long memory access time because dead-time corrections cannot be made with absolute accuracy, particularly when the dead time represents a large fraction of the data collection time.

Probably the most serious disadvantage of delay-line memories is their "volatility." Each bit in memory must be regenerated each cycle, in the neighborhood of 1,000 times per second. An electrical failure or an extraneous noise signal at any time can cause the loss of one or more bits of information. Furthermore, failure to recognize the start pulse properly can result in the clock oscillator getting out of phase with the stored information, with the resultant loss of all the data. Occasional failures of this kind may be tolerated when data runs are short, but when one experiment lasts for many hours (or even days), even infrequent failures can be very disconcerting.

Another problem associated with delay-line memories is the fact that they are difficult to repair. The failure of any element in the memory loop usually results in the loss of all signals at all points in the loop. When the "symptom" is characteristic of so large a number of possible "diseases," the serviceman's ingenuity may be severely taxed.

5.3   Magnetic-core Memories

Hysteresis in ferromagnetic materials provides the basis for a number of very useful information storage devices.   In many ferromagnetic materials, the magnetic flux density B is not uniquely determined by the

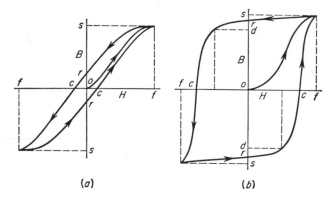

(a) (b)

FIG. 5.8   Typical hysteresis loops for ferromagnetic materials.   Curve b represents a "square-loop" material suitable for use in storage cores in coincident-current memories.

applied magnetic field intensity H, but depends also upon the magnetic history of the material. If H is varied cyclically, the value of B is observed to lag behind the changes in H in a manner, and by an amount, which is characteristic of the particular magnetic material. If B is plotted as a function of H, one obtains a hysteresis loop for the material. Two typical hysteresis loops are shown in Fig. 5.8.   Many of the properties that determine the suitability of a particular magnetic material as a memory element can be read from its hysteresis loop.   These are the saturation flux density B_s (distance os in Fig. 5.8) and the associated saturating field intensity H_s (of); the residual flux density or remanence (or); and the coercive force (oc), which is the magnetic field intensity that is required to reduce the flux density from its remanent value to zero.

A sample of magnetic material can be used as a memory element by virtue of the magnetization that remains after the removal of an applied magnetic field. This residual magnetism can have either of two polarities, depending on the polarity of the applied magnetic field, which can be used to represent the binary digits 0 and 1. Information can be stored in a piece of magnetic material if it is included in a magnetic circuit that is linked one or more times by an electrical conductor. Of the many possible geometric configurations, the most common consists of a magnetic toroid wound with one or more turns of copper wire. A current pulse in one direction in the wire writes a 1 in the core, while a current pulse in the other direction writes a zero.

To read the information stored in a magnetic core, it is necessary to determine the polarity of the remanent magnetic flux. This is usually done with a read pulse that sets the core to the 0 state. The electrical signal induced in a "sense" winding on the core indicates whether or not this changes the remanent flux. A change indicates that the core held a 1, while no change indicates a stored 0. The voltage E induced in the sense winding is

$$E = n \frac{d\phi}{dt} \tag{5.1}$$

where n is the number of turns in the sense winding and ϕ is the magnetic flux. If the read pulse extends over a time interval Δt, then

$$\int_0^{\Delta t} E \, dt = n \, \Delta \phi \tag{5.2}$$

where $\Delta \phi$ is the change in the remanent flux produced by the read pulse. If the core contains a 0, the read pulse produces no net flux change, so the time integral of the induced voltage is zero. This does not mean, of course, that no electrical signal is induced in the sense winding. During the read pulse the flux density changes from r to s and back to r again (Fig. 5.8), so that $d\phi/dt$ is not equal to zero. However, the time integrals of the positive and negative parts of the induced signal are equal, so that the average value of the net voltage impulse is zero. If the core contains a 1, then switching it to 0 induces an asymmetrical signal in the sense winding which has a net integrated value proportional to the distance between the points marked r on the hysteresis loop.

If the read 1 signal is to be easily distinguished from the read 0 signal, it is clearly advantageous to use a magnetic material in which the distance rr is large compared with the distance rs. A "square" hysteresis loop like Fig. 5.8b, therefore, is better for memory cores than one like Fig. 5.8a.

When a magnetic-core memory has only a small number of bits, it may be practical to provide each core with separate read-write and sense windings. A read-write pulse generator would be required as well as an electronic switch capable of directing the generated pulses to each of the memory cores individually. Some economy could be achieved by connecting all, or many, of the sense windings in series so that only one, or a few, sense amplifiers would be required. Still, the system is entirely impractical for a large pulse-height-analyzer memory. A typical instrument might have 100 channels, with 16 storage bits in each channel. To address each core with an individual read-write winding would require a 1,600-pole electronic switch.

The number of addressing elements can be substantially reduced by employing "coincident-current" [4] addressing. Magnetic cores are available which have a coercive force (oc in Fig. 5.8b) which is appreciably

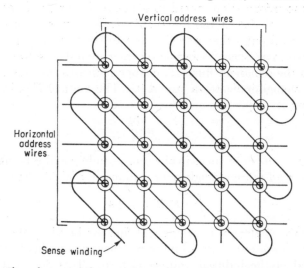

FIG. 5.9   Section of a magnetic-core storage plane, showing the address wires and the sense winding. Threading the sense winding diagonally through the cores results in partial cancellation of the disturb signals.

greater than one-half the saturating magnetic field intensity *of*. This means that, if the core is in one residual flux state, there exists a value of switching current that will change it to the opposite saturation state, while one-half of that switching current will produce only a negligible perturbation in the original residual flux. This property is exploited in coincident-current memories in which each core is threaded by two addressing wires. The cores are generally assembled in a two-dimensional matrix of horizontal and vertical wires, with a core located at each intersection (Fig. 5.9). To select a particular core in the matrix, the horizontal and vertical wires threading it are pulsed simultaneously with currents, each of which is half that required to saturate the core. The selected core is thus subjected to a full saturating magnetomotive force, while other cores, which are threaded by only one of the selected addressing wires, receive only half of a saturating magnetomotive force, which leaves their residual flux substantially unaltered. The selected core can be set to either the 1 state or the 0 state, depending upon the polarity of the two addressing currents.

The information stored in a core is read by pulsing that core, via its two addressing wires, to the 0 state and observing the signal in a sense wire threading the core. Since, for coincident-current addressing, the cores must have very square hysteresis loops, the read signal obtained from a core in the 0 state is considerably smaller than that obtained from a core in the 1 state.

The sense windings on all the cores in each memory plane are generally connected in series to a single read amplifier. Only one read amplifier is required per plane because only one core in each plane can be read at any one time. The signal at the input to the read amplifier represents a composite of the desired read signal from the selected core (either a large read 1 signal or a small read 0 signal) combined with a number of small "disturb" signals from the half-selected cores that share either a horizontal or a vertical address wire with the selected core. While the disturb signal from a single half-selected core is small, corresponding to either the small reversible flux change rs or rd (Fig. 5.8b), the accumulation of disturb signals from the half-selected cores in a large array may be greater than a read 1 signal from the selected core. This difficulty is minimized by threading the sense wire through the core array in such a way that the disturb signals tend to cancel in pairs. One way to do this is to thread the sense wire in a diagonal zigzag pattern, as shown in Fig. 5.9. The disturb signals from one half of the half-selected cores are then opposite in phase to the disturb signals from the other half-selected cores. It follows, of course, that the read 1 signals may be either positive or negative, depending upon the direction of the sense winding through the selected core. The sense winding is therefore connected to the primary of a pulse transformer whose center-tapped secondary is connected to a full-wave rectifier (Fig. 5.10). Both polarities of signal at the pulse transformer primary thus produce signals of the same sign at the read amplifier input.

The individual cores in a pulse-height-analyzer memory can be associated with the various pulse-height channels in a number of ways. A common arrangement is to associate each core in a memory plane with a different pulse-height channel. Each plane, in turn, is associated with a particular binary digit in the numbers stored in the pulse-height channels. For example, a pulse-height analyzer with 100 channels and 16 bits of storage per channel would have 16 core planes, each with 100 cores arranged in a 10×10 matrix. Each plane is connected, via its read amplifier, to a one-bit electronic register (usually a flip-flop), which collectively make up the "memory register." The contents of a particular pulse-height channel are transferred from the core memory to the memory register by pulsing the appropriate horizontal and vertical address wires. It is not necessary to have a separate set of address-current pulse generators for each memory plane. Information is usually transferred between the core memory and the memory register in parallel; that is, all of the bits of a given pulse-height channel are read simultaneously. Since all of the bits in a channel occupy the same coordinate location in each memory plane, the horizontal and vertical addressing wires of all planes may be connected in series and pulsed simultaneously. Thus, by pulsing only one horizontal wire and one vertical wire, all of the bits in a selected pulse-height channel can be transferred from the core memory to the memory register. In the case of a 100-channel, 16-plane memory, each address wire is threaded through 160 cores, 10 in each plane.

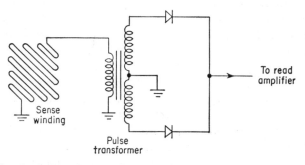

FIG. 5.10   Circuit showing how read signals of either polarity from a magnetic-core plane are converted into signals all having the same sign.

All communication between the core memory and the other circuits of the pulse-height analyzer is done via the memory register. Data for display and printout are derived from the memory register. In addition, during data acquisition the memory register participates in the process of adding 1 to the stored count in a channel whenever it is selected by the analog-to-digital converter section. This is most simply accomplished by connecting the stages of the memory register together, in sequence, with suitable coupling circuits to make it operate as a binary scaler. To tally a count in a particular channel, the contents of that channel are transferred to the memory register. A single pulse is then applied to the first stage of the register scaler, increasing the number stored by 1. The new contents of the memory register are then transferred back to the core memory. Because of its participation in the addition process, the memory register is usually referred to as the arithmetic or "add 1" scaler.

Whenever a number is read from memory, whether the count is increased by 1 as in data accumulation or whether it is left unchanged as in data display, it is necessary to transfer the number in the arithmetic scaler back to the core memory.   This results from the fact that the read process is destructive, since in the process of reading all the cores in the selected channel are set to the 0 state.   The reading process is relatively simple because all of the selected cores are pulsed in the same direction, in the direction of the 0 state.   However, it is not so straightforward to write combinations of 0's and 1's.   The address wires are common to all planes and must, therefore, send the same information to all planes. Writing in the various planes is individually controlled, therefore, by equipping each plane with another winding, called the "inhibit" winding, which threads all the cores in the plane in the same sense.   To write a number in a memory address, the horizontal and vertical wires corresponding to that address are each pulsed with a half saturating write 1 pulse.   The current in each inhibit winding is controlled by the state of the corresponding arithmetic scaler stage, so that, in those planes in which a 1 is to be written, the inhibit winding is not pulsed and the sum of two half saturating currents writes a 1.   In those planes in which a 0 is to be written, the inhibit winding is supplied with a half saturating current in the write 0 direction.   The selected cores then receive two half write 1 currents and one half write 0 current.   The net current, a half write 1 current, is too small to switch the selected cores, so they remain in the 0 state.   The other cores in the plane that share either a horizontal or a vertical address wire with the selected core receive a half write 1 current and a half write 0 current.   This has no net value so those cores, of course, retain their original magnetization.   The remaining cores in the plane receive a half write 0 current pulse, which is too small to switch them, so they remain in their original state also.

    The memory cycle in a coincident-current magnetic-core memory can be summarized as follows.   A reset pulse sets all stages of the arithmetic scaler to 0.   The address scaler then directs the read current pulses to one horizontal and one vertical address wire.   Each current pulse is half that required to produce core saturation and is in the direction to set the selected cores to 0.   In those planes in which the selected core contains a 1, signals induced in the sense windings set the corresponding stages of the arithmetic scaler to 1.   In those planes in which the selected core contains a 0, the signals induced in the sense windings are too small to trigger the corresponding arithmetic scaler stages, so they remain in the 0 state. At this time, if the instrument is operating in the data storage mode, a pulse is applied to the input of the arithmetic scaler which increases its count by 1.   In the display and printout modes this step is omitted. Next, the inhibit-pulse generator directs half saturating current pulses, in the 0 direction, to all those planes whose arithmetic scaler stage contains a 0.   Shortly after the start of the inhibit pulses, and while the inhibit current continues to flow in the appropriate planes, the rewrite pulses are directed by the address scaler to the same horizontal and vertical address wires as before. The rewrite pulses are the same amplitude as the read pulses but opposite in polarity. This causes a 1 to be written in the selected core in each plane whose arithmetic scaler stage contains a 1, which completes the memory cycle.

While the coincident-current technique greatly simplifies the memory addressing problem, it introduces problems of its own which stem from the fact that memory cores do not have perfectly square hysteresis loops. With cores that are currently available, it is necessary to hold the addressing and inhibit currents within fairly narrow limits if the read 1 signals are to be reliably distinguished from the various disturb signals. Variances of as little as 10 per cent from the optimum values can cause memory errors.

The tolerance to address- and inhibit-current variations can be considerably increased by taking advantage of the fact that the read 1 signals differ from the disturb signals not only in amplitude but also in duration. Because the losses in the memory cores associated with flux reversal are not zero, the flux in a selected core does not change instantaneously. The read 1 signals, therefore, last somewhat longer than the disturb signals and may be close to their maximum value when the disturb signals have almost completely decayed. If the read signals are examined at the optimum time, read 1 signals can be distinguished from disturb signals even if the address currents are so far from the optimum value that the disturb signals are larger than the read 1 signals. This is done by gating the read amplifiers with a "strobe" signal, suitably delayed with respect to the beginning of the read addressing currents, so that it occurs at a time when the disturb signals are small but the read 1 signals are still large.

Another variation in the coincident-current addressing technique is also effective in reducing the disturb signals, thus increasing the memory reliability by increasing the address-current tolerances. This technique, employed in a pulse-height analyzer designed at the Atomic Energy Research Establishment at Harwell, England [5], divorces the address-selection function from the memory function. Information is stored in a set of small magnetic cores, 2 mm in diameter. The storage cores are arranged in 100 columns, with 16 cores in each column. The cores are threaded by 100 vertical address wires and 16 horizontal sense wires which are also used to control writing in the memory. Larger cores, 8 mm in diameter, arranged in a 10×10 coincident-current matrix, supply address currents for reading and writing in the storage cores.

The addressing cores are normally biased to negative saturation by a fixed bias current flowing in a winding linking all cores in the address matrix. A storage channel is selected by supplying address currents, opposite in sense to the bias current, to a selected row and column winding in the address matrix. The address core at the intersection of the selected row and column winding is switched from negative to positive saturation. The address current in the half-selected cores is sufficient to overcome the bias magnetomotive force, but because of the squareness of the hysteresis loops, the cores remain in saturation.

A secondary winding on each address core drives the address wire of a corresponding set of 16 storage cores. The flux change in the selected address core must be capable of producing a flux reversal in as many as 16 storage cores. If the address and storage cores were the same size, the secondary windings on the address cores would have to have at least 16 turns to drive the single-turn address wires on the storage cores. However, the address cores used have about ten times the cross-sectional area of the storage cores. The use of 4 secondary turns, therefore, is more than sufficient to ensure that all 16 storage cores are driven to saturation before the switch core saturates.

Once the sum of the currents in an address core is sufficient to carry it from negative saturation to the knee of the magnetization curve, the address core becomes an efficient current transformer. Address current in a half-selected address core is not efficiently coupled to the storage cores because the address core, in saturation, is a poor transformer. The current that does flow in half-selected storage cores is kept small by placing a small resistance, about 0.5 ohm, in series with the address winding. This resistance is large compared with the output impedance of the address-core current transformer when the core is saturated but small compared with its output impedance when the core is being switched. As a result, the address current flowing in half-selected storage cores is only about 5 per cent of the current that flows in fully selected cores, and the corresponding read signal from half-selected cores is about 1 per cent of the signal from fully selected cores. This reduction in the amplitude of the disturb signal, by about an order of magnitude, is the principal advantage of the switch-core system of addressing. It means that, for a 100-channel memory, it is unnecessary to strobe the read signals or to balance the disturb signals in pairs. The sense windings, therefore, pass through all the storage cores in the same direction, so that the read signals all have the same polarity.

Writing in the memory is accomplished, almost automatically, at the end of the read address-current pulse. Let us assume that each half-selecting component of read address current produces a magnetomotive force in an address core exactly equal and opposite to that produced by the bias current. Then, the current induced in the secondary winding when the address currents are removed is equal and opposite to that induced when the address currents are turned on. This current is, therefore, sufficient to set all the storage cores in the selected channel to the 1 state.   Those cores which are to be maintained in the 0 state receive a half saturating current pulse, via the sense winding, in the direction to inhibit the writing of a 1.   The inhibit current in each sense line is controlled, of course, by the state of the corresponding stage of the arithmetic scaler.

An alternative writing method makes use of slightly larger address-current components in the address matrix, each of which produces a magnetomotive force somewhat larger than that produced by the bias current, but not large enough, by itself, to drive an address core out of saturation. The reading current induced in the address wire linking the storage cores is, then, larger than the writing current, and by proper adjustment of the bias and address currents in the address matrix a 2 to 1 ratio between reading and writing currents can be achieved.   The read current is large enough to set all the cores in the selected channel to 0, but the write current pulse, which occurs when the address currents are turned off, is not large enough by itself to set the cores to 1.   A simultaneous half saturating current in the sense line causes the appropriate cores to be set to 1, while the other cores remain in the 0 state.   This additional current component, like the inhibit current in the previous case, is controlled by the individual stages of the arithmetic scaler.

Both writing techniques work equally well and the choice between them is an arbitrary one.   In either case, if the count in a channel is to be increased by 1, the add 1 pulse is applied to the arithmetic scaler after the read pulses have decayed but before the address currents are removed. The increased count is then returned to the storage cores when the address currents are removed.   When the analyzer is operated in the data display mode, the add 1 pulse is omitted, and the number is returned to the storage cores without alteration.

An additional advantage of the address-core technique is that it can be extended to three dimensions and permits the use of triple-coincident-current addressing for large memories [6].   A larger bias current is used which balances the magnetomotive force due to two address-current components.   Only the core at the intersection of the three selected core planes receives three address-current components and is driven out of saturation. Of course, with larger memories the disturb signals are more troublesome, and it becomes necessary to employ integrating or strobing techniques.

Magnetic cores are eminently satisfactory as pulse-height-analyzer memory elements.   Core memories are nonvolatile, and because the cores are passive devices, they are capable of a high order of reliability. An additional virtue is that they are random-access systems, i.e., any memory address can be selected at any time.   The access time (the time to read and rewrite at a single address) is usually in the neighborhood of

10 μsec, although with the development of new core materials and the application of low-temperature techniques, the access time of magnetic memories is being considerably shortened.

Magnetic memories in current use still have a few disadvantages, but these are being overcome. One is the high cost of the tedious hand assembly of magnetic-core planes. Other arrangements of magnetic elements, such as apertured plates, thin evaporated films, and woven magnetic wire matrices, show promise of being less expensive than core arrays. Another disadvantage, the destructive nature of the memory reading process, can be eliminated in at least two ways. One technique is to employ memory elements with two apertures so arranged that a reading current through one aperture samples, but does not significantly alter, the flux distribution around the other aperture. The other technique makes use of reading current pulses which are so short that the core magnetization is only temporarily altered and, at the end of the read pulse, reverts automatically to its original condition.

5.4 Cathode-ray-tube Memories

A number of digital computers and a few nuclear data storage devices make use of memories in which information is stored as a charge-distribution pattern on an insulating surface in a cathode-ray tube. The storage surface may be the phosphor screen in a standard cathode-ray oscilloscope tube or it may be a sheet of mica, or some other material, in a specially built memory tube.

A widely used cathode-ray-tube storage system, using standard oscilloscope tubes, was developed by Williams and Kilburn [7] in 1949. Its operation depends on the fact that, at the usual cathode-ray-tube accelerating voltages, the secondary electron emission ratio of the phosphor screen is greater than 1. This is, in fact, essential to the normal operation of a cathode-ray tube because, if it were not true, electron bombardment of the insulating phosphor screen would charge the point of impact negatively. The accumulating negative charge would repel the electron beam so that the point of impact would not be uniquely related to the deflection-plate voltage. With the passage of time the whole phosphor screen would charge negatively to cathode potential, and the electron beam would no longer be able to reach it.

But because the secondary emission ratio is greater than 1, the screen charges in the positive direction. Let us consider a cathode-ray tube whose phosphor screen has not been charged by the beam and is, therefore, an equipotential surface at the potential of the ultor.[1] Now, if the

---

[1] The ultor is the conducting coating on the inside surface of the side wall of a cathode-ray tube, at the target end of the tube. It is normally the most positive electrode in the tube.

electron beam is allowed to impinge on the phosphor screen, more electrons leave the point of impact than arrive, so this region of the screen charges positively. Charging continues until the point of impact becomes so positive that it pulls back enough of the secondary electrons to reduce the net secondary emission ratio at that point to 1. An equilibrium condition is thus established in which the number of electrons in the beam that reach the impact point is exactly equal to the number of secondaries that leave it.

The secondary electrons leave the phosphor screen with an energy distribution that is peaked in the neighborhood of a few electron volts. The electric field near the screen is directed toward the screen because of the positive potential on the ultor, so many of the lower-energy secondary

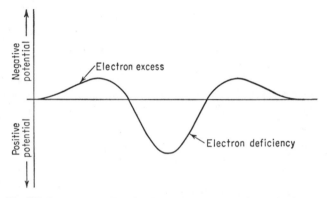

FIG. 5.11   Equilibrium charge distribution on the screen of a cathode-ray tube in the neighborhood of the point of impact of the primary electron beam.

electrons return to the screen. Most of the secondary electrons, as they leave the screen, have a radial velocity component in addition to an axial component. Very few of the secondaries, therefore, return to the point of origin. The point of return for any particular electron depends upon both its energy and its direction. Since both the radial and the axial velocity components are generally small, most of the secondary electrons fall back on the screen in a small circular area immediately surrounding the point of impact. The secondary electrons return to the screen with too little energy to liberate additional secondaries, so they accumulate as a patch of negative charge surrounding the positively charged point of impact. Ultimately, this patch becomes sufficiently negative to repel any additional secondaries. The secondaries are then either collected on the ultor or fall back on more remote areas of the phosphor screen. A cross section of the final equilibrium potential distribution in the neighborhood of the point of impact of the primary beam is shown in Fig. 5.11.

The beam may be considered to have dug a positive hole and to have piled the electrons from the excavation around the edge of the hole.

Let us suppose, now, that the primary electron beam is deflected slightly so that it falls on a portion of the negative rim surrounding the positive hole. Because the secondary emission ratio is greater than 1, the excess electrons are quickly removed and a new positive hole is dug. The original positive hole, lying on the rim of the new hole, is filled by electrons from the new excavation and disappears. If we consider the first hole as representing a binary 1 and the second hole as representing a binary 0, we see that writing a 0 can erase a 1 and, conversely, writing a 1 can erase a 0. The phosphor screen of most cathode-ray tubes is a high-quality insulator so that, once a set of numbers has been written on the screen, it can be stored for a considerable period of time, provided that the primary electron beam is turned off. The double-dot storage system described here is only one of many possible charging systems. Others in use include the double-line system in which the spots are changed to short line segments by adding a small high-frequency voltage to the deflection signal on one set of deflection plates; the dot-circle system in which a 1 is represented by a dot and a 0 is represented by a circular trace surrounding it, the circle being generated by small high-frequency signals, in phase quadrature, applied to both sets of deflection plates; and the dot-blur system in which a 1 is represented by a sharply focused spot and a 0 is represented by a superimposed, slightly defocused blur. These more complex arrangements are somewhat more tolerant of slight deflection errors and therefore usually result in more reliable memories.

A 3-in. cathode-ray tube can accommodate more than 1,000 discrete information storage locations which are well enough separated so that the spray of secondaries produced by writing at one location discharges the neighboring locations only slightly. Each storage location is, in effect, two locations, one for storing 1 and the other for storing 0.

Information is read from a Williams memory with the aid of a pickup electrode mounted close to the phosphor screen on the outside of the cathode-ray tube. As with a magnetic-core memory, reading is destructive and is accomplished by writing a 0 at the address to be read. If the address contains a 0, i.e., if the corresponding location on the phosphor screen has been charged to equilibrium with the primary beam deflected to the 0 side of that location, then writing 0 again at that location does not produce any redistribution of charge on the storage surface, so only a small signal, induced by the space charge in the beam, is observed on the pickup electrode. If the address contains a 1, then writing 0 digs a new positive hole and fills the old one. This charge redistribution induces a larger signal on the pickup electrode which is interpreted to mean that the interrogated address contained a 1.

If one examines a storage location containing a 1 before and after a reading operation which writes 0 at that location, one finds that the net equilibrium charge on the storage surface is not changed. The charge pattern has merely been moved slightly. Why, then, should a signal be induced on the pickup electrode when the net charge that it is exposed to is unaltered? The answer is that the net induction is zero, but it has a transient value that is different from zero because the digging and filling operations proceed at different rates. The entire primary electron beam is active in the digging process, so digging proceeds rapidly. It is associated with a large positive current to the screen which lasts for the short time required to dig the new hole. Filling, on the other hand, proceeds more slowly because only a fraction of the secondary electrons fall in the old hole. The negative filling current (opposite in polarity to the digging current) is smaller than the digging current, but flows for a longer period of time in order that it may return as much charge to the old hole as is removed from the new one.

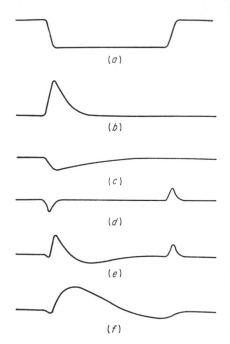

Fig. 5.12 Signals associated with reading a 1 in a double-dot Williams memory. (a) Electron beam; (b) current component associated with "digging" a new positive potential hole; (c) current component associated with "filling" the old hole; (d) current induced by the space charge in the beam; (e) net current signal; (f) voltage signal that results when (e) is integrated at the amplifier input.

When the primary electron beam is turned on (Fig. 5.12a), both the digging and the filling currents rise rapidly to their peak values and then decay to zero, approximately exponentially, as the new equilibrium condition is established. The two current components are shown, plotted as a function of time, in Fig. 5.12. The positive digging current (Fig. 5.12b) is large and has a short decay time constant, while the negative filling current (Fig. 5.12c) is small and has a longer decay time constant. A third current component is also shown (Fig. 5.12d). This is the current induced in the pickup electrode circuit by the sudden appearance of the space charge associated with the primary beam, when the beam is turned on, and the disappearance of this space charge when the primary beam is turned off.   The duration of the space-charge current components is determined, primarily, by the rate of rise and fall of the cathode-ray-tube grid waveform which, in turn, determines the build-up and decay time of the space charge.

The net signal current is a composite of waveforms b, c, and d and is shown as Fig. 5.12e.   The amplifier signal-to-noise ratio can be maximized by integrating this signal current on the stray capacitance associated with the pickup electrode and the amplifier input circuit.   The resultant voltage waveform is shown as Fig. 5.12f.

The permissible spacing between storage locations on the phosphor screen is determined by how much writing at each location degrades the information stored at neighboring locations.   If the spacing is too close, the spray of secondary electrons produced by writing at one location may fill in the positive hole of an adjacent location to the point where the information at the second location cannot be read unambiguously.   As the spacing between storage locations is increased, the degrading effect of the secondary electron spray is decreased, but it is never entirely eliminated.   This means that, if a particular storage location is consulted a sufficient number of times, the information stored in neighboring locations must ultimately be lost.

The loss of information is prevented by periodically regenerating the stored-charge pattern.   This is done by addressing each storage location in turn, reading and then rewriting the information stored there.   Each rewriting operation reestablishes the equilibrium charge distribution which might have been partially destroyed by writing at neighboring locations or by leakage of the storage surface.   The number of memory consultations that can be permitted between regeneration operations is determined by the "read-around ratio."   The read-around ratio is defined as the number of times a memory location can be consulted at a particular storage location, uninterrupted by a regeneration cycle, without causing the loss of information stored at a neighboring location. The read-around ratio is the most commonly used figure of merit for a cathode-ray-tube memory.   It depends not only on the spacing between storage locations but also on the spot size, the beam current, the time duration of reading and writing beam pulses, the amount of deflection defocusing and astigmatism in the cathode-ray tube, the gain of the read amplifier, and the bias of the discriminator that distinguishes 0 read pulses from 1 read pulses.   Typical values for the read-around ratio for a well-constructed cathode-ray tube storing 1,024 bits in a square 32 × 32 array range between 50 and 100.   As the number of bits increases, the read-around ratio falls rapidly.   It is interesting that a 3-in. cathode-ray tube can store as many bits as a 5-in. tube, without sacrifice in read-around ratio. This results from the fact that larger cathode-ray tubes generally have a proportionally greater spot size.

In the Williams system, memory locations are addressed by applying voltages to the cathode-ray-tube deflection plates which direct the electron beam to the storage location of interest. It is, of course, a random-access system because storage locations can be selected in any order. The deflection voltages are an analog representation of a set of digital storage locations. They must be restricted to a discrete set of reproducible values so that information stored can be located and read at a later time. This can be done with a digital-to-analog converter circuit which

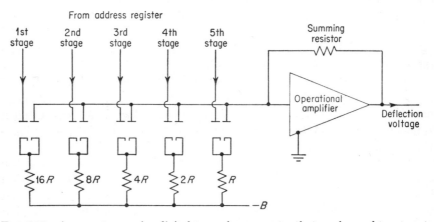

FIG. 5.13   A current-summing digital-to-analog converter that can be used to generate the address voltage for a cathode-ray-tube memory.

translates a digital number stored in an electronic register into a corresponding analog voltage. Figure 5.13 shows a current-summing digital-to-analog converter suitable for converting a digital address contained in a five-stage address register into a proportional deflection voltage. The output voltage from a register stage is assumed to be positive if the stage contains a 0 and negative if it contains a 1. The five graduated resistors connected to the diode cathodes determine five current values, weighted in binary fashion. When a register stage contains a 1, its associated weighted current flows through a right-hand diode to the input of the operational amplifier. When a register stage contains a 0, the current is diverted into the left-hand diode and the right-hand diode is cut off. The current components in the right-hand diodes are added by the operational amplifier which produces an output voltage proportional to the digital value of the number stored in the address register. If two converters of this type are used, one for horizontal deflection and one for vertical deflection, the beam can be directed to 1,024 storage locations in a square 32 × 32 array on the storage surface.

A complete memory might contain one or a number of storage tubes, depending upon the required storage capacity. For example, 16 tubes with their deflection plates connected in parallel could store up to 2^{16} counts in each of 1,024 storage channels. Alternatively, a single tube could be used to store up to 2^{16} counts in 64 channels. Of course, with all the data on a single tube the count in each channel must be read and written one bit at a time. In this mode of operation the Williams memory, like a delay-line memory, is compatible with a serial binary adder.

The limitations of a Williams memory result mainly from the fact that reading and writing operations spray the entire storage surface with secondary electrons which tend to degrade the stored-charge patterns.

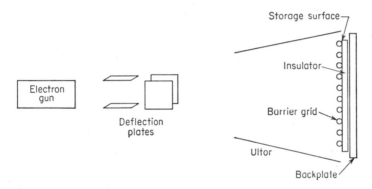

FIG. 5.14 Schematic representation of the construction of a barrier-grid storage tube.

This effect can be substantially reduced, and the quality of the memory correspondingly improved, by using barrier-grid storage tubes in place of standard cathode-ray tubes. The construction of a barrier-grid storage tube is illustrated schematically in Fig. 5.14. It contains a standard cathode-ray-tube gun and deflection assembly, but the phosphor screen is replaced by a target consisting of an insulating surface (usually mica) with a fine-mesh grid in contact with its inside surface and a conducting back plate on its outside surface. The barrier grid is usually maintained at ground potential, the cathode being at a high negative potential and the ultor (often referred to as the collector) being about 100 volts positive with respect to the barrier grid. Most of the secondary electrons that leave the storage surface with appreciable radial velocity components strike the barrier-grid wires and are collected there. Those which leave the storage surface more or less normally pass through the barrier grid and are accelerated to the more positive collector. Thus, very few of the secondary electrons that leave the storage surface are able to fall back on other storage locations and degrade the information stored there.

With the secondary electron spray virtually eliminated, it is necessary to employ a writing and reading technique somewhat different from that used in a Williams memory. When the primary electron beam strikes a previously uncharged portion of the storage surface, enough secondary electrons are ejected to charge the storage surface positively with respect to the barrier grid. The charging continues until, at a positive potential of a few volts, an equilibrium condition is attained at which the electric field between the storage surface and the barrier grid attracts enough secondary electrons back to the storage surface to reduce the net secondary emission ratio to unity. This same equilibrium condition is established regardless of the initial potential of the storage surface. If it is initially positive, secondaries are not allowed to leave and the primary beam charges the surface negatively to the equilibrium potential. The time to reach equilibrium depends on the current density in the primary electron beam, the storage surface secondary emission ratio (ideally equal to two for equal positive and negative charging time), and the difference between the initial and the equilibrium surface potential. With the operating potentials and beam current normally used, equilibrium charging takes a few microseconds.

Writing of information on the storage surface is controlled by the back-plate potential. If, with the barrier grid grounded, the back-plate potential is changed positively by an amount ΔV, capacitive coupling to the storage surface changes its potential by a substantial fraction of ΔV, perhaps as much as $\Delta V/2$. If, now, the primary electron beam is turned on and directed to a particular storage location, that portion of the storage surface is brought to the equilibrium potential, a few volts positive with respect to the barrier grid. Returning the back plate to its initial potential returns the storage surface to the same potential as before, except for the storage location just addressed which is now negative with respect to the barrier grid by approximately $\Delta V/2$. Alternatively, the selected storage location could have been charged positively by driving the back plate in the negative direction, pulsing the beam, and returning the back plate to ground.

Information is read from the storage surface with the back plate at ground potential. The primary electron beam is directed to the storage location of interest and is pulsed on. If the storage location is at the equilibrium potential with respect to the barrier grid, no net current flows to the storage surface. Because the storage surface is slightly more positive than the barrier grid, very few of the secondary electrons strike the barrier grid. The secondary electron current, which is very nearly equal to the primary beam current, is almost entirely collected on the ultor, producing a standard voltage pulse across a load resistor connected between the ultor and its power supply. If the storage location had been charged negatively in a previous writing operation, then addressing that location with the back plate grounded would result in a secondary electron current considerably larger than the primary current, until equilibrium were established. The negative pulse at the ultor is therefore initially larger than the standard value. Alternatively, if the previous writing operation had left the addressed storage location charged positively, then the read signal would have been, initially, smaller than the standard value. Assignment of the names 0 and 1 to these charge conditions is, of course, arbitrary and any consistent definition can be used.

The reading system just described suffers from the difficulty that the signals at the ultor have the same polarity, regardless of whether a 0 or a 1 is being read, the difference being only in the signal amplitude. This means that the beam current, the read amplifier gain, and the read discriminator level must all be well stabilized if 0 and 1 read signals are to be reliably distinguished. The target reading system developed by Hines et al. [8] is much more tolerant of instabilities and, therefore, results in a more reliable memory. If the target assembly, consisting of the barrier grid, the storage surface, and the back plate, is separated from ground by a suitable impedance, the net target current can be measured by observing the signal pulse across this impedance during reading. The net target current may be zero, positive or negative depending on whether the back plate, at the time of writing, was at barrier-grid potential, or positive or negative with respect to the barrier grid. Therefore, in order to read the information stored at a memory address it is not necessary to measure the amplitude of the read signal; it is sufficient to observe its polarity.

In a typical barrier-grid storage tube, the capacitance between the storage surface and the back plate is approximately 0.001 μf. It is advisable, therefore, to consider the entire target assembly as a single electrode when reading the stored charge. In this way the signal charge produces a relatively large signal voltage across the low read amplifier input capacitance rather than a very small signal voltage across the large capacitance between parts of the target assembly. Figure 5.15 shows how the back-plate-to-barrier-grid potential can be changed for purposes of writing while, at the same time, maintaining a high a-c impedance between target assembly and ground so that the read signal voltage can be large. The back-plate pulse is applied between back plate and barrier grid via a miniature coaxial cable. The cable is coiled around a magnetic core so that the inductive reactance between target assembly and ground is large enough to appear as a high impedance to the read signal observed at the target. In this way the back-plate pulsing and reading operations are made almost independent of each other.

In barrier-grid electrostatic memories high bit-storage densities can be achieved with good read-around ratios. In a well-designed system more than 8,000 bits can be stored on a single tube with a read-around ratio of 1,000 or more. Therefore, only a small fraction of the system operating time need be wasted in memory regeneration. However, regeneration is still necessary, and largely because of the circuit complexity associated with regeneration, cathode-ray-tube memories have not been widely used in pulse-height analyzers.[1]

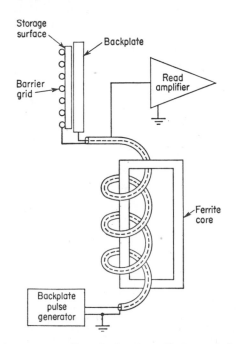

FIG. 5.15 System for target reading of a barrier-grid storage tube reported by Hines et al. [8]. The signal is developed across the inductance formed by winding the back-plate driving coaxial cable on a ferrite core.

A notable exception is the pulse-height analyzer of Porter and Bor-kowski, referred to in Art. 4.3. The beam-deflection quantizing tube converts input-pulse amplitudes into quantized analog voltages which can be used directly to address a barrier-grid storage tube. The simplicity and high speed of the addressing system make this an attractive arrangement, despite the necessity for regeneration. Since a single storage tube is used as the memory, it is necessary to do serial arithmetic. One set of deflection plates selects the storage channel and the other set of

[1] This is not true in the Soviet Union, where cathode-ray-tube memories are quite popular [9].

deflection plates selects the bits in sequence, starting from the least-significant bit. Addition of 1 follows the pattern used with delay-line memories and described in Art. 5.2. This means that, for a 16-bit channel storage capacity, it may be necessary to make as many as 16 memory consultations to complete the addition of one count in a storage channel. However, this is necessary only very infrequently. One-half of the addition operations require but a single memory consultation and one-quarter of the operations require two consultations. More extended memory consultations occur less and less frequently, and on the average the number of consultations per addition is two. Therefore, with respect to memory-cycle time, the barrier-grid memory is not at a significant disadvantage with respect to magnetic-core memories, even when the addition is done serially. When combined with a beam-deflection quantizer, it results in a pulse-height analyzer that is considerably faster than those using magnetic-core memories.

REFERENCES

1. Kandiah, K., and D. W. Chambers: Multi-electrode Counting Tubes, *J. Brit. IRE*, vol. 15, no. 4, April, 1955.
2. Hutchinson, G., and G. Scarrott: A High Precision Pulse Height Analyzer of Moderately High Speed, *Phil. Mag.*, vol. 42, p. 792, 1951.
3. Gallagher, J., and J. McKibben: 100-channel Pulse Height Analyzer Using Delay Line Storage, *Los Alamos Sci. Lab. Rept.* LA-1917, May, 1955.
4. J. Rajchman: Static Magnetic Matrix Memory and Switching Circuits, *RCA Rev.*, vol. 13, p. 183, June, 1952.
5. Koch, H., and R. Johnston (eds.): Multichannel Pulse Height Analyzers, *Natl. Acad. Sci.–Natl. Research Council Publ.* 467, p. 76, 1957. Remarks by E. Cooke-Yarborough.
6. Wells, F., and J. Page: A 1000-channel Neutron-velocity Spectrometer Using Ferrite Data Storage, *Proc. IEE (London)*, vol. 104, part B, Suppl. 7, 1957.
7. Williams, F., and T. Kilburn: A Storage System for Use with Binary-Digital Computing Machines, *Proc. IEE (London)*, vol. 96, part II, p. 183, 1949.
8. Hines, M., M. Chruney, and J. McCarthy: Digital Memory in Barrier-grid Storage Tubes, *Bell System Tech. J.*, vol. 34, p. 1241, 1955.
9. Melnikow, G., L. Artemenkov, and Y. Golubev: Multichannel Amplitude Analyzer with Potentialoscopic Registration, *Pribory i Technika Eksperementa*, no. 6, p. 57, 1957.

CHAPTER 6

PHOTOGRAPHIC PULSE-HEIGHT ANALYZERS

The relatively sophisticated instruments described in Chaps. 4 and 5 are capable of recording pulse-height distributions with high accuracy over a wide range of counting rates. While individual instruments have advantages and disadvantages in particular applications, all of them can be used successfully in the large majority of experiments. However, versatility and accuracy are not achieved without cost. The digital multichannel pulse-height analyzers in current use are complicated instruments that are expensive to build, subject to frequent failures, and often difficult to repair. In many cases the experiment is so demanding that it is necessary to invest in a large digital pulse-height analyzer, but there are many problems that can be solved with simpler, less expensive equipment. In institutions where competent electronic maintenance is not easily available or where equipment budgets are modest, multichannel pulse-height analysis is often done photographically. In this chapter we shall consider three photographic pulse-height analyzing systems and discuss their applications and their limitations.

6.1 Densitometer Analysis

A simple, qualitative pulse-height analyzer can be made with a triggered sweep oscilloscope, a camera, and an optical densitometer. The output of the linear amplifier is connected to the oscilloscope input, and the controls are set so that each signal, above a selected threshold level, triggers a sweep. The input signals are thus represented by a family of traces on the oscilloscope screen. If the counting rate is high, the pulse-height distribution can be estimated by eye. Prominent peaks in the pulse-height spectrum are associated with frequent traces at the corresponding level on the oscilloscope screen and can be recognized as bright bands, while valleys in the spectrum show up as relatively darker bands. Of course, a visual estimate of a pulse-height distribution is relatively inaccurate and is sensitive only to the most prominent spectral features. Also, at low counting rates the eye cannot integrate over a sufficiently large number of events to make a useful estimate of a pulse-height distribution. By taking a time exposure of the screen with an oscilloscope camera, the integration can be extended over any desired time interval (see Plate A). Also, it is possible to extract semiquantitative intensity information from the photograph. The blackening of the photographic emulsion at each pulse-height level is a measure of the integrated count at that pulse height. With some photographic emulsions there is an approximately linear relationship between exposure and blackening over as much as a 100 to 1 ratio. Furthermore, even if the relationship is not linear, it can be determined by calibration. The pulse-height distribution can be determined, with sufficient accuracy for at least some experiments, by measuring the blackening of the developed emulsion with an optical densitometer.

The accuracy that can be achieved by this method is limited primarily by the vagaries of the photographic process. The sensitivity of photographic emulsions varies somewhat from batch to batch and also with the age of the emulsion. Additional uncertainties are introduced by variations in the age and temperature of the developer and by the amount of agitation during the developing process. The extent of these uncertainties is difficult to predict because they depend largely on the skill of the photographer. In any case, results can be improved by including at least one calibration shot, made with a standard radioactive source, on each roll of film. This will also help to compensate for any changes that might occur in the oscilloscope sweep speed or trace brightness.

The calibration process is somewhat complicated by an often troublesome photographic anomaly, the failure of the reciprocity law. It might reasonably be expected that the blackening of a photographic emulsion would depend only on the total amount of light to which it had been exposed and not on the length of the exposure interval. Exposure to weak illumination for a long period of time should produce the same amount of blackening as exposure to bright light for a short time, provided that, in both cases, the integrated light flux were the same. In other words, for a given amount of emulsion blackening, the product of the illumination intensity I and the time t should be constant. Unfortunately, no emulsion follows this reciprocity law exactly, and many depart from it considerably. For most emulsions, a closer approximation is

$$It^n = \text{constant} \qquad (6.1)$$

where, at least for times greater than 0.01 sec, n is a fraction with a value between 0.5 and 0.8. If, therefore, the length of an experimental exposure is different from the length of the calibration exposure, it is necessary to correct for the failure of the reciprocity law. If the value of n is not known accurately, it is advisable to calibrate with a source whose intensity is comparable to that of the unknown, so that equal exposure times can be used.

6.2   Gray-wedge Pulse-height Analysis

The gray-wedge technique [1,2] makes it possible to obtain, with only a slight increase in complexity, much more nearly quantitative photographic pulse-height analyzers.   With a gray-wedge analyzer, the determination of the relative counting rates at various pulse heights in a given spectrum does not depend on calibration of the emulsion and the development technique, but only on the highly stable characteristics of an optical filter.   However, the determination of absolute intensities depends upon photographic factors and is therefore no more accurate than the photography or the calibration procedure.

The gray-wedge analyzer makes use of a pulse-stretching circuit (see Art. 4.2) and a triggered sweep oscilloscope.   Each input signal is maintained at its peak amplitude for the duration of the sweep and appears, therefore, as a horizontal line of constant brightness on the oscilloscope screen.   The vertical distance from a reference base line to the trace is proportional to the peak amplitude of the input signal.   As with the densitometer analyzer, the counting rate at each amplitude level determines the average brightness at the corresponding vertical position on the oscilloscope screen.

The oscilloscope display is photographed through a gray wedge mounted close to the phosphor screen (Plate B).   A gray wedge is a neutral-density optical filter, whose optical density varies linearly from nearly zero at one edge to some suitable maximum value at the opposite edge.   It can be constructed by grinding a piece of uniformly gray filter glass into the shape of a wedge or, alternatively, by mounting a pair of optical flats with a small angle between them and filling the space with gray gelatin.   Gray wedges can also be made photographically, but these are generally less satisfactory because the silver grains in a photographic gray wedge tend to scatter light rather than absorb it, and the resultant redistribution of light can spoil the resolution in a pulse-height spectrum.

When the oscilloscope is viewed through a gray wedge, the horizontal traces appear to vary in brightness from one side of the screen to the other. The apparent length of the traces depends on their repetition rate.   At low-counting-rate positions the traces become almost invisible a short distance from the transparent edge.   At high-counting-rate positions the traces can still be seen at or near the opaque edge.   If the oscilloscope is photographed through the gray wedge, the horizontal extent of the emulsion blackening at each vertical pulse-height level is a measure of the counting rate at that pulse height.   Of course, the blackening does not end abruptly, but varies continuously over an appreciable range.   The extent of the gray range between the overexposed and the virtually unexposed portions of the emulsion depends upon the wedge angle, the choice of emulsion, and, to a smaller extent, the developing procedure.   If a high-contrast emulsion is used (like that used for microfilm photocopying), the transition region can be made quite small.   The contrast may be further enhanced, and the transition region correspondingly reduced, by printing on a high-contrast photographic paper.   With a suitable choice of photographic materials, the full transition can be made to correspond to a counting-rate variation of less than 15 per cent, and an isodensity line can be drawn by eye in the middle of the gray region with an uncertainty that corresponds to an error in relative counting rate of less than 5 per cent.[1]

The transmission of light through an absorbing medium decreases exponentially with the thickness of the medium and can be written

$$I = I_0 e^{-t/\lambda} \tag{6.2}$$

where I is the transmitted light intensity, I_0 is the incident light intensity, t is the absorber thickness, and λ is a distance that characterizes the opacity of the medium.   In a linearly tapered wedge the thickness t varies linearly with the distance from the sharp edge x, so Eq. (6.2) can be rewritten

$$I = I_0 e^{-(x \tan \theta)/\lambda} \tag{6.3}$$

where θ is the wedge angle.

For a particular exposure time, the emulsion is exposed to the middle of its contrast range by a specific average illumination intensity.   This value of illumination I_c occurs at a horizontal position x_c which is related to the incident light intensity I_0 and can be determined by solving Eq. (6.3) for x.   Thus

$$x_c = \frac{\lambda \log_e (I_0/I_c)}{\tan \theta} \tag{6.4}$$

It follows, therefore, that the horizontal length of the exposed portion of the emulsion is a measure of the logarithm of the counting rate at each pulse height.   The full-scale counting-rate ratio depends upon the wedge constants λ and θ, while the absolute counting-rate calibration depends upon the exposure time, the oscilloscope trace speed and brightness, and I_c. I_c, in turn, is a function of the emulsion speed and the lens aperture.

---

[1] When less accuracy is acceptable, satisfactory results can be obtained using Polaroid film.   Some accuracy is lost because of the low contrast of the emulsion and the relatively poor control of the developing process.   However, because of the convenience of rapid developing, Polaroid film is generally used in gray-wedge pulse-height analysis for qualitative work.

Furthermore, because of reciprocity failure, I_c also depends somewhat on the exposure time.

The logarithmic nature of the intensity calibration makes the gray-wedge analyzer unique among pulse-height analyzers currently in use. Because pulse-height spectra frequently cover a wide counting-rate range, the logarithmic scale can be a distinct advantage. If the wedge constants are chosen to cover a large counting-rate range (perhaps 100 or 1,000 to 1), high- and low-counting-rate portions of the spectrum can be recorded in a single photograph. Also, because of the logarithmic scale, exposure times do not have to be accurately adjusted to the counting rate; a change in exposure time merely displaces the spectrum on the counting-rate axis without changing its shape. Gray wedges could, of course, be fabricated for other types of scale, but because the logarithmic scale is convenient and easy to achieve, it has been used most frequently. Maeder [3] has achieved performance similar to that obtained with a gray wedge by using a nonlinear horizontal sweep so that the spot velocity and, therefore, its apparent brightness vary across the screen. Many different counting-rate-calibration curves can be obtained with suitable nonlinear sweep waveforms. For example, an exponential sweep, produced by charging a capacitor through a resistor connected to a fixed voltage source, leads to a linear counting-rate calibration.

Plate C shows a pulse-height spectrum obtained with a scintillation counter and a gray-wedge pulse-height analyzer. The logarithmic scale was superimposed on the spectrum in the printing process. The scale was obtained by photographing a piece of semilog graph paper and adjusting the enlargement to correspond to the counting-rate range of the gray wedge.

It is difficult to define the resolution of a gray-wedge pulse-height analyzer because, unlike the digital instruments, it does not have discrete channels. It is probably best characterized by the observed width of the line produced by a monoenergetic input signal as simulated with a stable pulse generator. The line width is due, almost entirely, to the finite diameter of the focused spot on the cathode-ray-tube screen. It is not difficult to focus a 5-in. cathode-ray tube so that the distance between half-intensity points on the spot is less than 0.04 in. Therefore, with a gray wedge 2 in. wide, the resolution of a gray-wedge pulse-height analyzer is comparable to that obtained with a 50-channel digital pulse-height analyzer. Of course, sharpness of focus is not uniform over the surface of a cathode-ray tube. This results in slight variations in the instrument resolution over the useful pulse-height range, but it is not accompanied by the spectral distortion that one associates with channel-width variations in digital instruments (see Art. 3.4). Since the total light in a cathode-ray-tube spot is largely independent of the sharpness

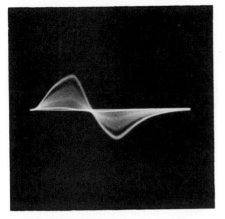

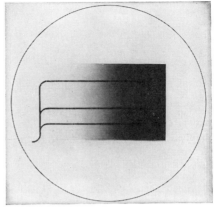

PLATE A   Triggered sweep oscilloscope photograph of amplified signals from a NaI scintillation detector. The bright band at the top was produced by photo-electric conversion of the 667-kev gamma ray from Cs^{137}.

PLATE B   An optical gray wedge. The horizontal lines represent stretched input pulses as they would be displayed on the screen of the cathode-ray tube.

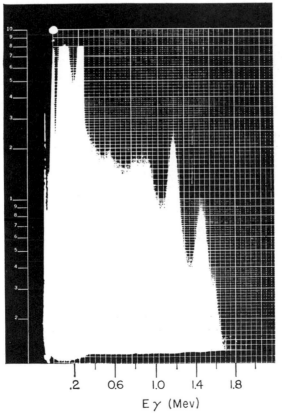

PLATE C   A scintillation-counter spectrum as recorded with a gray-wedge pulse-height analyzer. The logarithmic scale was superimposed in the printing process.

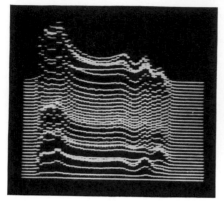 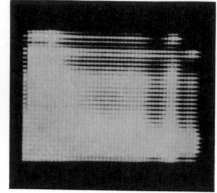

PLATE D   A set of curves illustrating the two-dimensional spectrum of the gamma rays from Co[60], obtained with two sodium iodide scintillation counters. Energy increases from left to right and from top to bottom.

PLATE E   Intensity display of the two-dimensional spectrum of the gamma rays from Co[60]. Energy increases from left to right and from bottom to top. The oscilloscope brightness is a nonlinear representation of the information stored in the analyzer memory.

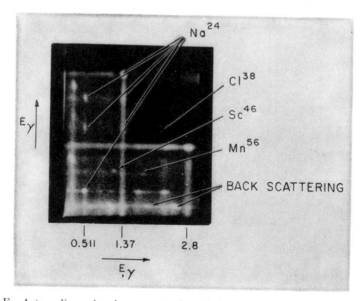

PLATE F   A two-dimensional representation of the gamma rays from a mixture of radioactive sources obtained by Grodzins [Chap. 8, Ref. 7] by photographing dots on a cathode-ray-tube screen.

of focus, the contribution of each trace to the area under the pulse-height-distribution curve is independent of the focus.

6.3 Moving-film Analysis [4]

The photographic pulse-height analyzers already described represent the accumulated count at the various pulse-height levels by analog quantities (optical density or linear extent of the exposed region).   The moving-film analyzer, on the other hand, is a digital instrument.   Its principal virtue is that it is, electronically, very much simpler than any of the digital pulse-height analyzers so far considered.   Mechanically, however, it is rather more complex.   It recommends itself, therefore, to those experimenters who have confidence in their mechanical ability and who are distrustful of electronic systems.

In the moving-film analyzer the amplitude of an input signal is represented by the vertical height of a dot on the face of a cathode-ray tube. The dots are recorded on photographic film that moves continuously through an oscilloscope camera, in a horizontal direction, at a velocity commensurate with the input counting rate.   The signals are provided with a flat top by a pulse-stretching circuit (Art. 4.2) and are applied to the vertical deflection plates of the cathode-ray tube.   After a suitable delay, to allow the input signals to reach peak amplitude, a gate circuit is triggered which turns on the cathode-ray-tube beam for a short time (about a microsecond) and, after turning it off again, discharges the pulse stretcher.   The result is a set of bright dots whose vertical position on the screen represents the amplitude of the corresponding input pulses.

After the data have been collected, the film is developed and scanned by a specially constructed reader.   The reader contains an optical system and a photomultiplier tube which scans a narrow region of the film for dots as it passes through at high speed.   At the end of each traverse, the scanning region is displaced slightly and the film is passed through the reader again.   The channel width, determined by an aperture in the optical system, is usually adjusted to be about equal to the diameter of the dots.   This results in about 50 to 100 useful channels with a standard 5-in. cathode-ray tube and 35-mm film.

The scanning channels may include all, or only part, of each recorded dot.   An amplitude discriminator circuit following the photomultiplier tube decides how much of each dot must fall within the channel to be counted.   If the discriminator bias is adjusted to accept half a dot or more, and if the spacing between adjacent scans is made equal to the channel width, each dot will be counted in one, and only one, channel. However, because it is not possible to make these adjustments perfectly, and because the size of a focused spot varies somewhat over a cathode-ray-tube screen, there must always be gaps or overlaps between channels.

Furthermore, the variation in spot size results in channels that are not exactly equal in width, so it is important to use a cathode-ray tube that has a minimum of astigmatism and deflection defocusing.

The accuracy of the moving-film analyzer is also limited by mechanical considerations. The film, as it moves through the camera and the reader, must be guided with high precision if repeatable, high-resolution results are to be obtained. With 35-mm film the channel will usually be about 0.01 in. wide so that, to avoid loss of resolution, the guidance system should not allow an uncertainty in film position greater than a few thousandths of an inch. A mechanical system suitable for use at high film speeds is described in Ref. 4.

Except for the fact that all the data are collected simultaneously, the moving-film analyzer is, in essence, a scanned single-channel pulse-height analyzer. If, therefore, the input-signal counting rate is high, the system does not process the data any more rapidly than a single-channel analyzer. It is only when the source is decaying or otherwise varying that the moving-film analyzer would be used at high counting rates. At low counting rates, on the other hand, it exhibits the advantages of a true multichannel system because it records all of the input signals presented to it, and the data processing time can be short compared with the data collection time.

When collecting data with a moving-film analyzer, it is important to select the film speed judiciously. If the film speed is too low, a significant fraction of the dots may be recorded too close together to be resolved by the reader. This not only results in a loss of data but also leads to spectral distortion, because unresolved dot pairs are more likely to occur at peaks in the spectrum than in other parts. Too high a film speed, on the other hand, is wasteful of film and developing and scanning time. The best compromise depends somewhat on the shape of the spectrum being studied. If the distribution is reasonably smooth and does not contain very prominent peaks, a dot density of about a hundred to the linear inch is usually acceptable. If, however, the spectrum is concentrated in one or a few well-resolved peaks, it is advisable to record fewer dots per inch.

An ingenious scheme, suggested by Choudhury and Banerjee [5,6], substantially reduces the probability of recording unresolved dot pairs and, at the same time, permits recording at a high average dot density. Instead of allowing the dots to be randomly distributed along the film, their technique regularizes the dot spacing so that the horizontal distance between a pair of dots is never allowed to be less than a preassigned minimum value, which is generally made slightly greater than the dot diameter. Immediately following the recording of each dot, the cathode-ray-tube beam is deflected horizontally, in the direction opposite to the film motion, by an amount that slightly exceeds a dot diameter. The beam is then permitted to return to its home position at a velocity that exactly matches the film speed.   Thus, if two events occur before the film can move appreciably, the dots are separated by the cathode-ray-tube horizontal deflection.   Because the film and the beam move at the same speed during the return interval, all pulse pairs separated by less than this interval produce dots that are separated by an amount equal to the horizontal beam displacement.   In addition, the second event of a closely spaced pair causes another horizontal displacement of the beam, so that a third event, closely following the other two, produces a dot which is separated from the second by the standard distance.   Figure 6.1 shows a

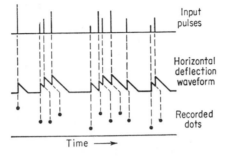

FIG. 6.1   A technique for regularizing the spacing between dots recorded with a moving film-pulse-height analyzer.   The horizontal deflection has been exaggerated for clarity.

typical random input-pulse spacing, the corresponding horizontal deflection waveform, and the resultant location of the recorded dots.   Even though the input pulses are randomly spaced, the recorded dots are almost uniformly spaced.   The film is thus utilized with very little waste. Of course, each input counting rate is still associated with a minimum allowable film speed.   If the film speed is too low, the accumulation of horizontal beam deflections will carry the beam off the face of the cathode-ray tube.

REFERENCES

1. Maeder, D.: Elektronenröhren-Spektograph zur Messung von Ionisationskammerimpulsen, *Helv. Phys. Acta*, vol. 20, p. 139, 1947.
2. Bernstein, W., R. Chase, and A. Schardt: Gray Wedge Pulse-height Analysis, *Rev. Sci. Instr.*, vol. 24, p. 437, 1953.
3. Maeder, D., and H. Medicus: Measurement of Converted Gamma-radiation by the Proportional Counter Technique, *Helv. Phys. Acta*, vol 23, suppl. III, p. 175, 1950.
4. Zaffarano, D., F. Boley, and W. Hunt: A Multichannel Pulse Height Analysis System Utilizing Photographic Recording on 35-mm Film, *U.S. Atomic Energy Commission Rept.* ISC-253, 1952.
5. S. Choudhury and B. Banerjee: Improved System of Dot on Film Records for Pulse-height Analysis, *Rev. Sci. Instr.*, vol. 27, p. 1080, 1956.
6. Maeder, D.: Photographic Recording Methods in Nuclear Spectrometry, *Nuclear Instruments*, vol. 2, p. 299, 1958.

CHAPTER 7

TIME ANALYZERS

The time relationships between signals from radiation detectors can provide information about nuclear properties that cannot be determined from studies of pulse-height distributions alone. Time-distribution studies are used in the following three kinds of investigation:

1. Determination of particle energies by measuring their velocities. This is an important way of measuring neutron energies, in particular, because the amplitude of a signal from a neutron detector is rarely related to the particle energy in an unambiguous way. It is also a useful technique for measuring the energy of energetic charged particles that cannot be brought to rest in a detector of reasonable size.

2. Measurement of the lifetimes of radioactive nuclear states and unstable particles. Lifetimes can be determined by measuring the time intervals between signals announcing the birth and death of the states of interest.

3. Coincidence investigations which study the correlation between events that occur simultaneously, or nearly so. These include experiments devoted to the determination of nuclear decay schemes and counter telescope experiments which define particle beams as distinguished from scattered radiation.

In the first two classes of experiment, the desired result is a frequency distribution of time intervals, somewhat analogous to the pulse-height distributions already considered. In the third class, the characteristic of primary interest is simultaneity. It is the purpose of the instrumentation to distinguish correlated signals from uncorrelated signals, the distinction being based on whether or not the signals occur simultaneously. This is usually done with one of a number of types of coincidence circuit. Since coincidence circuits also play an important role in at least some of the time-distribution measurements, it will be worthwhile to study them first before proceeding to a consideration of other types of time-distribution analyzers.

148

7.1 Coincidence Circuits

When we say that two events occur simultaneously, we really mean that, if there is any time interval between them, it is too short for us to detect. A coincidence circuit, in like manner, records two events as being simultaneous if their time separation is less than the circuit resolving time τ, and rejects them if their time separation exceeds this value. It is, of course, desirable that the resolving time be short, in order to distinguish between truly correlated events and those events which, by chance, occur at nearly the same time. However, the resolving time must not be made indefinitely short, because the time of occurrence of nuclear events cannot be determined with absolute precision. If the uncertainty in the detection time were greater than the coincidence-circuit resolving time, then truly correlated events might be rejected. In general, the resolving time is adjusted, for a particular experiment, so that the number of recorded chance coincidences is not so large, compared to the true coincidences, that it excessively limits the accuracy of the determination of the true coincidence counting rate. If this cannot be done without making the resolving time shorter than the uncertainty in the detection time, it may be necessary to redesign the experiment.

In order to choose the resolving time intelligently, it is necessary to be able to predict, at least approximately, the number of chance coincidences that will be recorded. Consider two detectors, A and B, receiving uncorrelated signals at counting rates n_1 and n_2, respectively. All signals from detector B, which are separated from an A signal by a time interval less than τ, are recorded as chance coincidences. Each of these B signals must, of course, fall within one of a set of time intervals, each of length 2τ, associated with, and symmetrically bracketing, the A signals. These intervals represent a fraction $2\tau n_1$ of the total data collection time, provided the fraction is small enough so that an insignificant number of the intervals overlap. If we multiply this fraction by n_2, the counting rate from detector B, we obtain the chance coincidence counting rate R.

$$R = 2\tau n_1 n_2 \qquad (7.1)$$

In general, both n_1 and n_2 in Eq. (7.1) are proportional to the intensity of the radiation source. The chance coincidence rate, therefore, is proportional to the square of the source intensity. If some of the events detected are truly correlated in time, the true coincidence counting rate is, of course, proportional to the source intensity. The ratio of true-to-chance coincidences is, therefore, inversely proportional to the source intensity. If, in a particular experiment, the chance coincidence counting rate, as indicated by Eq. (7.1), is so large that the true coincidence rate cannot be determined with sufficient accuracy, the true-to-chance ratio can be improved by reducing the source intensity. This, of course, increases the time required to record a statistically significant number of coincidences. The source intensity should not, therefore, be reduced excessively. Based on statistical considerations alone, the source intensity that leads to the most accurate determination of the true coincidence counting rate, in any given counting interval, is that intensity which makes the true and chance coincidence counting rates equal.

A convenient way to visualize the performance of coincidence circuits, and one that, in fact, is an accurate physical representation of the operation of many of them, is to consider each input signal as occupying a time interval equal to the circuit resolving time. When input signals are close enough for their associated time intervals to overlap, they are recorded as coincident. This applies not only to twofold coincidence circuits but also to circuits having three or more inputs. When the time intervals associated with all inputs overlap, a multiple coincidence is recorded. With this in mind, we can calculate the chance coincidence counting rate for a threefold coincidence circuit with resolving time τ and input counting rates n_1, n_2, and n_3, corresponding to inputs A, B, and C, respectively. From Eq. (7.1), the counting rate of AB coincidences is $2\tau n_1 n_2$. Each of these coincidences is associated with an overlap time interval whose length lies between 0 and τ. Since, with uncorrelated input signals, all of the possible overlap times are equally likely, the average length of the overlap intervals is $\tau/2$. C signals that occur during these overlap intervals, or precede them by less than τ, are recorded as being coincident with them. For each AB coincidence, therefore, there is a time interval of average length $\tau + \tau/2 = 3\tau/2$ during which a C signal is recorded as being coincident with AB. Multiplying this by the AB coincidence rate, we obtain $3\tau^2 n_1 n_2$ as the fraction of the data collection time during which C signals are recorded as coincident. The threefold chance coincidence rate is determined by multiplying this fraction by n_3.

$$R = 3\tau^2 n_1 n_2 n_3 \qquad (7.2)$$

In a similar way, the chance coincidence counting rate can be derived for circuits having more than three inputs. Each additional input reduces the chance counting rate substantially, the reduction being of the order of the fraction $n\tau$. The general expression for the chance counting rate for an m-fold coincidence circuit is

$$R = m\tau^{m-1} n_1 n_2 \cdots n_m \qquad (7.3)$$

Practical coincidence circuits can take many different forms. A study of the literature pertaining to nuclear electronics reveals a greater number and variety of coincidence circuits than of any other circuit type. We shall not attempt, therefore, to consider all of the coincidence circuits in use at present, but shall confine ourselves to a few general remarks and to several representative circuit configurations.

If the signals to be combined in a coincidence circuit are standardized with respect to amplitude and duration, very simple coincidence con-figurations are possible. For ex-ample, the signals may be added linearly and the sum presented to an amplitude discriminator such as a biased diode (Fig. 7.1). The discriminator bias is adjusted to reject single amplitude pulses re-sulting from signals at only one input and to accept double ampli-tude pulses that result when two input signals partially or com-pletely overlap. In an alternative current-summing configuration, the

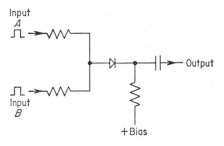

FIG. 7.1   A pulse-addition coincidence circuit suitable for use with standardized input signals.

two signals are applied to the grids of two vacuum tubes that have a common anode load resistor (Fig. 7.2). Again, a biased discriminator passes only those signals that result from the simultaneous presence of standardized signals at the two inputs. This same circuit can also be used with input signals that do not all have the same amplitude, by taking

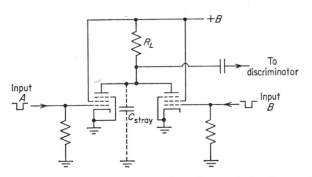

FIG. 7.2   Current-summing coincidence circuit. The same circuit arrangement is a Rossi coincidence circuit if R_L is large enough for the pentodes to "bottom."

advantage of the limiting properties of vacuum tubes. All input signals sufficiently large to drive the tubes from their normal conducting condi-tion to cutoff produce current pulses of standard amplitude in the load resistor. The discriminator is biased to reject output signals produced by cutting off only one tube but to accept the larger pulses which result from cutting off both tubes. Pentodes are to be preferred over triodes in this configuration when the input signals are short in duration, because with triodes large negative input signals may produce displacement currents in the plate-to-grid capacitance that are comparable to the plate current.

The arrangements of Figs. 7.1 and 7.2 are satisfactory for twofold coincidence circuits where the effective input amplitude variation is restricted (by limiting or otherwise) to a range smaller than 2 to 1, or for multiple coincidence circuits where the range of amplitude variation is correspondingly smaller. Much greater tolerance to signal amplitude and bias variation can be achieved, however, by employing nonlinear mixing circuits. One such arrangement makes use of the circuit of

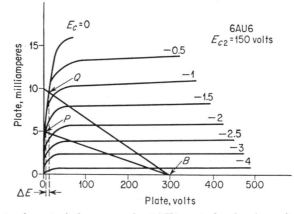

FIG. 7.3   Plate characteristic curves of a 6AU6 pentode, showing suitable load lines for use in a Rossi coincidence circuit.

Fig. 7.2 where the anode load resistor is much larger than in the linear mixer just discussed.[1] The load resistor is so large that the tubes are operating in the "bottomed" condition (point P on the pentode plate characteristics, Fig. 7.3). The load line is drawn to correspond to an anode resistor having twice the value of the resistor R_L in the circuit because, normally, the load current is shared by both tubes. If, now, one tube is driven to cutoff by an input signal, the slope of the load line for the conducting tube is determined by R_L alone, and the operating point shifts to point Q, resulting in a small positive output signal ΔE (see Fig. 7.3). If, however, both tubes are cut off simultaneously, the operating point shifts to B, producing an output signal nearly equal to the

[1] The first circuit of this type, described by Rossi [1] in 1930, employed triodes operating in the bottomed condition. Pentodes are to be preferred, however, because of their lower dynamic plate resistance when bottomed and because of their lower plate-to-grid capacitance.

full plate supply voltage, which is very much larger than, and easily distinguished from, ΔE.

This arrangement, with a properly chosen anode load resistor, is also very useful for multiple coincidence circuits. If $n - 1$ tubes in an n-fold coincidence are cut off simultaneously, all of the current in the load resistor flows in the one conducting tube. If the load resistor is large enough, that tube remains in the bottomed condition and the output signal is small. Cutting off the last tube results in a large output signal.

Junction transistors have pentode-like collector characteristics that are usually associated with very low values of collector resistance in the bottomed or "saturated" condition. Typical values for the saturation resistance of high-frequency, low-power germanium transistors are 5 to 20 ohms, while high-power transistors have still lower values. Junction transistors, therefore, are almost ideally suited to parallel coincidence circuits of the Rossi type. Figure 7.4 shows a fourfold coincidence circuit of this kind. To make certain that the circuit remains in saturation, even if three transistors are cut off, the ratio between the base resistors R_b and the collector load resistor R_L is made less than the forward current transfer ratio β.*

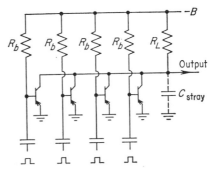

FIG. 7.4 Fourfold parallel coincidence circuit using junction transistors biased to saturation.

In the parallel coincidence circuits of Figs. 7.2 and 7.4, the duration of the input signals sets an upper limit on the circuit resolving time. The resolving time is further limited by the output time constant $R_L C_{stray}$ and the bias and switching time of the subsequent discriminator. The effective resolving time is determined by subtracting from the input-signal duration the amount of signal overlap necessary to allow the output signal to rise to the discriminator threshold. There is, of course, no lower limit on the resolving time that can be achieved, but when it is made short compared with the input-signal duration, the resolving time becomes critically dependent upon the discriminator sensitivity. When coincidence circuits are used to measure time distributions, an accurate knowledge of the resolving time is essential. Practical limitations on the stability of fast discriminator circuits dictate, therefore, that the resolving time should not be much shorter than the input-signal duration.

The shortest resolving time that can be achieved with good stability is

---

* It is often worthwhile to make R_b two or three times smaller than βR_L to allow for variations in the value of β from transistor to transistor.

determined by the rate of rise of the output signal which, in turn, depends upon the current switched and C_{stray}. In the case of the pentode circuit allowable anode current is limited by the relatively low screen dissipation rating rather than by the higher anode dissipation rating. (In the bottomed condition most of the cathode current goes to the screen, and only a small fraction is collected on the anode.) This circuit configuration is not used, therefore, to achieve very short resolving times.

In the transistor circuit (Fig. 7.4) where screen dissipation need not be considered, large currents can be switched. Two other effects, however, combine to reduce the resolving time with respect to the input-signal duration. In saturated transistors the number of minority carriers present in the base is more than sufficient to account for the full collector current. The excess carriers have a finite lifetime in the base, so that collector current continues to flow for a short time after the base input current has been removed by the input signal. The time during which collector current is completely cut off is, therefore, somewhat shorter than the duration of the input signal. The size and duration of the output signal and, consequently, the resolving time are also somewhat decreased by the current that flows in the base-collector circuit when the transistors are driven to cutoff by the input signals. In a transistor with an appreciable reverse bias across the collector-base junction, only a little displacement current flows in the small collector-base capacitance. However, in a saturated transistor, the collector-base junction is forward-biased and the base and collector are coupled by the considerably larger junction diffusion capacitance. As the base is driven to cutoff, the stored charge that flows out the base lead divides between the emitter and the collector circuits. For an appreciable time interval, this current component in the collector circuit may be enough to override the output signal.

In a nonlinear parallel coincidence circuit designed by Garwin [2], the resolving time can be more nearly equal to the input-signal duration because the switching elements are not operated in the bottomed condition. A threefold version of the Garwin circuit is illustrated in Fig. 7.5. The three pentodes are normally conducting approximately equal currents I. Resistors R_1 and R_2 are both large compared with R_f, the forward resistance of diode D, and are so proportioned that slightly more than two-thirds of the total anode current flows in the diode. (This is accomplished by making R_1 slightly greater than $2R_2$.) The anode of the diode is bypassed to ground by a large capacitor C so that, as far as short impulses are concerned, the dynamic impedance in the anode circuit of the three pentodes is very nearly equal to the low forward resistance of the diode. If one of the pentodes is driven to cutoff by an input signal, the total anode current decreases by I, the current change occurring almost entirely in the diode because R_1 is much larger than R_f. This gives rise to a small positive output signal IR_f. If two pentodes are driven to cutoff, the change in anode current, $2I$, is still less than the initial current in the diode, so it continues to conduct slightly, the anode circuit impedance remains low, and the signal at the output, $2IR_f$, is still small.   If, however, all three pentodes are cut off simultaneously, the diode also cuts off, and if the subsequent circuit loading is negligible, the output rises to power supply potential.   Therefore, in the Garwin circuit as in the Rossi circuit, when all tubes are cut off, the output signal is much larger than when one or more are left conducting.   However, in the Garwin circuit the current available to drive the output stray capacitance may be considerably greater.   Since the tubes are not bottomed, only a

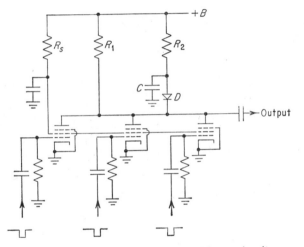

FIG. 7.5   Threefold Garwin coincidence circuit.

small fraction (about one-fourth) of the cathode current flows to the screens, so the anode current can be reasonably large without exceeding the screen dissipation rating.   The Garwin circuit is, therefore, more suitable for use with short resolving times.

The Garwin circuit performs very well at moderate input-signal counting rates but has a serious defect at high counting rates.   Whenever one or more of the pentodes are cut off, the diode current is smaller than its quiescent value.   The current in R_2 is then larger than the diode current, and capacitor C charges positively.   When all tubes return to conduction, a disproportionately large share of the total anode current flows in the diode, at the expense of current in R_1.   When a coincidence occurs, the current available to charge the stray capacitance at the output (the total plate current less the diode current) is less than that at low counting rates.   This means that more nearly perfect overlap of the input signals is required in order to produce an output signal that exceeds the discriminator bias. In other words, the effective resolving time is shorter at high counting rates than at low counting rates.

A first-order compensation for this duty-cycle effect can be achieved by a proper choice of screen dropping resistor R_s. At high counting rates the tubes spend an appreciable fraction of the time cut off, and the average screen potential rises by an amount determined by the value of R_s. The rise in screen potential can increase the anode current, during the conducting intervals, so that, despite the increase in the diode

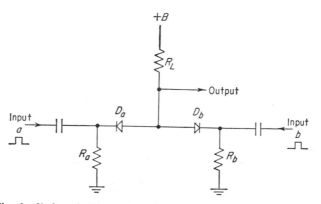

FIG. 7.6 Simple diode coincidence circuit. The output is approximately equal to the smaller of the two input signals.

current, the available output current remains independent of the counting rate.

Figure 7.6 shows a diode coincidence circuit that is popular largely because of its simplicity. Quiescently, current flows from the positive power supply through R_L and divides, approximately equally, between the two diodes and resistors R_a and R_b. R_a and R_b are small resistors, of the order of the forward resistance of the diodes, and R_L is much larger. A positive input signal at input a cuts off D_a, forcing the current that previously flowed in that diode to transfer to D_b. This current, flowing in D_b and the parallel combination of R_b and the b input source impedance, produces a small positive output signal. If, however, signals are simultaneously present at both inputs, both diodes are driven in the cutoff direction, and the output potential rises until it is limited by conduction of one or both diodes. This occurs at an output potential approximately equal to the amplitude of the smaller of the two input signals. With large input signals, the coincidence output can be much larger than the output resulting from a single input. By reversing the diodes and the power supply polarity, the circuit can be made to accept negative input signals.

The practical resolving time limit for the diode coincidence circuit depends critically on the diodes used. With vacuum diodes the circuit fails when the input signals are so short that the displacement current in the diode capacitance becomes comparable to the current in R_L. With semiconductor diodes the limit is usually imposed by the finite reverse resistance recovery time (see footnote, page 77).

It has been assumed in the coincidence circuits already considered that all input signals have the same duration and, in some circuits, the same amplitude as well. However, most radiation detectors do not give signals of uniform size, and despite similarities in shape, amplitude differences

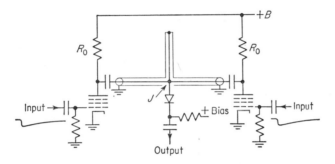

FIG. 7.7   Coincidence circuit of Bell, Graham, and Petch.

lead to different effective signal durations. A large signal applied to a switching element in a coincidence circuit keeps that element switched for a longer interval of time than would a smaller signal, even though both signals have similar shapes. Furthermore, linear pulse-shaping operations, such as RC or delay-line differentiation, do not alter the fact that large signals have longer durations than small ones. In order to standardize the effective duration of detector signals it is necessary, first, to standardize their amplitudes. This can be accomplished with a regenerative discriminator circuit or with a nonregenerative limiter circuit. Slow- and medium-speed coincidence circuits (with resolving times of the order of 10^{-8} sec and longer) frequently employ regenerative amplitude-standardizing circuits. However, transit time delays in the elements of regenerative feedback loops limit their switching speed and make them unsuitable for use in faster systems.

A highly successful fast coincidence system, described by Bell, Graham, and Petch [3], combines the functions of amplitude limiting, mixing, and pulse-duration standardization in a single circuit (Fig. 7.7). The charge signals from the detectors are integrated on stray capacitance,[1] amplified, if necessary, and presented to the coincidence circuit as negative pulses, long compared with the detector rise time.   The signals drive the limiter pentodes from zero bias to cutoff, producing current pulses in the anode circuit that are standardized in amplitude but uncertain in duration. R_0 is made equal to the characteristic impedance of the coaxial transmission line at the anode of each tube, so that the net impedance at each anode is equal to $R_0/2$.   If the current I in one of the limiter tubes is cut off by an input signal, a voltage pulse $IR_0/2$ propagates down the transmission line to the junction J.   At this point, the signal, reduced in amplitude because of the lower net impedance, divides and propagates down the shorting stub and also along the transmission line to the other tube anode.   The signal component that reaches the second anode is absorbed in the terminating resistor R_0.   The signal component that travels down the shorting stub is reversed in polarity at the short circuit and returns to junction J.   If the characteristic impedance of the stub matches the net impedance of the two transmission lines at J, the reflected signal exactly cancels the incident signal, so that the voltage pulse at J has a duration equal to twice the signal propagation time in the stub.   The impedance match is accomplished by using coaxial cable for the stub that has half the characteristic impedance of the cable used for the anode transmission lines.   The reflected signal returning to the junction divides between the two transmission lines, propagates to their respective terminations, and is absorbed.   The net result is a standardized signal at J having an amplitude of $IR_0/8$ and a duration (which determines the circuit resolving time) of twice the time length of the stub.   If both limiter tubes are cut off within the resolving time, and the anode transmission lines are the same length, the signal at J achieves double amplitude during the overlap time.   The diode is biased to reject single amplitude signals but to pass the double amplitude signals resulting from coincident input signals.   If the anode transmission lines have different lengths, the circuit becomes a delayed coincidence circuit and records pulse pairs only if they are separated in time by the difference in propagation time in the two transmission lines.

[1] Some coincidence systems make use of the short, fast-rising current pulses from the detectors instead of the longer signals that result from integration.   This is accomplished by using a very small load resistor at the detector so that the time constant determined by this resistor and stray capacitance is short compared with the duration of the detector current pulses.   This may lead to serious difficulties, however, because of the statistical nature of the detector current pulses.   The detector current is, in fact, made up of a collection of discrete charge pulses.   If these charge pulses are not integrated, a single event may produce more than one discrete signal at the coincidence-circuit input.   This effectively increases the singles counting rate, with the result that the accidental coincidence rate may be substantially increased.

Most of the advantages of this circuit result from the fact that each input is associated with only one fast active circuit element, the limiter pentode. By employing high-transconductance, low-capacitance limiter tubes, stable operation is readily achieved with resolving times as low as 10^{-9} sec. A minor disadvantage of the circuit is that it does not perform properly if the negative input signals have positive overshoots. During a positive overshoot at one limiter grid, the current in the limiter tube is temporarily increased. If another signal arrives during the overshoot and drives the limiter to cutoff, the anode current pulse is abnormally large, and the resultant signal at the diode may be large enough to be recorded as a coincident pair. To prevent the recording of these spurious coincidences, it is necessary to remove the positive overshoot from the input signals. This can be done with diodes in series with the limiter grids, oriented to pass negative signals and to reject positive ones.

The coincidence circuits so far discussed are sometimes classified as "parallel" circuits because the input switching elements are connected in parallel. Coincidence circuits can also be made in which the output-signal current flows through the switching elements in series. For an output signal to occur, all of the series switches must be closed simultaneously. Coincidence circuits of this type can be made with multigrid vacuum tubes, biased to cutoff at more than one grid. A number of vacuum-tube types are suitable for this sort of application. The 6AS6, a pentode with a closely wound suppressor grid, is often used. With the anode and screen at about 100 volts, 10 volts of bias at either the control grid or the suppressor is enough to prevent the flow of anode current. A positive pulse at the control grid alone allows cathode current to flow to the screen, but no anode current flows unless a positive pulse is simultaneously present on the suppressor grid.

Fischer and Marshall [4] have described a fast series coincidence circuit based on the 6BN6 tube. The advantages of this circuit stem from the fact that the 6BN6, a gated beam tube of unique design, can be cut off at either of two control grids with biases of as little as 3 volts. Furthermore, the anode current limits sharply in the positive-grid region, and very little grid current flows. The circuit is, therefore, sensitive to small input signals, but still capable of accepting large input signals without serious feed-through or bias-stability problems. An interesting characteristic of the 6BN6 tube is that, even though anode current is cut off by negative bias at both control grids, cathode current flows to the accelerator electrode. The tube can, therefore, be self-biased even in the cutoff condition.

Figure 7.8 shows a series coincidence circuit made with junction transistors. A threefold circuit is illustrated, but more (or fewer) transistors can be used. Initially, all the bases are at ground potential, so that all the transistors are cut off and no current flows in the load resistor. To produce an output signal, it is necessary to supply current to all three bases simultaneously. If the input signals are large enough to drive the transistors to saturation, the coincidence output signal is a positive pulse nearly equal to the power supply voltage.

The series transistor circuit is frequently used as a logical "and" circuit in digital computer systems but is rarely employed for nuclear coincidence counting. Its principal drawback is its rather uncertain resolving time caused by minority carrier storage in saturated transistors. A single input signal to T_1 cannot produce an output signal, but it does inject minority carriers into the transistor base. If, after this signal has decayed, but while some of the minority carriers are still present in the base, input signals are applied to T_2 and T_3, current will flow in the load resistor. The effective resolving time, therefore, depends upon the minority carrier lifetime.

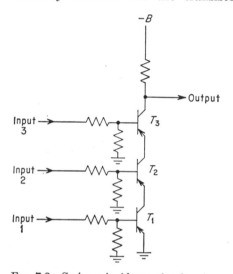

Fig. 7.8   Series coincidence circuit using junction transistors normally biased to cutoff.

A third class of coincidence circuits includes various forms of balanced configurations. In these circuits individual input signals produce a pair of output signals which cancel each other. Coincident signals, on the other hand, are combined in a nonlinear circuit element which renders the cancellation imperfect, so that a net output signal results. Although balanced coincidence circuits have been built in many different ways [5–9], all of the published circuits have at least two features in common: (1) When carefully balanced, they can accept input signals with a wide range of amplitudes (as large as two orders of magnitude) and can successfully reject single events without resorting to pulse-amplitude standardization. (2) They are sensitive to small signals (less than 1 volt) because the signals need only be large enough to establish slight nonlinearity in a circuit element (usually a diode) and do not have to switch currents completely on or off.

Figure 7.9 shows a balanced coincidence circuit designed by Bay [7]. The circuit accepts negative input signals with a variety of amplitudes and shapes and delivers negative output signals when the inputs are coincident. A signal at input B, unaccompanied by a signal at A, is blocked by the high reverse resistance of diode D_2 and produces a negligible output signal.   A signal at A, on the other hand, drives both diodes D_1 and D_2 in the forward direction, so that a charging current flows in capacitors C_1 and C_2.   If the capacitors are equal, the diode forward resistances are matched, and resistor r is equal to the impedance of the B signal source (represented by r_B), a signal at A delivers equal amounts of charge to C_1 and C_2.   If a negative signal is present at input B during part or all of the signal at input A, the current flowing through D_2 is reduced so that the charge on C_1 exceeds the charge on C_2.   The function of the remainder of the circuit is to compare the charge on the two capacitors and to present a signal at the output when, because of coincident input signals, the two charges are unequal.

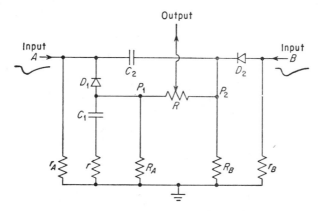

FIG. 7.9   Bay balanced coincidence circuit.

After the A input decays, C_1 discharges through resistors r and R_A in series, while C_2 discharges through R_B and the impedance of the A signal source r_A which, like r_B, is equal to r. R_A and R_B are adjusted to be equal and large compared to r so that the discharge time constants associated with the two capacitors are equal and long compared with the charging time constants.   The discharge of C_1 in R_A produces a negative, exponentially decaying signal at P_1, whereas the discharge of C_2 in R_B produces a positive signal at P_2, decaying with the same time constant. The output signal at the center tap of R (large compared to R_A and R_B) represents the algebraic sum, and therefore the absolute difference, of the signals at P_1 and P_2 and is a measure of the difference in the amount of charge deposited on C_1 and C_2.   This difference is zero when only one input is present but has a finite negative value when simultaneous signals are present at the two inputs.

The resolving time of the Bay circuit is determined by the duration of the input signals, the sensitivity of the output recording circuit, and, to a certain extent, the amplitude of the input signals.   With large input signals only a small amount of signal overlap is necessary to produce a detectable difference in the amount of charge on the two capacitors, whereas small signals must overlap more and are, therefore, associated with a smaller value of resolving time.   Increasing the output-circuit sensitivity decreases the amount of overlap necessary to produce a detectable output pulse, thus increasing the resolving time for both large and small signals but preserving the resolving-time dependence on pulse amplitude.

A differential coincidence circuit described by Meunier [9] features a resolving time which is more nearly independent of input-signal amplitude.   Furthermore, if the input signals are longer in duration than a

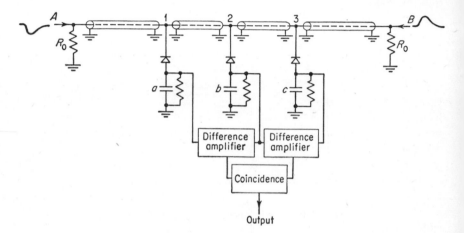

FIG. 7.10   Meunier differential coincidence circuit.

minimum value determined by the length of a delay line, the resolving time is also independent of the signal length.   The operation of the circuit will be described in terms of a block diagram (Fig. 7.10).

The circuit accepts negative input signals from the anode of a photomultiplier tube at A and positive signals from the last dynode of another photomultiplier tube at B.   If a B signal occurs alone, it propagates down the tapped transmission line and is absorbed at the termination at the A end.   The diodes at tap points 1, 2, and 3 are pulsed in the reverse direction, so no charge is deposited on the capacitors at a, b, and c and no signals are presented to the difference amplifiers.   A negative signal at A, which occurs alone, also travels down the transmission line and is absorbed at the far end, but in passing points 1, 2, and 3 it causes the deposition of equal amounts of charge on the small capacitors at a, b, and c.   Since each difference amplifier receives equal signals at both inputs, neither sends an output to the final coincidence circuit.   "Singles" are thus rejected in much the same way as in the Bay circuit, at one input because they have the wrong polarity to pass through the circuit diodes, and at the other input because the resultant output signals are equal and cancel each other.

If signals are impressed simultaneously at inputs A and B, they arrive at tap point 2 at the same time. Because the two signals have opposite polarity, the net signal at point 2 is smaller than that which would be produced by the A input alone. Depending upon the lengths of the two input signals, they may or may not overlap at points 1 and 3 as well, but in any case the overlap at 1 and 3 is not as complete as it is at 2. The signals at a and c, therefore, will be larger than the signal at b. The differences $a - b$ and $c - b$ both have a finite amplitude, so both difference amplifiers send signals to the final coincidence circuit which generates an output signal.

Now let us consider what happens if the A and B signals do not occur exactly simultaneously. If the A signal precedes the B signal, the overlap increases at point 3 while it decreases at 2 and 1. When the time separation between the input signals is equal to the time required for a signal to propagate between points 2 and 3 on the transmission line, the overlap at point 3 is equal to that at point 2 and the b and c signals are equal. The difference $c - b$ vanishes and the final coincidence circuit, lacking an input on the right-hand side, produces no output. Similarly, if the order of the input signals is reversed, when the time separation becomes equal to the propagation time between 1 and 2, $a - b$ vanishes and the coincidence circuit fails to receive an input on the left-hand side. For smaller time separations between the input signals both differences $a - b$ and $c - b$ are finite and have the appropriate polarity for driving the final coincidence circuit.

If the transmission-line segments 1-2 and 2-3 are equal and have a propagation time τ, then input signals that are separated by more than τ are rejected, while those separated by less than τ are recorded as being coincident. Notice that this applies, at least in theory, regardless of the amplitude and duration of the input signals, provided that each signal duration is at least equal to τ. This is based on an assumption that the final coincidence circuit is sensitive to finite values of the differences $a - b$ and $c - b$, no matter how small. In a practical system, where the sensitivity of the coincidence circuit is not infinite, the resolving time is largely, but not entirely, independent of the amplitude and duration of the input signals.

7.2 Defining Pulse-arrival Time

The resolution of all coincidence and pulse-timing systems is limited, ultimately, by the uncertainty with which the detector signals characterize the arrival time of the primary particles.[1] If we neglect the time required for the primary particle to traverse the detector, we can say that each particle arrives at a unique point in time. The resultant detector signal, however, is not of infinitesimal duration. In order to optimize the system time resolution, it is necessary for us to determine which point in the detector signal represents the true moment of arrival with the least uncertainty. There is, unfortunately, no single solution to this problem because it depends on both the characteristics of the detector and the energy of the detected radiation.[2]

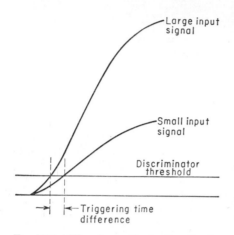

In general, the early part of a detector signal is subject to less statistical uncertainty than later parts. Many timing systems, therefore, derive pulse-time information from the earliest practical point on the detector charge signal. A discriminator or limiter circuit is biased to switch at a point very close to the beginning of the detector signals. Since the discriminator cannot have infinite sensitivity, it is, of course, impossible to switch precisely at the beginning of the signals. Nor would it be advisable even if possible, because if the discriminator is made too sensitive, it will trigger often on the system noise. This may increase the counting rate to the point where the accidental coincidence rate becomes excessive.

Fig. 7.11 Waveforms illustrating the dependence of the triggering time of a discriminator on the amplitude of the input signals.

Figure 7.11 shows how a finite discriminator bias causes signal timing to be dependent on pulse amplitude. The signals are drawn as if there were no statistical uncertainty in their shapes. In practice, however, statistical fluctuations in the leading edge incur additional timing uncertainties which are random and of a fundamental nature. These statistical fluctuations determine the ultimate time resolution attainable. The systematic amplitude-dependent uncertainties, on the other hand, are not fundamental and can be eliminated in several ways.

One way to eliminate the amplitude-dependent time uncertainties is to restrict the input signals to a narrow amplitude range. This is often done

---

[1] See Chap. 1 for a discussion of some of the sources of time uncertainty in various detectors.

[2] See Refs. 10 and 11 for detailed studies of the statistics governing time measurements with scintillation counters.

in a "fast-slow" coincidence system like that illustrated in Fig. 7.12. Each input signal, in addition to going to the fast (i.e., short resolving time) coincidence circuit, also goes to a single-channel pulse-height analyzer which is set to accept only those signals that fall in a narrow amplitude range. The output signals from the two pulse-height analyzers are combined with the output of the fast coincidence circuit in a slow triple coincidence circuit which produces an output signal only when the time and amplitude restrictions are simultaneously satisfied. This eliminates amplitude effects, but at the expense of a large amount of the available data because time measurements are only made on those few signals that satisfy the amplitude requirements.

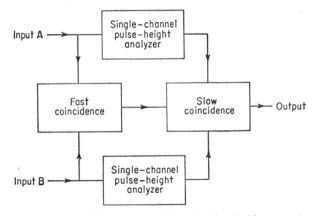

FIG. 7.12   Block diagram of a "fast-slow" coincidence system.

Amplitude-dependent timing errors can be eliminated without sacrificing data in two ways. One arrangement we shall call the "linear" system because nonlinear limiters or discriminators are not used to prepare the input signals for the coincidence circuit. The balanced coincidence circuits described in the previous article operate in the linear system. In the linear systems the effective time of arrival of a signal is marked by the centroid of the detector current pulse rather than by the leading edge, so the statistical uncertainties may be greater than in the nonlinear leading-edge systems. However, the increased data collection rate that results from accepting signals of all amplitudes frequently justifies a slight sacrifice in time resolution.

Another class of amplitude-independent timing systems makes use of special discriminator circuits which trigger at a fixed phase point on the input signals, regardless of the signal amplitude. These can be further divided into two groups. In one group, advantage is taken of the fact that double-differentiated signals from linear amplifiers pass through zero at a time which is independent of the signal amplitude. In the other group, a fixed increment is applied to a delayed part of the signals which causes them to pass a voltage threshold, different from zero, at a time independent of their amplitude. The first circuit of this type was described by Weinzierl [12] in 1956 and another, similar at least in principle if not in execution, by Arecchi [13] in 1959.

A detailed discussion of all the published circuits in these two groups is hardly warranted because they all yield approximately the same results. In each case, by suitable adjustment of the pulse-shaping elements it is possible to use any phase point on the input signals as the time reference point. In nearly all of the published circuits, however, the half-amplitude point on the integrated charge signal, corresponding to the centroid of the detector current pulse, has been chosen. The most important difference among the published circuits is that the zero-crossing circuits are easier to build and to understand, so we shall confine our consideration to them.

Fairstein et al. [14] and Grühle [15] have shown that a Schmitt trigger circuit can be biased to mark the zero transition of a double-differentiated input signal. If the trigger circuit bias is made exactly equal to its hysteresis (see Art. 3.1), the trailing edge of its output waveform corresponds in time to the zero crossing of the input signal. Since the time of zero transition is independent of the pulse amplitude, a signal derived from the trailing edge of the Schmitt trigger waveform can be used for amplitude-independent timing.

A minor disadvantage resulting from the use of a Schmitt trigger circuit is that the bias must be fixed (or the hysteresis must be made to vary with the bias) if it is to recover at the time of zero transition. In the circuit [16] of Fig. 7.13, the discriminator bias can be varied continuously over a 100-volt range without altering the circuit recovery time. The circuit threshold sensitivity is determined by two independently adjustable biases derived from two potentiometers P_1 and P_2. With P_2 set to zero, P_1 is set to a bias exactly equal to the circuit hysteresis. An arbitrary additional bias is then imposed by P_2. When the circuit triggers, the voltage across P_2 is reduced to zero, thus removing the second bias component. The circuit recovery is thus governed only by the bias imposed by P_1, independent of the setting of P_2. Therefore, if P_1 is properly adjusted, the circuit recovers just as the input signal passes through zero.

P_1 and P_2 impose negative bias currents in diode D_1. D_1 is included in a negative feedback loop consisting of T_1 and T_2 in such a way that the circuit input impedance at point Q is very low so long as D_1 is conducting. T_2 and T_3 constitute a difference amplifier with T_2 quiescently conducting more heavily. Positive input signals that are large enough to drive a current through R_1 larger than the net bias current cut off D_1. The base of T_2 then goes positive, causing current to shift from T_2 to T_3.

The positive excursion at the collector of T_3 is coupled, through emitter follower T_4, to the regenerative feedback loop composed of transistors T_5, T_6, T_7, and T_8. When the circuit triggers, T_8 is driven from cutoff to saturation, thus reducing the voltage drop across P_2 from 10 volts to a few tenths of a volt and almost entirely removing the second

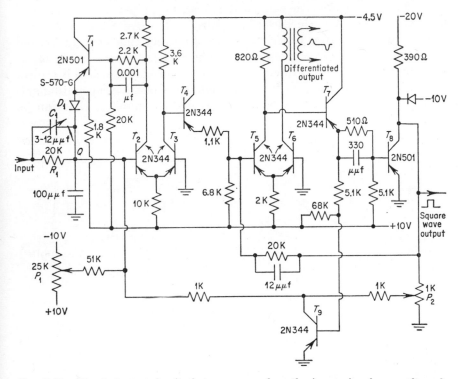

Fig. 7.13 Discriminator circuit that recovers when the input signals pass through zero. The recovery time is independent of both the input-signal amplitudes and the discriminator bias setting.

bias component. The small residual part of this bias component, which results from the finite saturation voltage drop in T_8, is almost entirely eliminated by T_9, which is driven to a saturation voltage drop of a few millivolts by T_7. Capacitor C_1 is included to compensate for the finite switching speed of the circuit. It is adjusted empirically, in association with P_1, to minimize the variation in recovery time with signal amplitude. This variation can be adjusted to be less than 2×10^{-8} sec over a range of input-signal amplitudes from 5 to 100 volts.

7.3 Chronotrons

Coincidence circuits distinguish simultaneous events from those which do not occur simultaneously. By a simple extension of the coincidence technique (the introduction of a time delay between one input signal and the coincidence circuit), the circuit can be made to recognize events that do not occur simultaneously but are separated by a specific time interval equal to the inserted delay. By counting so-called "delayed coincidences" for a set of different delay intervals, one can measure time-distribution functions which can yield information about the lifetimes of nuclear states or the velocities of particles.

Coincidence counting experiments are often very time-consuming, and delayed coincidence experiments even more so, because at each setting of the delay interval only a fraction of the time-correlated events is tallied. Since the practical limit on the resolution of a coincidence counting system is usually determined by the resolving-time stability that can be

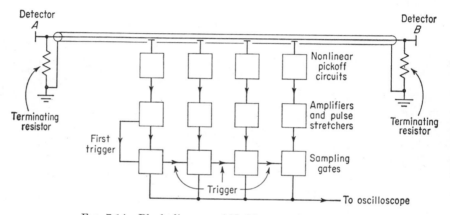

FIG. 7.14   Block diagram of Neddermeyer's chronotron.

achieved, long experiments do not generally yield as good time resolution as short ones. Experimental time can be reduced, and resolution correspondingly improved, by employing multichannel time-measuring systems in delayed coincidence work. Delay-line chronotrons are one of several classes of multichannel time-interval measuring devices.

In essence, a chronotron is a set of delayed coincidence circuits. Each coincidence circuit is connected to the two signal sources with different amounts of relative time delay, so that a number of points on the delay distribution curve can be recorded simultaneously. The appropriate time relationships can be established with either one or two signal delay lines. The first chronotron circuit, published by Neddermeyer et al. [17] in 1947, made use of a single tapped transmission line driven at opposite ends by the two signal sources (see Fig. 7.14). Input signals, with durations comparable to the time separation between taps on the transmission line, overlap to a greater or lesser degree at the various tap points, depending on their relative time of arrival. Pickoff circuits at each tap point produce output signals whose amplitudes are related to the degree of overlap. An essential characteristic of these pickoff circuits is their nonlinearity. A linear pickoff circuit, with poor high-frequency response, would produce an output proportional to the time integral of the short voltage signals at its input. But the time integral of linearly combined signals depends only on the amplitude and duration of the signals and not on the extent of their overlap. A biased nonlinear device (diode, vacuum tube, etc.), on the other hand, can emphasize the large signals produced by overlapping pulses with respect to the smaller signals that result when the two signals arrive at the tap point at different times.

If the input-signal durations are greater than the time separation between tap points, signal overlap may occur at more than one pickoff circuit. The timing of the two signals can then be inferred from the relative amplitudes of the signals from the pickoff circuits, since these are a measure of the extent of signal overlap at the various tap points. In the original system of Neddermeyer et al. the signals from the pickoff circuits were stretched and then sampled sequentially and displayed as a train of pulses on a triggered sweep oscilloscope. The pulse trains were photographed and examined, individually, to determine the time separation of the input signals.

Photographic techniques of this type are useful for low-counting-rate experiments, but they are impractical when a large number of events must be studied. In a chronotron reported by O'Neill [18] in 1955, the outputs of the various pickoff circuits are compared automatically, the largest output is recognized, and a count is tallied in the appropriate one of a set of message registers. O'Neill's chronotron makes use of two transmission lines, rather than one,[1] with a set of 6BN6 coincidence circuits connected to tap points on each line (see Fig. 7.15). The output signals from the coincidence circuits are compared with the aid of another tapped delay line with a relatively long time interval (0.5 μsec) between taps. Each coincidence is connected to a tap point on this "slow" line through an isolating diode, so that a train of evenly spaced pulses appears at the output of the line, each of which is a measure of the extent of the input-signal overlap at one of the coincidence circuits. Each pulse in the train is compared with its predecessor with the aid of an additional 0.5-μsec section of delay line and a difference amplifier. The arrival of the

---

[1] While there is no fundamental difference between a two-line chronotron and a single-line chronotron, the two-line system is more tolerant of imperfect transmission-line terminations. In the case of a single-line chronotron both sources must match the characteristic impedance of the transmission line to prevent spurious reflections. In a two-line chronotron a proper match at either end of each line is sufficient to suppress reflections.

largest coincidence pulse at the difference amplifier is marked by a reversal in the polarity of the difference-amplifier output. A pulse is directed to one of the set of tallying circuits, the selection being based on the time at which the difference-amplifier output changes sign. This involves the use of a second slow delay line, shown at the bottom of Fig. 7.15. A

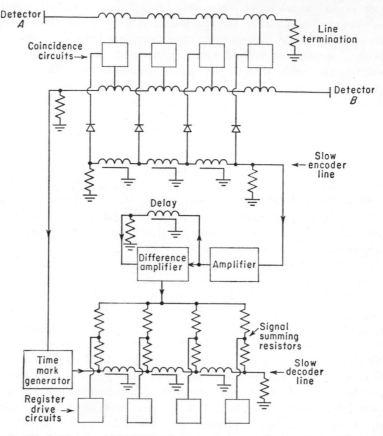

FIG. 7.15   Block diagram of O'Neill's chronotron, showing how the coincidence circuit with the largest output is automatically recognized.

time-marker pulse, triggered by one of the two chronotron input signals, propagates down this second slow line and combines with the difference-amplifier output to trigger one of the register drive circuits.

If the resolving time of the coincidence circuits in a chronotron is shorter than the propagation time between tap points on the transmission line, then an output appears at only one coincidence circuit and the tallying system can be much simpler [19]. Each coincidence circuit may then be connected to a scaling circuit through a suitable amplifier and discriminator. Of course, in this case, there are gaps between the sensitive time intervals during which input information is lost, whereas there are no gaps between time channels in the previous, more complicated, system.

Multichannel chronotrons are, in some respects, analogous to multidiscriminator pulse-height analyzers, because each requires a separate active circuit (coincidence circuit or amplitude discriminator) to mark each of the channel boundaries. As a result, both instruments are limited, by considerations of cost and complexity, to a modest number of channels. In addition, both are beset by serious problems associated

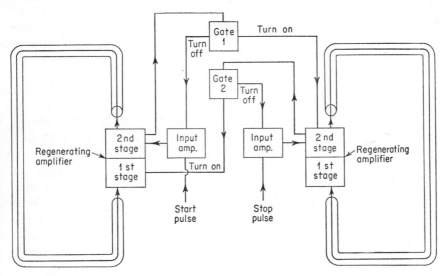

FIG. 7.16   Block diagram of the vernier chronotron of Lefevre and Russell.

with the measurement, adjustment, and stability of the effective widths of the various channels.

An interesting variation on the chronotron, published by Lefevre and Russell [20], has a large number of adjacent, nonoverlapping time channels, yet it employs only a single fast coincidence circuit. The instrument, called a vernier chronotron, has two long signal transmission lines, with the output of each connected to its input through a fast pulse-regenerating amplifier (see Fig. 7.16). If certain essential gating conditions are satisfied, a signal presented to each of the transmission lines circulates indefinitely in the closed loop, consisting of the line and the regenerating amplifier, until an externally imposed "kill" signal turns off the amplifier. The recirculation period, determined by the line length and the transit time through the regenerating amplifier, is made slightly different in the two lines, the difference corresponding to the width of the chronotron time channels.   The gating conditions permit signals to be inserted in the two loops only if they occur in pairs separated in time by less than the recirculation period.   On each pass through the lines the time difference between the circulating pulses decreases by an amount equal to the difference in the two loop periods.   After a number of passes through the lines, proportional to the initial time separation, the pulses emerge from the two lines simultaneously and trigger the coincidence circuit.   The output of the coincidence circuit turns off both regeneration amplifiers for a time interval greater than the recirculation period, thus clearing the lines in preparation for new signals.   The initial time separation is measured by counting the circulating pulses with a scaling circuit each time they pass through the regenerating amplifier.   The count in the scaler is used to address a magnetic-core memory (see Art. 5.3) where each event is tallied in a channel corresponding to the time separation of the input signals.

Figure 7.16 shows the interlocking arrangement of gate circuits which discards "start" pulses that are not followed by "stop" pulses within the period of the start line and accepts stop pulses only if they are preceded by start pulses.   The same gate circuits also prevent the insertion of a pulse in either line if a pulse is already circulating in that line.   Gate 1 is controlled by the second stage of the start-pulse regenerating amplifier and turns off the start-pulse input amplifier immediately after a start pulse has been accepted.   In the same way, gate 2 turns off the stop-pulse input amplifier after a stop pulse has been accepted.   Gate 1 also turns on the second stage of the stop-pulse regenerating amplifier so that stop pulses can be admitted once a start pulse has arrived.   When a stop pulse is admitted, gate 2 is triggered.   In addition to preventing a second stop pulse from entering the stop line, gate 2 turns on the first stage of the start-pulse regenerating amplifier.   This permits the start pulse, already present in the start line, to continue circulating.   If a stop pulse does not occur before the start pulse has completed its first trip around the start line, the start pulse finds its regenerating amplifier blocked and is, therefore, discarded.

The width of the time channels in the vernier chronotron, as previously mentioned, is determined by the small difference (typically of the order of 10^{-9} sec) in the propagation periods of the relatively long transmission lines.   The ratio of the line period to the channel width determines the maximum number of channels, which can be quite large, so that the limit is more likely to be determined by the capacity of the memory.   The minimum time length of the transmission lines must be longer than the resolving time of the address scaler.   Lefevre and Russell used lines about 300×10^{-9} sec long and a 256-channel memory.   The channel widths are determined to an accuracy of about 10^{-10} sec by adjustment of the line lengths. Finer control of the channel widths is made by adjusting the screen potentials in the regenerating amplifiers; this has a significant effect on the signal transit time through the amplifiers.

7.4 Time-to-Pulse-height Converters; Time Expanders

Chronotrons measure short time intervals directly in terms of signal propagation times in transmission lines. Alternatively, short time intervals can be measured by converting them, with suitable circuits, into other quantities that are more readily measurable using conventional techniques. The most common procedure is to charge a small capacitor linearly during the time interval to be measured. The peak capacitor potential can then be measured using a pulse-height analyzer. The virtue of this procedure lies in the fact that it is difficult to subdivide short time intervals for purposes of measurement, but it is relatively easy to subdivide a range of pulse amplitudes using any of a number of quantitative, readily available instruments. As an alternative to measuring the capacitor voltage directly, the capacitor can be allowed to discharge at a constant current much smaller than the charging current. The net result is the conversion of short time intervals into proportional long time intervals. Long time intervals are, of course, readily measurable by conventional techniques, as is evidenced by the fact that many modern pulse-height analyzers convert input-pulse amplitudes to time intervals to facilitate quantitative measurement. It is clearly of minor importance whether short intervals are converted to long ones in a single circuit or through the mechanism of separate time-to-height and height-to-time converters. Direct conversion is, of course, simpler, but it depends on the capacitor voltage being reasonably large so that the end point in its discharge can be recognized by a discriminator of reasonable sensitivity. An advantage of the two-step process is that a linear amplifier can be interposed between the time-to-height converter and the height-to-time converter so that the latter can operate in a convenient voltage range.

The short time interval to be measured is bounded by a "start" pulse and a "stop" pulse. At least one of these signals is derived from a radiation detector, while the other may be derived either from another detector or from a periodic "clock." Two detectors might be used to measure the flight time of a charged particle as it traverses the distance between them (as in a counter telescope) or to measure the lifetime of an excited nuclear state whose birth and death are heralded by the emission of radiation. A single detector and a clock are more likely to be used when measuring the velocities of neutrons produced by particle accelerators. The clock is then a periodic-signal generator that is synchronized in phase with pulses of energetic particles from the accelerator. For example, the radio-frequency accelerating voltage in a phase-focused cyclotron is often used as a time reference for measuring the velocity of neutrons produced when the short beam pulses (one per cycle) strike a target. Similar measurements are made with Van de Graaff generators in which the output beam is modulated by deflecting it across a slit with a large high-frequency voltage.

We distinguish between clock measurements and two-detector measurements because there are some essential differences in the techniques employed. Let us first consider some of the ways of measuring the time intervals between the aperiodic signals from two detectors and then discuss the additional problems that arise when one of the signals is periodic.

The following are three different ways in which the start and the stop pulses can be applied to switching circuits to control the charging of a capacitor.

1. Both signals can be applied to the same control electrode of a tube or transistor. The signals are opposite in polarity and are applied to the control electrode via isolating diodes (or other suitable elements) such that the start pulse charges the stray capacitance at the control electrode and the stop pulse discharges it. The result is a square pulse at the control electrode whose width is equal to the time interval between the start and the stop pulses. During this pulse the current through the tube or transistor has a constant value different from its quiescent value. The circuit output impedance (at the anode or collector) is made large so that the current change (either an increase or a decrease) is integrated on the output capacitance. The output voltage is then a measure of the time interval of interest.

2. The two signals can be applied to separate control electrodes in such a way that the start pulse turns on a charging current and the stop pulse turns it off. The two electrodes may be two grids in a multigrid tube, one quiescently biased on and the other biased off, or they may be in separate tubes or transistors which are connected in parallel, one normally conducting and the other cut off. As in the first case, the start and stop pulses are opposite in polarity.

3. Two control electrodes are used (either in series or in parallel), but they are biased so that a charging current flows in the output capacitor only when signals are present at both electrodes. These are, in effect, coincidence circuits, and charging current flows only during the time that the start and stop pulses overlap. These circuits measure the time interval between the leading edge of the stop pulse and the trailing edge of the start pulse. Therefore, in order that the results be meaningful, it is essential that the start pulse have a unique, well-defined duration. The width of the stop pulse need not be accurately determined, but it should be at least equal to the width of the start pulse. The output signal is not a direct measure of the time interval between the start and the stop pulses

T but is, rather, proportional to $L - T$, where L is the length of the start pulse. If the start-pulse duration is well determined, this is, of course, just as good as measuring T directly.

So long as both start and stop pulses are present and occur in the proper order, all three arrangements produce unambiguous results. However, if these conditions are not satisfied, each arrangement can, under certain circumstances, produce meaningless or ambiguous results. For example, if a start pulse is not accompanied by a stop pulse, 1 and 2 produce very large output signals while 3 gives no output. If a stop pulse precedes a start pulse, 1 gives a very large output signal, 2 may or may not produce an output depending on the duration of the two signals, and 3 yields an output proportional to the interval between the leading edge of the start pulse and the trailing edge of the stop pulse.

These difficulties can be avoided, where necessary, by employing a standard delayed coincidence circuit in conjunction with the time-to-pulse-height converter. The coincidence-circuit delay and resolving time are adjusted so that an output is produced only when the start and stop pulses are suitably related in time. The output of this coincidence circuit is used to control the pulse-height analyzer that measures the output of the time-to-pulse-height converter, so that only meaningful signals are recorded.

A circuit reported by Beghian et al. [21] illustrates the first of the three methods of time-to-pulse-height conversion (see Fig. 7.17). A negative start pulse at the grid of T_1 is limited and clipped, by the short-circuited delay line at the anode, to a duration of 3×10^{-9} sec. This short impulse charges the stray capacitance at the grid of T_4 via diode D_1, producing a positive step which remains until removed by a stop pulse, or if no stop pulse occurs, until the charge on the stray capacitance leaks off through the grid resistor and the reverse resistance of diodes D_1 and D_2. Quiescently, a current of 1 ma flows through diode D_3 and resistor R_1 to the negative power supply. The positive signal at the grid of T_4 raises its cathode potential slightly, cutting off D_3 and diverting its current to the tube. While the grid of T_4 remains positive, a constant current flows in its anode circuit[1] and charges capacitor C_1 negatively. Note that, even though the potential at the grid may drop slightly as the stray capacitance discharges, the voltage across R_1 departs only slightly from 150 volts, so that the cathode current in T_4 does not change appreciably. When a negative stop pulse arrives at the grid of T_2, it is limited and clipped, like the start pulse, and applied as a short positive signal to the grid of T_3.

---

[1] Immediately following the positive step at the grid of T_4, the current in T_4 would be higher than normal while the stray capacitance at its cathode is being charged. However, C_2 can be adjusted to supply the charging current for this stray capacitance so that it does not flow in T_4 and is not integrated by C_1.

The short current pulse in T_3 discharges the stray capacitance at the grid of T_4 and drives it to its quiescent cutoff potential where it is caught by conduction in diode D_2. Meanwhile, C_1 has been charged at constant current during the interval between the arrival of the start and stop pulses and now has a potential which is a measure of this time interval. This signal is coupled, via cathode follower T_5, to a linear amplifier and pulse-height analyzer.

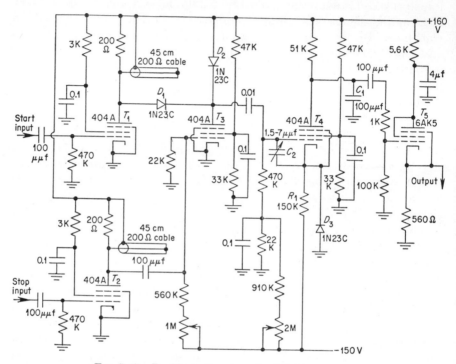

FIG. 7.17   Beghian's time-to-pulse-height converter.

The longest time interval that the circuit can measure is determined by the time required for leakage currents to discharge the stray capacitance at the grid of T_4. With the circuit elements shown in Fig. 7.17, this time is of the order of 10^{-7} sec. The shortest time interval that can be measured, without inserting external delays, is determined by the duration of the clipped start pulse. If the start and stop pulses overlap, the discharge of the stray capacitance at the grid of T_4 may be incomplete because of competition between the signals. It may not then be possible to interpret the charge signal on C_1 unambiguously because the incomplete cutoff allows excessive charge to reach C_1. An associated coincidence circuit, as pointed out above, may then be necessary to resolve the ambiguity.

A time expander that makes use of the second of the three conversion schemes was published by Moody [22] in 1952 and is shown, in part, in Fig. 7.18. Start and stop signals are provided by fast discriminator circuits (not shown). The stop pulses are assumed to occur after the start pulses and to be somewhat longer in duration, so that a stop pulse never ends while a start pulse is still present. The start-pulse duration is at least as great as the longest time interval to be measured. Quiescently, T_1 is conducting and T_2 is biased to cutoff. The current in T_1 (about 50 ma) exceeds the 30 ma flowing in R_1, the 20 ma difference flowing in the low forward resistance of diode D_1. A negative start signal at the grid of

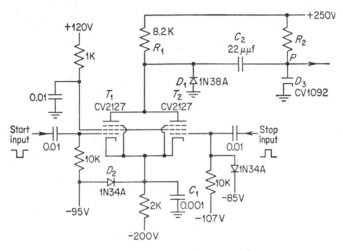

Fig. 7.18   Moody's time expander.

T_1 drives it to cutoff. A small capacitor C_1, at the common cathode connection between T_1 and T_2, prevents rapid changes in the cathode potential, so T_1 cuts off sharply. When, after a while, the cathode potential drops a few volts, it is caught by diode D_2. With T_1 cut off, D_1 stops conducting and the current in R_1 charges the plate circuit capacitance positively. This capacitance consists of the parallel combination of stray capacitance to ground and the small capacitor C_2 which is connected to ground through the forward resistance of diode D_3. Since C_2 is approximately twice as large as the stray capacitance, it receives about two-thirds (20 ma) of the current in R_1. At the end of the time interval to be measured, a positive stop signal turns on T_2. The surge of cathode current flowing into bypass capacitor C_1 causes the initial value of the plate current to be large, thus quickly discharging the stray capacitance and once more driving D_1 into conduction. This negative signal at the anodes drives D_3 to cutoff, leaving an accumulated charge on C_2 that is proportional to the time interval between the leading edges of the start and stop pulses. With the left-hand terminal of C_2 clamped to ground, the negative excursion of its right-hand terminal P is also a measure of the time interval of interest. This voltage is converted to another, much longer, time interval by allowing C_2 to be recharged by a very small current in R_2. This time interval begins with the fast negative voltage step at P and ends when the linear recharge of C_2 returns point P to ground, at which potential it is once more caught up by D_3.

A circuit designed by Green and Bell [23] illustrates the third way of converting short time intervals into proportional pulse amplitudes. The circuit (Fig. 7.19) is a variation of the coincidence circuit of Fischer and Marshall (see Art. 7.1). A 6BN6 tube is driven at each of its control

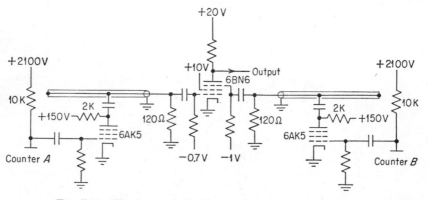

Fig. 7.19   Time-to-pulse-height converter of Green and Bell.

grids by signals from a pair of limiter pentodes. The limiters are driven to cutoff by the integrated charge signals from two scintillation detectors. The durations of the limited signals are determined by differentiating (clipping) the limiter output signals with short-circuited transmission-line stubs. The 6BN6 is operated with a very low voltage at the anode and accelerator electrode (20 volts and 10 volts, respectively) so that a quiescent bias of only 1 volt at either control grid prevents the flow of anode current. When nearly simultaneous signals are present at both inputs, anode current flows in the 6BN6 during the time the limited and clipped signals overlap. This current is integrated on the stray capacitance at the 6BN6 anode, producing a voltage signal proportional to the time interval between the leading edge of the stop pulse and the trailing edge of the start pulse.

Each of the systems discussed can be applied to the measurement of the time of arrival of a detector signal with respect to the phase of a clock, if suitable precautions are taken to deal with the profusion of clock pulses.

Since the clock signals are periodic, it is of little consequence whether the detector signal is timed with respect to the clock pulse that precedes it or the one that follows it. However, to avoid a large number of false starts, the detector usually provides the start pulses, and stop pulses are derived from the clock. The design of the timing circuit depends on the relationship between the clock period and the range of time intervals of interest. If the range of time intervals to be measured is less than half the interval between clock pulses, any of the schemes used with two detectors can also be used for clock measurements. If, on the other hand, detector pulses of interest occur at all phases of the clock, additional gating circuits are necessary. In methods 2 and 3, for example, the duration of the start pulse is made equal to the largest time interval to be measured and the duration of the stop pulse is made slightly greater still. If measurements are to be made over the entire clock period, the start-pulse duration must be at least equal to the clock period and the stop-pulse duration must be greater than the clock period. But if every clock pulse produces a stop pulse, then stop pulses will always be present and no meaningful output signals will ever be obtained. It is necessary, therefore, to select for use as stop pulses only those clock pulses that are preceded by detector pulses.

Figure 7.20 shows a circuit designed by Weber et al. [24] that includes a gate circuit for selecting clock pulses. Tubes T_1 and T_2 constitute a biased difference amplifier that accepts negative input signals with an amplitude greater than some preassigned value and delivers negative cutoff signals to the grid of T_3. T_{1a} and T_2 are connected as a White cathode follower (see Art. 2.3) so that the cathode of T_{1a} can follow fast negative input signals. Because of a positive feedback connection between the anode of T_4 and the grid of T_3, T_3 and T_4 act as a trigger circuit. The trigger circuit is somewhat unusual in that the duration of its output signal is determined by the length of the short-circuited delay line in the anode circuit of T_3, regardless of the length of the input signal. The line length is chosen so that the positive output signal at the cathode of T_4 has a duration equal to the interval between clock pulses. The signal is applied to the second control grids of both dual-control tubes T_5 and T_6. The first control grid of T_6 is normally at zero bias, so it starts to conduct as soon as the start pulse arrives, its anode current being integrated on the small capacitor C_1. T_5, on the other hand, is normally biased to cutoff at its first grid, so that it does not conduct until a clock pulse arrives. The first clock pulse following the beginning of the start pulse is passed by gate tube T_5 and cuts off T_6 at its first control grid, thus interrupting its anode current and terminating the integration process. The result is a negative signal at the anode of T_6 which is proportional to the time interval between the leading edge of the start pulse and the next clock pulse.

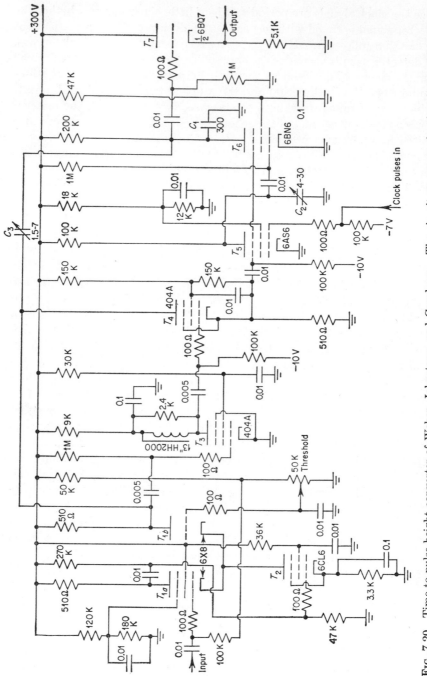

Fig. 7.20 Time-to-pulse-height converter of Weber, Johnstone, and Cranberg. The circuit measures the time interval between a detector pulse and the next pulse from a periodic clock.

It will be observed that, since T_5 is normally biased to cutoff at both control grids, clock pulses that are not preceded by start pulses have no effect on T_6.   When T_5 does pass a selected clock pulse, the anode current is integrated on C_2, which is adjusted so that T_6 remains cut off at its first control grid for at least the duration of the start pulse from T_4. C_3 couples a small negative signal to the anode of T_6 to compensate for the displacement current flowing in the second-control-grid-to-anode capacitance of T_6.

This timing arrangement has been used with clock frequencies as high as 5 megacycles, the limit being imposed by the width of the clock pulses at the first control grid of T_5.   Due to the width of the clock pulses, there is a time interval in each cycle during which the measurements are ambiguous, when the beginning of the selected stop pulse precedes the start pulse.   At very high clock frequencies, this time interval can represent so large a fraction of the cycle as to render the system useless.

R-F Vernier Technique.   An important new technique for time-interval measurements was reported by Cottini et al. [25,26] in 1956. The system is applicable to both two-detector and clock measurements. It can be operated in either a linear or a nonlinear mode (see Art. 7.2), so that signal timing can be based either on the leading edges of the signals or on their centroids.   An important advantage of the system is that for clock measurements data can be collected over nearly the entire clock cycle, even when the frequency is high.

The r-f vernier technique is similar in principle to the vernier chronotron of Lefevre and Russell (see Art. 7.3), the most important difference being that the r-f system deals with sinusoidal waveforms rather than with short impulses so that relatively simple, narrowband circuits can be employed.   Let $A \sin (\omega_1 t + \phi)$ and $B \sin (\omega_2 t + \theta)$ represent two r-f signals with different frequencies, and let us assume that they are combined in an ideal modulator which generates an output proportional to the product of the input signals.   By invoking a simple trigonometric identity we obtain, for the modulator output,

$$A \sin (\omega_1 t + \phi) \cdot B \sin (\omega_2 t + \theta) = \frac{AB}{2} \cos \left[(\omega_1 - \omega_2)t + (\phi - \theta) \right]$$

$$- \frac{AB}{2} \cos \left[(\omega_1 + \omega_2)t + \phi + \theta \right] \quad (7.4)$$

The first term on the right of Eq. (7.4) represents the "beat note" between the input signals and is seen to have a phase representative of the phase difference between the input signals.   In particular, at any instant in time when the input signals have the same phase, the beat note has a maximum value, and when the input signals are in phase quadrature, the instantaneous beat-note amplitude is zero.

Two high-Q resonant circuits, tuned to slightly different frequencies, are used to measure the time interval between two impulses. Each input signal is coupled to one of the resonant circuits, linearly for centroid timing or through a limiter circuit for leading-edge timing. Two damped r-f signals are generated, each having a phase determined by the time of arrival of the impulses that produce it. The two r-f signals are combined in a nonlinear modulator circuit which gives rise to sum and difference output frequencies. It is merely necessary to measure the phase of the low-frequency beat note to determine the time interval between the two input signals. If the two r-f signals have very nearly equal frequencies, the frequency of the beat note is low and its phase can be measured to high precision. The low-frequency beat note is easily separated from the r-f input signals and other modulation products by means of a low-pass filter. Its phase can be determined by measuring the time between one of the input pulses and a standard phase point on the beat note. Since the r-f input signals and, therefore, the beat note are decaying exponentially (because of the finite Q of the resonant circuits), it is most convenient to use one of the zero transitions of the beat note as the standard phase point. The zero transitions can be recognized, nearly independently of the beat-note amplitude, by a sensitive amplitude discriminator circuit.

The r-f vernier technique accomplishes a time expansion equal to the ratio of the frequency of the resonant circuits to the beat frequency. In theory, there is no limit to the time expansion that can be achieved, since by making the difference between the tuned circuit resonant frequencies sufficiently small, the beat frequency can be reduced indefinitely. A practical limit is imposed, however, by stability considerations, because when the beat frequency is low, its value is very sensitive to slight relative changes in the resonant frequencies of the tuned circuits. With reasonable care stabilities of the order of 1 per cent can be achieved with time-expansion factors of as much as 100.

Application of the r-f vernier technique to clock timing is very simple [27], since the clock signal can be used in place of one of the pulsed r-f signals. An advantage of this system is that the duration of the input signals does not detract from the useful measuring time, so that nearly all of the clock period can be utilized, even at high clock frequencies.

7.5 Slow-neutron-velocity Spectrometers

So far, we have been concerned with the measurement of short time intervals and with electronic circuits operating at or near their ultimate speed. We shall now shift our attention to the problems of measuring long time intervals, of the order of hundreds or thousands of microseconds in duration.   Interest in this time range results, almost entirely, from the wealth of interesting resonance interactions between nuclei and thermal and epithermal neutrons.   Because of the large number of these resonances, very precise neutron-energy measurements are often necessary in order to resolve them.   The two most useful tools for high-resolution measurement of slow neutron energies are the diffraction spectrometer and the velocity spectrometer.   Diffraction spectrometers, which employ a crystal lattice as a diffraction grating for neutrons, do not fall within the province of pulse spectrometry.   We shall, therefore, confine our attention to velocity spectrometers.

In a velocity spectrometer the energy of a neutron is determined by measuring its time of flight over a standard path length.   Neutrons are launched at specific times, in short bursts produced either by a particle accelerator that is pulsed or by a high-speed shutter that intercepts a neutron beam from a nuclear reactor.   The neutron burst is normally made as short as possible so that the desired resolution can be achieved with the shortest possible flight path.   A long flight path is undesirable because it leads to low neutron-detection efficiency.   Neutron-burst durations usually are in the range from a fraction of a microsecond to several microseconds.

The development of velocity spectrometers has followed a course analogous to that of the pulse-height analyzers.   Starting with single-time-channel instruments with scaler memories, they progressed through multi-time-gate instruments (the analog of multidiscriminator pulse-height analyzers) to the modern matrix-addressed machines, some with more than 2,000 channels of digital storage.   In many ways, particularly with respect to data storage, the electronic techniques employed in velocity spectrometers are similar to those used in pulse-height analyzers, so it will not be necessary for us to consider them in great detail.

Single-channel velocity spectrometers are no longer used.   Experimental time at facilities capable of supplying neutrons in large quantities is so costly that it is economically foolish to waste time with single-channel data collection.   We shall, therefore, confine our discussion to the multichannel instruments.

In all velocity spectrometers the beginning of the time interval to be measured is marked by a t_0 signal, derived either from the signal that pulses the accelerator ion source, from a particle detector in the primary beam of the accelerator, or from a light pulse that passes through a neutron shutter ("chopper") at the same time as the shutter passes a burst of neutrons from a reactor.   The t_0 signal generally triggers an adjustable delay circuit which marks the beginning of the time interval in which the detection of neutrons is to be recorded.   This interval is subdivided into a number of time channels commensurate with the desired resolution, each channel being connected to a tallying system which counts the neutrons detected therein.

In the early velocity spectrometers [28,29] the boundaries of the time channels were defined by a series of identical gate circuits which were triggered in sequence by signals from a clock oscillator. Each gate circuit was connected to one input of a coincidence circuit, the other input being connected to the neutron detector. The output of each coincidence circuit was connected to a scaling circuit and/or a mechanical register. A signal from the neutron detector would pass through the coincidence circuit controlled by the gate that happened to be on at the time, and would be tallied by the appropriate counter.

In velocity spectrometers, as in pulse-height analyzers (see Art. 4.1), it is important that the channels have equal width. In the case of the multi-time-gate spectrometers it would seem that, if the sequential triggering of the gates were controlled by an accurately periodic clock oscillator, the channel widths would automatically be equal. This would be true if the gates opened and closed in zero time. However, in practical circuits the switching time is finite and, in addition, may vary somewhat from circuit to circuit. When the time gates are short, it is very difficult to make the switching-time uncertainties small compared to the gate width. Furthermore, when a neutron pulse (whose width is necessarily finite) straddles the boundary between two time gates, it may be tallied in both channels, or if a delay has been inserted between time channels to prevent this, some pulses may be lost between channels. It will be seen later that these difficulties are not confined to the multi-time-gate spectrometers. In the more modern spectrometers they are eliminated by the use of time-quantizing circuits (see below).

The primary disadvantage of the multi-time-gate spectrometers is that they require a very large number of circuit elements per channel. When the number of time channels is large, an alternative matrix addressing scheme[1] is much to be preferred because it makes possible substantial savings in cost and complexity, as well as a corresponding improvement in reliability. The simplest matrix addressing system makes use of two sets of time gates. The first set of gates, which is advanced by a clock oscillator, closes upon itself to form a "ring scaler," and the second set of gates is advanced one step each time the ring scaler makes a full revolution. A 4×4 matrix addressing system is illustrated in Fig. 7.21. It will be seen that only 8 gate circuits are required for a 16-channel spectrometer. In general, a square matrix of N^2 elements requires only $2N$ gates, as compared with N^2 gates for the multigate system. In large

---

[1] Unpublished work on matrix-addressed velocity spectrometers at Argonne and Brookhaven Laboratories is described in a general review of time-of-flight instrumentation by Higinbotham [30].

systems with, for example, 10×10 or 16×16 channels, the saving in gate circuits is very substantial.

The system can be operated in either of two ways, depending upon the neutron counting rate. When the neutron flux available for time-of-flight experiments is so low that the probability of detecting as many as one neutron in the measuring time associated with a single neutron burst is

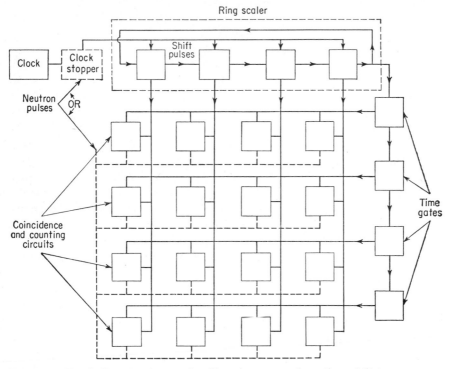

Fig. 7.21 Block diagram of a matrix addressing system for a time-of-flight spectrometer. A 4×4 matrix is illustrated for the sake of simplicity. Practical systems usually have more channels.

very small, the probability of detecting more than one neutron per burst is still smaller and, in many cases, can be neglected. Under these circumstances the simplest expedient is to stop the flow of pulses from the clock oscillator to the ring scaler when a neutron is detected. This can be done either by stopping the clock or by blocking a gate circuit connected between the clock and the ring scaler. The two sets of time gates are then left in a condition which is a unique representation of the number of clock pulses presented to the ring scaler from the start of the measuring interval to the detection of a neutron. No time-quantizing system is required because the same clock-stopping or gating circuit is involved, regardless of the time of arrival of the neutron. Any delays in this circuit apply equally to all time channels and, therefore, do not affect their relative widths.

With the clock stopped, one horizontal time gate and one vertical time gate are left in the ON condition while all the other time gates are OFF. The ON gates select one vertical and one horizontal address line which, together, energize the coincidence circuit at their intersection. Each coincidence circuit drives a tallying circuit which, for low-counting-rate experiments, may simply be a mechanical impulse register. In such a case, the functions of coincidence circuit and register driver can be combined in a set of dual-control thyratron tetrodes in which each thyratron has one control grid connected to a vertical address line and the other control grid connected to a horizontal address line.

When intense neutron sources are available, the probability of detecting more than one neutron per burst may not be negligible. If the clock-stopping technique described above were used, only the first neutron detected in each burst would be recorded. This leads not only to the loss of potentially valuable data but also to distortion of the velocity spectrum. At high counting rates the system becomes disproportionately insensitive to slow neutrons which are likely to be preceded by fast neutrons that stop the clock. These difficulties are avoided in a matrix-addressed velocity spectrometer designed by de Boisblanc and McCollom [31]. In their system, threefold coincidence circuits are used at the intersections of the addressing leads, the third input to all of the circuits being derived from the neutron detector. When a neutron is detected, a signal is routed to the appropriate tallying circuit by that coincidence circuit which is turned on by both sets of time gates. The clock is not stopped, so that if additional neutrons are detected from the same initial burst, they can also be tallied. However, as a result of the fact that the clock is not stopped, additional difficulties are encountered with respect to channel-width equality which are similar to those associated with the multi-time-gate system. The effective width of a time channel, assuming that the neutron pulses are negligibly short, is equal to the time that addressing signals are simultaneously present at two inputs of the associated coincidence circuit. In most cases this is equal to the width of the address signal from the ring scaler, which, of course, may vary somewhat from circuit to circuit owing to slight differences in switching speeds. An even larger variation is to be expected in the case of those channels addressed by the first stage of the ring scaler, because their addressing immediately follows a transition of the second set of gates and the associated switching time decreases the effective widths of these channels.

These channel-width variations are eliminated by a time-quantizing circuit which introduces small adjustments in the effective time of arrival of the neutron pulses, causing them to be presented to the coincidence circuits approximately in the middle of the time channels, when the switching transients are over. The time quantizer is a bistable trigger circuit (flip-flop) that is triggered from the 0 state to the 1 state when a neutron pulse arrives. The circuit is periodically pulsed by reset signals derived from the clock pulses, but delayed by approximately half the width of a time channel. When the flip-flop is in the 0 state, the reset pulses have no effect. However, if the flip-flop has been triggered to the 1 state by a neutron pulse, the next reset pulse returns it to the 0 state. The trailing edge of the flip-flop waveform always occurs at a standard clock phase, somewhere near the middle of a time channel, and is, in effect, a time-quantized version of the neutron pulse.

Matrix addressing reduces the number of gate circuits required in a multichannel spectrometer, but it does not reduce the number of tallying circuits. Therefore, when the number of channels is large, it is expedient to resort to computer memory systems for data storage rather than to the more costly and less reliable scaler and register circuits. The high resolution attainable with velocity spectrometers often justifies the use of so many time channels that computer memory systems are a practical necessity. All of the memory systems described in Chap. 5 have been used at one time or another, the particular choice being determined by the state of the memory art, by memory access time considerations, and by considerations of cost and reliability.

The first velocity spectrometer with a computer memory was built for use with the Yale linear accelerator by Schultz et al. [32]. A quartz delay line, with a period of about 1,000 μsec, is used as the memory element. The linear accelerator is pulsed in synchronism with the delay-line recirculation period, so that the memory operates in "real time." This is a substantial advantage in those cases where synchronization of the neutron source is possible because the memory addressing system is particularly simple. The next channel pulse following the detection of a neutron directs the adder to "add 1" to the count in the channel just emerging from memory.

Because the system operates in real time, the number of bits of storage per channel is limited by the length of time channels and the bandwidth of the memory and the adder circuits. Schultz was able to operate his system with a bit spacing of 0.2 μsec, so that 2-μsec channels could accommodate 10 bits, resulting in a 500-channel memory with a capacity of 2^{10} or 1,024 counts per channel.

Unfortunately, it is often inconvenient to synchronize the neutron source with a periodic memory. In those cases, random-access memories (e.g., magnetic cores or cathode-ray tubes) are generally used. The random-access memories are addressed via an address register which must be set to a state corresponding to the flight time of each detected neutron. When the neutron counting rate is sufficiently low to permit the use of the clock-stopping technique, addressing the memory is relatively simple. The address register is then merely a scaler which counts clock pulses. When the clock stops, the scaler is left with a count that is a digital representation of the neutron flight time which, through a suitable matrix, selects the corresponding memory storage location.

The situation is somewhat more complicated when the neutron counting rate is too high to permit the clock to be stopped. The problem has been approached in two different ways. A scheme used by Graham[1] at

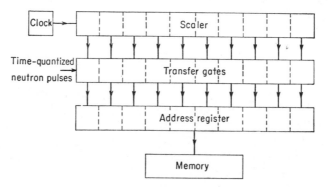

Fig. 7.22   Block diagram of a time-of-flight spectrometer in which detection of a neutron causes the contents of the clock scaler to be transferred to the address register, without stopping the clock.

Brookhaven National Laboratory uses separate circuits for the clock scaler and the address register (see Fig. 7.22). Each stage of the scaler is connected to a corresponding stage of the address register through a gate circuit. When neutrons are detected, they are time-quantized (by a circuit similar to that described above) and applied to the gate circuits. This causes the instantaneous state of the scaler to be transferred to the address register. A memory cycle is then initiated which adds 1 to the count in the memory location selected by the address register. During the memory cycle an auxiliary gate circuit prevents subsequent neutron pulses from altering the state of the address register. The scaler, however, continues counting clock pulses. At the end of the memory cycle the auxiliary gate circuit is turned on again so that slower neutrons, from the same burst, can be recorded. Neutrons can be recorded at any time in the interval of interest except during the relatively short memory cycles (about 10 μsec) associated with the recording of other, earlier, neutrons.

So long as the neutron pulses are time-quantized and the time channels

[1] Unpublished.

are moderately long, this system of reading the clock "on the fly" presents no difficulties. However, when the time channels are short, it is necessary to make allowance for the finite switching speed of the scaler stages. In conventional binary scalers each stage changes its state upon receipt of a triggering signal from the previous stage, when the previous stage switches from the 1 state to the 0 state. In the course of ordinary binary counting there are times when a number (perhaps all) of the stages are required to change their states simultaneously. Suppose, for example, that the first n stages of a scaler are in the 1 state. The next clock pulse triggers the first stage to the 0 state. This sends a "carry" signal to the second stage, switching it to the 0 state also. The switching of the second stage sends a carry signal to the third stage, and so on, the carry signal propagating through the first n stages, setting them to 0 and sending a carry signal to the $n + 1$ stage. The time for the carry signal to propagate from one stage to the next may be very short, but if the number of stages is large and the clock frequency high, the time for the carry signal to travel down the entire length of the scaler may equal or exceed the clock period. This means that some binary numbers, notably the "round" numbers ending in a long string of 0's, may never have time to "settle." If the transfer gates are pulsed by a time-quantized neutron pulse while the scaler is in an unsettled condition, the address register will be set to the wrong channel number. This difficulty can be avoided either by designing the scaler for very fast carry propagation or by delaying the time-quantized gate pulse slightly as it passes from stage to stage, so that it propagates at approximately the same rate as the carry signal.

Schumann [33] has published an ingenious alternative scheme for recording more than one neutron per burst which avoids the problems associated with reading the clock scaler on the fly. It is, in effect, a clock-stopping arrangement and, therefore, does not require a time-quantizing circuit. When a neutron is detected, the clock is stopped in the usual way and a count is added in the appropriate channel, the clock scaler performing the function of the memory address register. At the end of the memory cycle the count in the clock scaler is artificially advanced to the value it would have had if it had not been interrupted by the neutron pulse. The clock is then reconnected to the scaler, which continues to keep track of time as if there had been no interruption. As in the previous system, of course, the spectrometer is "dead" during each memory cycle.

The system of resetting the clock scaler to the correct time is considerably simpler than one would suppose at first, if the memory cycle time is adjusted to be equal to a round binary number of clock periods. Suppose that the length of the memory cycle is equal to 2^n clock periods so that, at the end of the memory cycle, the clock scaler would have lost 2^n counts.

Shortly before the end of the memory cycle, a signal pulse is applied to the input of the $n + 1$ scaler stage, causing it to reverse its state just as if it had received a carry pulse from the nth stage. This single pulse adds 2^n counts, replacing the counts lost during the memory cycle.

Occasionally, time-of-flight experiments are done under conditions in which the dead times associated with memory cycles as long as 10 μsec cannot be tolerated. If the over-all memory cycle time is to be significantly shortened, it is necessary to speed up each of the functions of addressing, reading, adding, and writing. An alternative, which is less demanding with respect to circuit speed, is to perform only part of the recording operation in real time, deferring the remainder for the free time between neutron bursts. This is a practical approach for a large group of pulsed accelerator experiments in which the interval between accelerator pulses is long while the flight times of interest are short. Hahn [34] and Garner et al. [35] have described a system of this kind for use with a synchrocyclotron that produces neutron bursts 60 times per second. The flight time interval of interest, following each neutron burst, is 200 μsec long and is divided into 2,000 time channels, 0.1 μsec long. The real-time part of the recording operation consists of writing a 1, whenever a neutron is detected, on the screen of a cathode-ray memory tube at a location corresponding to the channel number. This takes about 0.8 μsec. After each measuring interval, the long time interval before the next neutron burst is utilized for transferring the data just recorded to a magnetic-drum memory which has sufficient capacity for accumulating 2^{13} counts in each of the 2,000 time channels.

The use of an electrostatic memory for temporary storage of address information results in a short instrument dead time, even though the permanent memory has a long access time. The residual 0.8 μsec dead time is caused by the finite speed of the cathode-ray-tube deflection circuits and the settling time of the address scaler. A clock-stopping technique, similar to that used by Schumann, is employed to allow the scaler and deflection circuits to come to equilibrium before the cathode-ray-tube beam is turned on. The clock is stopped for 8 counts (0.8 μsec), allowing 0.4 μsec for settling, 0.3 μsec for writing, and 0.1 μsec for flipping the fourth scaler stage to make up for the 8 counts lost.

REFERENCES

1. Rossi, B.: Method of Registering Multiple Simultaneous Impulses of Several Geiger Counters, *Nature*, vol. 125, p. 636, 1930.
2. Garwin, R.: A Fast Coincidence-Anticoincidence Analyzer, *Rev. Sci. Instr.*, vol. 24, p. 618, 1953.
3. Bell, R., R. Graham, and H. Petch: Design and Use of a Coincidence Circuit of Short Resolving Time, *Can. J. Phys.*, vol. 30, p. 35, 1952.

4. Fischer, J., and J. Marshall: A 6BN6 Gated-beam Tube as a Fast Coincidence Circuit, *Rev. Sci. Instr.*, vol. 23, p. 417, 1952.
5. Dicke, R.: A High Speed Coincidence Circuit, *Rev. Sci. Instr.*, vol. 18, p. 907, 1947.
6. Baldinger, E., P. Huber, and K. Meyer: High Speed Coincidence Circuit Used for Multipliers, *Rev. Sci. Instr.*, vol. 19, p. 473, 1948.
7. Bay, Z.: New Type of High Speed Coincidence Circuit, *Rev. Sci. Instr.*, vol. 22, p. 397, 1951.
8. Strauch, K.: On the Detection of High Energy Particles with a Fast Coincidence System, *Rev. Sci. Instr.*, vol. 24, p. 283, 1953.
9. Meunier, R.: Circuit de coincidence differentiel, *Nuclear Electronics*, part I, p. 263, Proceedings of the International Symposium on Nuclear Electronics, organized by the French Society of Radio Electricians, Paris, 1958.
10. Baldinger, E.: Amplitude and Time Measurement in Nuclear Physics, *Advances in Electronics and Electron Phys.*, vol. VIII, p. 255, 1956.
11. Gatti, E., and V. Svelto: Theory of Time Resolution in Scintillation Counters, *Nuclear Instruments*, vol. 4, p. 189, 1959.
12. Weinzierl, P.: New Timing Method for Scintillation Events in Fast Coincidence Experiments, *Rev. Sci. Instr.*, vol. 27, p. 226, 1956.
13. Arecchi, F.: Fast Coincidences with Slow Scintillators, *Energia nucleare (Milan)*, vol. 6, p. 717, 1959.
14. Fairstein, E., T. Love, and R. Peele: A Pulse Crossover Pickoff Gate for Use with a Medium Speed Coincidence Circuit, *Proc. Sixth Tripartite Instrumentation Conf.*, AECL 804, part 4, p. 117, Apr. 20–24, 1959. Also Oak Ridge National Laboratory Instrumentation and Controls Division Annual Progress Report, July 1, 1957.
15. Grühle, W.: Impulse-Zeitformer für schnelle Koinzidenzstufen, *Nuclear Instruments*, vol. 4, p. 112, 1959.
16. Chase, R.: Multiple Coincidence Circuit, *Rev. Sci. Instr.*, vol. 31, p. 945, 1960.
17. Neddermeyer, S., E. Althaus, W. Allison, and E. Schatz: Measurement of Ultrashort Time Intervals, *Rev. Sci. Instr.*, vol. 18, p. 488, 1947.
18. O'Neill, G.: Direct Reading Analyzer for Short Time Intervals, *Rev. Sci. Instr.*, vol. 26, p. 285, 1955.
19. Ragsdale, R., and W. Stubbins: A Chronotron for Relativistic Neutron Time-of-flight Measurements, *IRE Trans. on Nuclear Sci.*, vol. NS-6, p. 31, March, 1959.
20. Lefevre, H., and J. Russell: Vernier Chronotron, *Rev. Sci. Instr.*, vol. 30, p. 159, 1959.
21. Beghian, L., G. Kegel, and R. Scharenberg: Fast Sodium Iodide Spectrometer and Its Application to Millimicrosecond Time Measurement, *Rev. Sci. Instr.*, vol. 29, p. 753, 1958.
22. Moody, N.: Time Expansion for Millimicrosecond Pulse Intervals, *Electronic Eng.*, vol. 24, p. 280, 1952.
23. Green, R., and R. Bell: Note on a Fast Time-to-Amplitude Converter, *Nuclear Instruments*, vol. 3, p. 127, 1955.
24. Weber, W., C. Johnstone, and L. Cranberg: Time-to-Pulse Height Converter for Measurement of Millimicrosecond Time Intervals, *Rev. Sci. Instr.*, vol. 27, p. 166, 1956.
25. Cottini, C., E. Gatti, and G. Gianelli: High Resolution Millimicrosecond Time Interval Measurements Based upon Frequency Conversion, *Nuovo cimento*, vol. 4, p. 156, 1956.
26. Cottini, C., and E. Gatti: Millimicrosecond Time Analyzer, *Nuovo cimento*, vol. 4, p. 1550, 1956.

27. Chase, R., and W. Higinbotham: Millimicrosecond Time-to-Pulse Height Converter Using an RF Vernier, *Rev. Sci. Instr.*, vol. 28, p. 448, 1957.

28. Bacher, R., C. Baker, and B. McDaniel: Experiments with a Slow Neutron Velocity Spectrometer: II, *Phys. Rev.*, vol. 69, p. 443, 1946.

29. Selove, W.: A Rotating-shutter Time-of-flight Spectrometer for the Slow-neutron Resonance Region, *Rev. Sci. Instr.*, vol. 23, p. 350, 1952.

30. Higinbotham, W.: Time-of-flight Instrumentation for Neutron Spectrometers, *Proc. Intern. Conf., Peaceful Uses Atomic Energy*, vol. 4, p. 53, Geneva, August, 1955. United Nations Publication 1956.IX.1.

31. De Boisblanc, D., and K. McCollom: MTR Time-of-flight Instrumentation, U.S. Atomic Energy Commission Document no. IDO-16159, Office of Technical Services, Oak Ridge, Tenn.

32. Schultz, H., G. Pieper, and L. Rosler: Multichannel Systems for Pulse-height and Time-of-flight Analysis, *Rev. Sci. Instr.*, vol. 27, p. 437, 1956.

33. Schumann, R.: 1024-channel Neutron Time-of-flight Analyzer, *Rev. Sci. Instr.*, vol. 27, p. 686, 1956.

34. Hahn, J.: A 0.1 Microsecond, 2000 Channel Electrostatic Storage System for Use as a Time of Flight Analyzer, *IRE National Convention Record*, Part 9, p. 57, 1957.

35. Garner, H., R. Miller, S. McMillon, and R. Graham: Multi-channel Analyzer for Time-of-flight Experiments, *IRE National Convention Record*, Part 9, p. 49, 1957.

CHAPTER 8

MULTIDIMENSIONAL ANALYSIS

In the previous chapters we have been concerned with instruments for the measurement of a single characteristic of the signals from radiation detectors for the purpose of determining an amplitude or time distribution. However, a single amplitude or time measurement does not necessarily exhaust the information available from a nuclear event. In this chapter we shall consider experiments in which more than one characteristic is to be recorded or in which signals from more than one detector must be analyzed simultaneously. It has become customary to think of each distinct observable property of an event as characterizing one of a number of "dimensions" with respect to which it can be described. Thus, if we measure the amplitude distribution of the signals from a radiation detector, we are recording one dimension of the set of events producing these signals. If, however, we measure both the amplitude and the time of arrival of each signal, we are concerned with a two-dimensional analysis; or if we use n detectors to observe the energies of n particles produced in a particular nuclear reaction, we are involved in an n-dimensional measurement.

Sometimes multidimensional techniques are employed to resolve some of the ambiguities that arise in one-dimensional observations when more than one mode of interaction between the radiation and the detector is possible. As a case in point, let us consider the problem of measuring gamma-ray energies with a scintillation counter. The detector signals do not uniquely characterize the incident gamma-ray energy because they may result from photoelectric conversion, Compton scattering, pair production, or a combination of these processes (see Art. 1.2). The pulse-amplitude distribution produced by monoenergetic gamma rays may, therefore, be moderately complex while that produced by gamma rays with many different energies may be so involved as to defy interpretation. Several techniques have evolved that employ more than one detector to simplify the interpretation of complex gamma-ray spectra.

8.1 Compton Spectrometer

The Compton spectrometer, first reported by Hofstadter and McIntyre [1] in 1950, employs two sodium iodide scintillation detectors in a coinci-

dence arrangement. The system is illustrated schematically in Fig. 8.1.
Gamma rays from the source are collimated so that they can strike the
first detector crystal but are prevented from interacting directly with the
second detector. Of the several competing interactions in the first detector, only Compton scattering is exploited in this application. Those
gamma rays which are scattered by electrons in the first detector can
recoil in any direction, the relative probabilities of the various directions
being dependent upon the gamma-ray energy. Some are scattered into
the second detector, where they may interact and give rise to an output
signal. Because the direction of arrival of the incident gamma rays is
defined by the collimator, any gamma ray that is scattered into the second
detector will have been deflected by a moderately well-defined angle θ,
determined by the geometrical arrangement of the two crystals and having

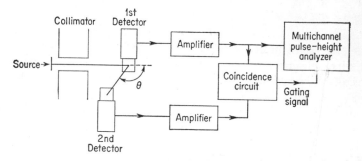

FIG. 8.1   Two-detector Compton spectrometer.

a range of variation determined by the size and separation of the crystals.
The energy of the scattered gamma ray is uniquely determined by the
incident gamma-ray energy and the scattering angle [see Eq. (1.1)]. The
difference between the incident and the scattered gamma-ray energies is
taken up by the scattering electron and measured by the amplitude of
the pulse from the first detector. If the scattering angle is known, the
electron recoil energy is also uniquely related to the incident gamma-ray
energy. The incident gamma-ray energy can, therefore, be unambiguously determined from the pulse-height spectrum obtained from the first
detector, provided that pulses are recorded only when the gamma rays
scatter through an angle θ and are detected in the second crystal. This
condition is established by gating the pulse-height analyzer only when
both detectors produce signals simultaneously.

    The Compton spectrometer yields spectra that are more easily inter-
pretable than those from a single detector. Its efficiency, however, is
considerably lower, because many of the scattered gamma rays miss the
second detector or fail to interact in it and because the collimation require-

ment reduces the geometrical efficiency of the first detector.   The Compton spectrometer is used, therefore, only when the source intensity is moderately high.   It has another limitation which results from the fact that other processes, in addition to the desired Compton scattering, can produce simultaneous pulses in both detectors.   If, for example, the source yields pairs of gamma rays in time coincidence, one of a pair of gamma rays can interact in the first detector while the other is Compton scattered from the collimator into the second detector.   Or if the gamma rays are sufficiently energetic, pair production can occur in the first detector (see Art. 8.2) and an annihilation gamma ray can be detected in the second detector.   It follows, therefore, that even though the spectra obtained with a Compton spectrometer are less complex than those obtained with a single detector, they can still be misinterpreted.

8.2 Pair Spectrometer

A three-detector coincidence arrangement, reported by Johansson [2] in 1950, is very useful for the unambiguous determination of gamma-ray

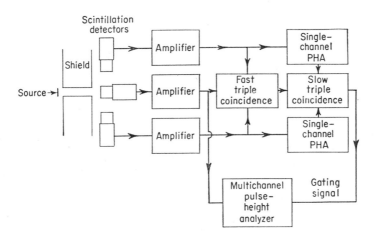

Fig. 8.2   Three-detector pair spectrometer.

energies in the energy range above the pair-production threshold (1.02 Mev).   The geometrical arrangement of source and detectors is shown in Fig. 8.2.   The three detector crystals are arranged in a straight line. Shielding is arranged so that only the central crystal is exposed to gamma rays from the source.   The amplitudes of signals from the central detector are analyzed only when there are simultaneous signals from the two side detectors.   The presence of simultaneous signals from the three detectors is a reliable indication that an incident gamma ray produced an electron-positron pair in the central crystal, since other competing scattering processes would not be likely to trigger more than two detectors.

In the pair-production process (see Art. 1.2 and Fig. 1.3) 1.02 Mev of the incident gamma-ray energy goes into the creation of the electron-positron pair and the remainder is carried off as kinetic energy of the two particles. The pulse amplitude from the central detector is a measure of this kinetic energy. When the positron comes to rest, it combines with an electron and the resulting annihilation process gives rise to two 510-kev gamma rays moving in opposite directions. If either or both of the annihilation gamma rays interact in the central crystal, the event is not recorded. If they both escape, the straight-line geometry makes it reasonably probable that they will both be detected, one in each side crystal, giving rise to the triple coincidence required to gate the pulse-height analyzer. The energy of the incident gamma rays is then simply determined by adding 1.02 Mev to the kinetic energy of the electron-positron pairs as measured by the recorded pulse-amplitude distribution.

One can imagine other interactions which could trigger all three detectors in such a way that the energy measurement would be in error, but they are all relatively improbable. The most important of these is a pair-production process in which one annihilation gamma ray escapes and is detected by one side crystal while the other is Compton scattered in the central crystal, the scattered gamma ray being detected in the other side crystal. The signal from the central detector would then be enhanced by the energy imparted to the scattering electron. The system can be made to discriminate against this and similar spurious interactions by imposing amplitude restrictions on the signals from the two side detectors with the aid of two single-channel pulse-height analyzers combined with the triple coincidence circuit in a "fast-slow" arrangement. The single-channel analyzers would be adjusted to accept only pulses whose amplitudes corresponded to photoelectric conversion of 510-kev gamma rays. The probability that spurious competing processes would impart this specific energy to the side crystals is sufficiently small to be neglected in nearly all cases.

In addition to eliminating the ambiguities from the energy measurement of high-energy gamma rays, the pair spectrometer may provide higher resolution than could be obtained with only one detector. The absolute width of a spectral line, as obtained with a pulse-height analyzer, always increases with the energy dissipated in the detector, approximately in proportion to the square root of the energy.[1] In the pair spectrometer, the energy measured is less than the incident gamma-ray energy by 1.02 Mev and therefore can be measured with less absolute uncertainty

[1] The relative line width, expressed as a fraction of the radiation energy, decreases with energy, despite the increase in absolute line width.

than would be the case with full energy measurement with the same detector. The resolution difference is particularly marked for energies only slightly above the pair threshold, because the measured energy is then only a small fraction of the total gamma-ray energy. For example, the line width associated with the measurement of a 1.32-Mev gamma ray with a pair spectrometer is the same as that which would be obtained for the measurement of a 300-kev gamma ray (1.32 Mev − 1.02 Mev) with the same detector in a single-crystal spectrometer. Unfortunately, the pair-production probability is quite low in the neighborhood of the threshold energy so that, even with intense sources, the recorded counting rate may be very low.

8.3 Multidimensional Events

In a great many cases one is interested in more than one property or aspect of a nuclear event. It may be helpful to cite several specific examples before discussing the associated electronic problems. It should be recognized, of course, that the variety of multidimensional problems is without limit, and the discussion that follows is merely illustrative and by no means a comprehensive study of the subject.

The radioactive decay of an excited nucleus to the ground state can often proceed, via a number of alternative paths, through various intermediate states. Measuring the energies of the particles and gamma rays emitted can provide clues to the initial and intermediate nuclear energy levels and spin states, but individual energy measurements are rarely sufficient for the complete determination of a complex decay scheme. As an example, consider the decay scheme of La[131] as reported by Creager et al. [3], illustrated in Fig. 8.3. If we were to attempt to construct this decay scheme starting only with a list of the beta- and gamma-ray energies involved in the various transitions, we would find that there are many alternative arrangements in which the energies add up properly. If, in addition, we were unaware or uncertain of some of the radiation energies, because of the limited resolution of our detectors, it would be hopeless to attempt to assign a unique set of values to the various energy levels.

Each transition from the initial excited state to the ground state can be thought of as an "event." The number of dimensions characterizing the event depends upon the number of steps involved in the transition. In Fig. 8.3, we can find transitions involving one, three, four, and five steps. The problem of unraveling such complex decay schemes would be greatly simplified if the more complicated events could be studied in their entirety instead of one dimension at a time. In decay-scheme work, three- and four-dimensional analyses are rarely attempted because of the relatively low probability that all of the characteristics of a complex event will be detected simultaneously. Two-dimensional studies, however, are quite common and usually yield sufficient information for the unique determination of even very complicated decay schemes. Two-dimensional pulse-height analysis involves the use of two detectors simultaneously observing the same source of radiation. When both detectors are triggered at the same time, as indicated by an output pulse from a coincidence circuit, the amplitudes of the pulses from both detectors are measured. The techniques for sorting and storing the results of these measurements will be considered later in this chapter.

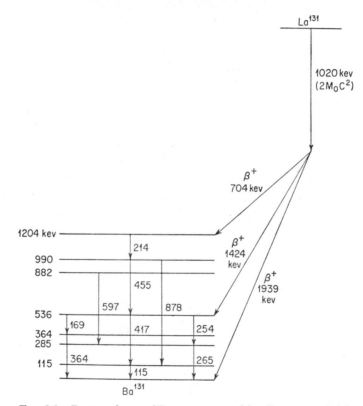

FIG. 8.3   Decay scheme of La[131] as reported by Creager et al. [3].

Multidimensional techniques are very useful in the study of neutron reactions. An event of interest might consist of the capture of a neutron by a nucleus and the subsequent radioactive decay of the compound nucleus. The quantities to be measured, each of which can be considered a "dimension" of the event, include the incident neutron energy and the energies of the particles and gamma rays emitted as the nucleus decays to the ground state. If the compound nucleus has a short half-life, as is often the case, two dimensions of the event can be measured with a single detector.   The amplitude of the detector signal can be a measure of the energy of a gamma ray, while its time of arrival, with respect to a suitable t_0 signal, is a measure of the neutron flight time and, therefore, its energy.

Most of the events studied by high-energy physicists are multidimensional in nature.   The dimensions in high-energy experiments tend to be geometric rather than energetic.   Direct energy measurements with radiation detectors are difficult at high energies, because the particles often cannot be brought to rest in detectors of reasonable size.   Radiation detectors can be used, however, to determine the number and angular distribution of the particles produced in high-energy reactions.   Large arrays of detectors are often used, so that suitable angular resolution can be combined with a reasonable probability of detecting all of the reaction products.

Each detector defines a solid angle with respect to a central target and can be considered to represent one coordinate of a multidimensional event. Each coordinate can have one of two values, a 1 representing the passage of a particle through a particular detector or a 0 indicating that no particle traversed that detector.   Sometimes the amplitudes of the pulses from the various detectors are measured because the specific ionization, indicated by the pulse height, may be useful in distinguishing various particle types.   A fairly crude measurement of specific ionization is often all that is warranted, and four to eight pulse-height channels provide adequate resolution.   Instead of only two values, then, each coordinate of a multidimensional event may be assigned one of several values corresponding to the detector pulse amplitude.

8.4   Multidimensional Data Storage

The problems of multidimensional data storage are not essentially different from the problems involved in the storage of one-dimensional data. The principal difference is that multidimensional systems, in general, require memory systems with more storage capacity.   If, for the moment, we restrict our consideration to digital memory systems using binary addressing techniques, then the memory size required is determined by the number of bits that are necessary to characterize each event and the number of events of each distinct type that must be tallied.   The number of bits required to describe an event is determined by adding the bits required for each coordinate of the event.   Each coordinate of the event need not necessarily be represented by the same number of bits.   The number, in each case, depends upon the resolution desired; very high resolution may be required for the measurement of neutron flight times, whereas low resolution, and therefore only a few bits, may be adequate for characterizing the specific ionization of high-energy particles.

In a binary memory the number of discrete addresses or storage channels is equal to 2^m, where m is the number of bits required to describe an event. If each address contains an n-bit number, 2^n events can be tallied in each channel. The total number of storage elements (magnetic cores, discrete charge storage locations on cathode-ray tubes, etc.) required to store 2^n m-bit events is $n2^m$. For example, a two-dimensional pulse-height analyzer having 2^6 or 64 channels in each coordinate direction and a storage capacity of 2^{16} events per channel requires 16×2^{12} or 65,536 storage elements. This is a relatively large memory for a nuclear data handling device, although by modern computer standards it is modest in size.

Now let us consider a three-dimensional instrument in which two pulse amplitudes and a neutron time of flight are to be measured simultaneously, and let us devote, as before, 64 channels to each pulse-height measurement and 256 channels to the time-of-flight measurement. For a capacity of 2^{16} events per channel, we now require 16×2^{20} or 16,777,216 storage elements. This is about an order of magnitude larger than the fast access memories in the largest modern digital computers. Until the cost per bit of high-speed memories is substantially reduced, it is unlikely that a memory of this size will be used for accumulating nuclear data.

As a third example, consider a high-energy experiment in which a target is surrounded by 50 detectors. Let us suppose that we are not interested in making amplitude measurements, so that each coordinate of our 50-dimensional system can be characterized by a single bit. Furthermore, because of the tremendous number of channels (2^{50}), let us suppose that we will accept a capacity of 2^4 or 16 events per channel. The number of storage elements is then 4×2^{50} or slightly more than 4×10^{15}, an absurdly large number. It is, however, almost inconceivable that in any real experiment all, or a large fraction, of the 50 detectors will be triggered simultaneously. If we accept the restriction that only events involving four detectors or less will be considered, we reduce the number of distinct events to about 250,000 and the number of storage elements required to tally 16 events per channel to about 1,000,000. Unfortunately, the problem of associating each of the 250,000 possible events with an address in the memory is a formidable one. One possibility involves the use of a 24-bit address, divided into four groups of 6 bits, so that each group can be a binary digital representation of the number of a triggered detector. However, this technique has the decided disadvantage that 24 bits represents about 1.7×10^7 channels, which is more than 60 times as great as the number that would be required if the optimum addressing system were employed.

From the foregoing examples, it is clear that the conventional memory techniques are inappropriate for many multidimensional experiments.

While there appear to be no entirely satisfactory alternatives, the current trend is toward the use of "address recording." In an address recording system, each event is reduced to a digital representation by suitable analog-to-digital conversion techniques, and the individual numbers are recorded, in order of occurrence, on a continuous recording medium such as punched paper tape, magnetic tape, or photographic film. The individual bits may be arranged serially on the recording medium, or in parallel, or in a combined serial-parallel format. In general, parallel recording is faster while serial recording can be done with less complicated equipment.

The principal virtue of the address recording technique is that it can employ a memory of practically unlimited capacity, since tape and film memories have an almost negligible cost per bit. For this reason, it appears to be the only practical choice in the more elaborate multidimensional systems where huge quantities of data must be stored. It has, however, some serious drawbacks which will certainly stimulate a search for more suitable storage systems. The primary disadvantage is that the stored information requires considerable processing before interpretation can be attempted. The data processing consists of reducing a long list of event descriptions (addresses) to a frequency distribution. No analog display of the frequency distribution is available during the experiment, or after it, until the data reduction has been effected. The data reduction can be accomplished with the aid of a conventional addressable memory [4,5]. The tape containing the stored addresses is scanned by a reader and selector system which picks out those events in which all coordinates but one have a preselected value or fall within a preselected range of values. These events are sorted and tallied in the addressable memory according to the value of the unspecified coordinate. The tape is passed again and again through the reader, with different sets of values being specified for the various coordinates. In this way, a set of one-dimensional frequency distributions is obtained, each one corresponding to a specified set of values for all the other dimensions.

This method of data reduction is practical only if the experimenter can restrict the number of passes through the reader to a reasonable value. It is not only the time involved in the scanning process that is important here, but the fact that, at the end of a large number of scans, the experimenter may be confronted with so large a number of one-dimensional spectra that he will be unable to analyze them. In the more elaborate multidimensional experiments, therefore, it will almost certainly be necessary to employ large automatic digital computers to perform much of the data reduction and analysis.

Although address recording seems the most promising technique for the more elaborate multidimensional experiments, there are many significant experiments that can be done with conventional memory systems. Two-dimensional decay-scheme studies, for example, are commonly carried out with a multichannel pulse-height analyzer. A typical experimental arrangement is shown in Fig. 8.4. A single-channel analyzer selects a portion of the pulse-height spectrum from detector B. Those signals from detector A that occur in coincidence with B signals in the selected energy range are measured by the multichannel pulse-height analyzer. The measurement is repeated with a number of different settings of the single-channel analyzer bias, and a family of one-dimensional spectra is obtained which constitutes a two-dimensional spectrum of the source.

Two-dimensional spectra of this sort have been recorded directly with instruments that are multichannel with respect to both coordinates. The largest instrument of this kind reported to date [6] devotes 6 bits of the

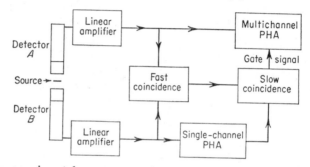

FIG. 8.4   An experimental arrangement for two-dimensional decay-scheme studies.

address (64 channels) to one detector and 5 bits (32 channels) to the other detector. It has 2,048 storage channels (64 × 32), each with a capacity of 65,535 events (16 binary bits). The memory consists of a high-speed magnetic drum with 32 read-write magnetic heads.

The multichannel two-dimensional instruments are related to the gated one-dimensional instrument of Fig. 8.4 in much the same way as the one-dimensional multichannel instruments are related to the single-channel instruments and have essentially the same advantages. In the case of two-dimensional measurements, however, these advantages may be even more significant, because the counting rates in coincidence experiments are often very much lower than the singles counting rates and many more channels must be filled with data. Even at singles counting rates as high as 10^5 per sec, it frequently takes a month or more of continuous counting to accumulate a two-dimensional spectrum with a coincidence-gated multichannel analyzer. The same experiment can be done in one day with a two-dimensional instrument, with far fewer problems associated with calibration drifts, instrument failures, and source decay.

An important advantage of accumulating two-dimensional data in an addressable memory is that they can be instantly displayed on a cathode-ray tube at the end of an experiment, or even while the experiment is in progress. The display can take several forms. Individual one-dimensional sections of the two-dimensional spectrum can be displayed as separate analog curves of accumulated count versus channel number. These curves can also be displayed simultaneously, in subgroups or all at once, slightly displaced from each other on the cathode-ray-tube screen, to give the illusion of a perspective view of a three-dimensional plot (see Plate D). Plate E shows an alternative display that greatly facilitates qualitative interpretation of a two-dimensional spectrum. The coordinates of each memory address are represented by the horizontal and vertical deflection of the cathode-ray-tube beam, and the beam intensity is made to correspond to the count stored at each address. If the beam intensity is made proportional to the stored count, the over-all presentation is a satisfactory qualitative picture of the spectrum; however, subtle features are difficult to see. These can be made more prominent, with a nonlinear biased amplifier preceding the cathode-ray-tube intensity control grid, to exaggerate the visual contrast in the neighborhood of a selected count level.

Before concluding this section on multidimensional data storage, mention should be made of a simple semiquantitative photographic system for two-dimensional pulse-height analysis [7]. The two input signals are connected to the horizontal and vertical deflection plates, respectively, of a cathode-ray tube through pulse-stretching circuits that sustain the signals at peak amplitude for a few microseconds. The intensifier grid of the cathode-ray tube is pulsed while the signals are at constant amplitude so that each pulse pair gives rise to a dot on the screen at a location corresponding to the amplitudes of both signals. A time-exposure photograph of the screen results in a display (Plate F) which is quite analogous to the brightness display obtained with a digital two-dimensional analyzer (Plate E). Approximate quantitative counting-rate measurements can be made by scanning the photograph with an optical densitometer.

REFERENCES

1. Hofstadter, R., and J. McIntyre: Measurement of Gamma-ray Energies with Two Crystals in Coincidence, *Phys. Rev.*, vol. 78, p. 619, 1950.
2. Johansson, S.: A Scintillation Spectrometer for High-energy Gamma-rays, *Nature*, vol. 166, p. 794, 1950.
3. Creager, C., C. Kocher, and A. Mitchell: The Disintegration of La[131], *Nuclear Phys.*, vol. 14, p. 578, 1960.
4. Birk, M., T. Braid, and R. Detenbeck: Two-dimensional Pulse-height Analyzer, *Rev. Sci. Instr.*, vol. 29, p. 203, 1958.

5. McMahon, J.: Argonne Three Dimensional Analyzer, *Nuclear Electronics*, Part II, p. 308, Proceedings of the International Symposium on Nuclear Electronics, organized by the French Society of Radio Electricians, Paris, 1958.
6. Chase, R.: A Two-dimensional Kicksorter with Magnetic Drum Storage, IRE National Convention Record, Part 9, p. 196, 1959.
7. Grodzins, L.: The Application of the XYZ Recorder to Radiation Studies, *Nuclear Electronics*, Part II, p. 241, Proceedings of the International Symposium on Nuclear Electronics, organized by the French Society of Radio Electricians, Paris, 1958.

CHAPTER 9

COUNTING LOSSES

Nuclear data handling problems differ from the problems encountered in other data processing systems largely because nuclear events tend to be randomly distributed in time. This means that, no matter how fast the circuits and no matter how low the average counting rate, occasionally two events will occur with so little time separation between them that they cannot both be measured correctly. This may happen so infrequently as to have only a negligible effect on the data; on the other hand, at high counting rates or with slow circuits the resultant errors may be sufficient to invalidate the experimental results.

Two types of error are possible when two events are insufficiently separated in time. One or both can be measured and recorded incorrectly, or one or both (but most often the latter) can be rejected entirely. For example, in a pulse-amplitude measuring system, if two pulses are separated by less than the pulse widths, the peak amplitude recorded is the result of the superposition of the two pulses and is a proper measure of neither of them. Furthermore, only one event is tallied. Suppose that, on the other hand, two events are separated by more than the pulse widths but by less than the resolving time (i.e., the measuring and recording time) of the pulse-height analyzer. Most pulse-height analyzers are equipped with gate circuits that prevent the second pulse from interfering with the measurement of the first, so the first pulse can be measured correctly. The second pulse, however, may have to be rejected.

Errors due to pulse superposition cannot, in general, be completely eliminated. They can be minimized by making the pulses as narrow as possible, consistent with the speed of the detector, the linear amplifier, and the pulse-height analyzer. On the other hand, it is usually possible to correct the data for errors introduced because of the finite resolving time of the pulse-height analyzer. These counting-loss corrections can be made in a number of ways. All of them, however, are based on the assumption that the amplitude distribution of the rejected pulses is essentially the same as that of the recorded pulses. This implies that, when pulses are admitted to the analyzer for measurement, they are accepted without prejudice with respect to amplitude. This condition is usually satisfied by designing the analyzer so that, after completing the measurement of a pulse, it accepts and measures the next pulse to arrive, regardless of its amplitude. A further requirement is that there be no correlation between the pulse amplitudes and their time of arrival. But if such correlation exists, it can, occasionally, be the cause of serious spectral distortion. Difficulties are most likely to arise when measurements are made on a source which has a radioactive state with a lifetime comparable to the instrument resolving time. If the system detects and measures a particle or gamma ray associated with the birth of the state, it may be busy with this measurement when the state decays, and, therefore, unable to measure the radiation that accompanies the decay. The detection of the first event adversely affects the probability of detecting the second event so that the recorded pulse-height spectrum is distorted in favor of the earlier event. The extent of this distortion depends upon the efficiency with which the first event is detected. If the efficiency is high, the probability of measuring the second event is low. In an extreme case, where the detection efficiency for the first event is 100 per cent and the associated instrument resolving time is long compared with the half-life of the state, the radiation emitted when the state decays can never be measured and will, therefore, be entirely missing in the recorded spectrum. On the other hand, if the efficiency for detecting the first event is sufficiently low, the resultant spectral distortion can be negligible. In the discussion that follows, we shall assume that the pulses to be measured are not time-correlated, or if they are time-correlated, that the detection efficiency is sufficiently low that the resultant spectral distortion can be neglected.

9.1　Calculating Counting Losses

Let us assume that the pulses to be analyzed occur randomly distributed in time, but at a constant average rate. This is the situation that would usually obtain when working with radioactive sources (if the lifetimes are long compared with the measuring interval) or with accelerators or nuclear reactors operating at constant intensity. Furthermore, we shall assume that the analyzer has no temporary storage facility (see Art. 4.2 and Fig. 4.14) so that, while it is occupied with the measurement or storage of an event, all subsequent events are rejected. Let R represent the number of events tallied in all channels in clock time t_c. Let C represent the total number of events in the energy range measured by the analyzer, including both those recorded and those rejected when the analyzer is busy with other signals. The measurement and recording of each of the R events requires a certain amount of instrument time. Let t_r represent the average value of this resolving time. During the total time interval

t_c, the instrument will be busy a part of the time, which we shall call the "dead" time t_d. The dead time, then, is

$$t_d = Rt_r \qquad (9.1)$$

The time during which the instrument is not dead we refer to as the "live" time t_L.

$$t_L = t_c - t_d = t_c - Rt_r \qquad (9.2)$$

Our assumption of a constant average counting rate implies that the average counting rate during the live time is equal to the average counting rate during the entire time interval t_c. Therefore,

$$\frac{R}{t_L} = \frac{C}{t_c} \qquad (9.3)$$

or

$$\frac{C}{R} = \frac{t_c}{t_L} = \frac{t_c}{t_c - Rt_r} \qquad (9.4)$$

C/R represents a correction factor which, because of our assumption that time correlations are unimportant, can be applied uniformly to the recorded count in each channel to determine the count that would have been tallied if the instrument resolving time were zero.

Calculation of the correction factor from Eq. (9.4) requires a knowledge of the average resolving time t_r. Unfortunately, in many pulse-height analyzers the resolving time is not constant but depends on the shape of the spectrum being measured. This is often true of analyzers that employ pulse-height-to-time conversion, because large pulses take longer to measure than small ones. In these instruments the signals tallied in each pulse-height channel must be associated with a different value of resolving time in order to determine the over-all dead-time correction. If the resolving time associated with channel j in an n-channel analyzer is t_{rj} and the count accumulated in that channel is R_j, then the total dead time can be written

$$t_d = \sum_{j=1}^{n} R_j t_{rj} \qquad (9.5)$$

and this summation must be used in place of Rt_r in Eq. (9.4) to determine the correction factor C/R.

If the analyzer contains a temporary or buffer storage mechanism (see Art. 4.2 and Fig. 4.14), the dead-time correction can be very substantially reduced, but its calculation becomes more difficult, particularly if the buffer is capable of storing more than one signal. To keep the discussion from becoming unduly complicated, we shall restrict our consideration to the case of a single buffer storage element. Furthermore, we shall assume that the buffer storage access time is negligibly small compared with the resolving time T of the remainder of the instrument and that the resolving time does not depend on pulse height.   This last assumption may not always be justified, but it greatly simplifies the development.

If r represents the average rate (in counts per second) at which events are stored in the main instrument memory, then the fraction of the time during which the basic instrument, exclusive of the buffer, is busy, is rT. If the input counting rate (also in counts per second) is n, then nrT events each second occur when the basic instrument is busy and must, therefore, be presented to the buffer.   Some of these events are accepted by the buffer and stored there until the basic instrument is ready to accept them. The time they spend in the buffer can vary from zero to T, depending upon when they occur with respect to the preceding event.   Other events, occurring when the buffer is busy, are rejected and constitute the counting loss to be evaluated.

In order to determine the counting loss it is first necessary to know the average value of the time that a signal spends in the buffer.   At low input counting rates, it is reasonable to expect that all values of time between zero and T would be equally probable and that, therefore, the mean time spent in the buffer T_b would be simply $T/2$.   At very high input counting rates, on the other hand, the probability that two input events will be separated by as much as T becomes small.   Almost as soon as the buffer is emptied, it is filled again so that T_b approaches T at high input counting rates.   In general, when an event is followed by another event at the end of an interval t and t is less than the main instrument dead time T, then the buffer is occupied by a time $T - t$.   The relative probability of an interval t is proportional to the probability that no events occur within the interval t.   For randomly occurring input events with an average counting rate n, the probability of no events within an interval t can be written e^{-nt} (see, for example, Ref. 5, Chap. 3).   The average of those values of t lying between zero and T is, therefore,

$$t_m = \frac{1}{T} \int_0^T t e^{-nt}\, dt \tag{9.6}$$

and
$$T_b = T - t_m \tag{9.7}$$

If we represent the ratio T_b/T by B, then by integrating Eq. (9.6) and substituting in (9.7), we obtain

$$B = 1 - \frac{1}{(nT)^2} + e^{-nt}\left[\frac{1}{nT} + \frac{1}{(nT)^2}\right] \tag{9.8}$$

Let r_b represent the mean rate at which events enter the buffer.   The fractional buffer dead time is, then, $r_b T_b$ and the fractional buffer live time is $(1 - r_b T_b)$.   The buffer counting rate is equal to the rate at which events are presented to the buffer multiplied by its fractional live time and is, therefore,

$$r_b = nrT(1 - r_bT_b) \tag{9.9}$$

Replacing T_b by BT and solving for r_b, we obtain

$$r_b = \frac{nrT}{1 + nrBT^2} \tag{9.10}$$

The rate at which events are rejected is equal to the difference between the input counting rate n and r, the rate at which events are stored. It is also equal to the difference between nrT, the rate at which events are

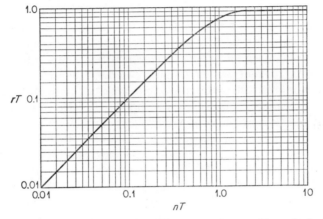

FIG. 9.1 Counting-loss-correction curve for an analyzer with a single fast buffer store and a main memory with a resolving time T. n represents the input counting rate and r represents the recorded counting rate.

presented to the buffer, and r_b, the rate at which they are accepted by the buffer. Therefore,

$$n - r = nrT - r_b \tag{9.11}$$

or

$$n - r = nrT - \frac{nrT}{1 + nrBT^2} \tag{9.12}$$

Solving for r, we obtain

$$r = n\,\frac{B(nT)^2 - 1 + \sqrt{B^2(nT)^4 + 4B(nT)^3 + 2B(nT)^2 + 1}}{2B(nT)^3 + 2B(nT)^2} \tag{9.13}$$

Equations (9.8) and (9.13) determine the relationship between the input counting rate n and the recorded rate r in terms of the main instrument resolving time T. Unfortunately, they are not in a convenient form for calculating n from experimentally determined values of r. This can be done, however, with the aid of Fig. 9.1, which is a graphical representation of the relationship between n and r in terms of the parameter T, obtained by numerical substitution in Eqs. (9.8) and (9.13). Figure 9.1 shows that, for values of nT less than 0.2, r differs from n by less than 0.5 per cent. At higher input counting rates, the disparity increases rapidly because, no matter how great the input counting rate, rT cannot exceed 1.

9.2   Measuring Live and Dead Time

It can be seen from the preceding paragraphs that the calculation of dead-time corrections, even when the instrument characteristics are accurately known, can be a tedious process. In addition, if the measuring and recording times are not known accurately or if some of the simplifying assumptions are not well justified, the calculations will not lead to accurate results. It is usually more convenient, and often more accurate, to determine counting losses by measurement rather than by calculation.

In order to prevent spectral distortion all modern pulse-measuring instruments, in which the processing time may be comparable to the mean interval between input pulses, are equipped with gate circuits which prevent input signals from entering while a signal is being processed. When the instrument is busy processing a signal and is, therefore, dead as far as subsequent signals are concerned, the gate is closed, but when the instrument is free and capable of accepting input signals, the gate is open. In order to determine the dead time, therefore, it is merely necessary to measure the time during which the gate is closed; the live time can, of course, be measured by the time the gate is open. A number of commercial and laboratory-built pulse-height analyzers contain live-time clocks controlled by the input gate circuits. Periodic pulses, derived either from the a-c power lines or from an internal oscillator, are counted when the gate is open and blocked when the gate is closed. The pulses may be counted with an external scaler or they may be tallied in the main instrument memory. In either case, the count accumulated during an experiment is a measure of the instrument live time. The data can be corrected for dead-time losses by multiplying the count in each data channel by the ratio of true clock time to the measured live time. It is, in fact, unnecessary to measure true clock time, since the counting rate in each channel is the ratio of the accumulated count to the measured live time.

The same input gate circuit can be used to obtain a direct meter indication of fractional dead time or live time. If a stabilized direct current is allowed to flow in a d-c milliammeter when the gate is open and is blocked when the gate is closed, the average meter deflection is a measure of the fractional live time. Similarly, if the current is turned on when the gate is closed and is turned off when the gate is open, the meter indicates dead time.   In either case, the meter indication represents the live or dead time averaged over an interval approximately equal to the meter response time.   The natural period of standard d-c meter movements is usually sufficiently long to permit measurements as accurate as the meter calibration, but with relatively slow analyzers it may be advisable to use a slow, sensitive movement, heavily shunted to provide an overdamped response.

If counting-loss corrections are to be based on live- or dead-time measurements, it is necessary that the average input counting rate be constant over the data-taking interval.   If the source decays appreciably or otherwise fluctuates during the measuring interval, the actual counting loss will be greater than that inferred from live- or dead-time measurements. However, the counting loss can still be determined accurately by direct measurement.   If N represents the total number of input events in the counting interval that trigger the input discriminator, then

$$N = R + L + S \qquad (9.14)$$

where R is the total number of events recorded in all data channels, L is the number of events lost, and S is the number of events which are discarded because they fall outside the instrument measuring range and, therefore, cause address overflow or the triggering of a surplus discriminator. R can be determined directly by adding the counts accumulated in all data channels. N can be measured with a scaler connected to the input threshold discriminator.   Another scaler, counting the surplus discriminator output or the number of times the address overflows, determines the value of S.   The counting loss can then be readily determined from Eq. (9.14).   Since $R + S$ represents the number of pulses arriving during the instrument live time, the stored data can be corrected for dead time by multiplying the count in each channel by $N/(R + S)$.   This correction can be applied without error even though the average counting rate fluctuates during data accumulation, provided, of course, that the input spectral distribution remains constant despite intensity variations.

9.3 Pulsed Sources

Many high-energy-particle accelerators produce short bursts of energetic particles separated by relatively long time intervals.   If efficient use is to be made of pulsed accelerators, the data accumulating and analyzing equipment should be able to record data at a rate commensurate with the rate at which it is available.   This puts a substantial premium on instruments with very short resolving times.   An instrument with a short resolving time might be able to record a large number of events per burst and collect statistically significant data in a reasonably short time, whereas an instrument with a resolving time greater than the burst duration is restricted to a single event per burst and requires much more machine time to collect a comparable amount of data. Burst durations and repetition frequencies vary widely among existing and contemplated accelerators, so it is difficult to generalize with respect to the suitability of various analyzers for use with pulsed accelerators. In some cases the fastest possible analyzer is essential to efficient operation; in other cases, where burst durations may be as long as several tens of milliseconds, relatively slow analyzers may be suitable for many experiments and stability, linearity, and reliability may be more important than speed. In those cases where conventional moderate-speed instruments are suitable, nothing more need be said. We shall, therefore, confine our attention to the problem of accumulating as much information as possible in very short time intervals.

The fastest of the conventional pulse-height analyzers are the multi-discriminator instruments, and one logical approach to the pulsed accelerator problem is to concentrate on the development of very fast discriminator and anticoincidence circuits. However, in order to operate vacuum tubes or transistors at their ultimate speeds, one must necessarily sacrifice reliability and stability. Since, even at moderate speeds, multidiscriminator instruments are neither notably reliable nor stable, there is some doubt that high-speed instruments of this type will prove to be very useful, unless high-speed components with more inherent stability than vacuum tubes or transistors are employed. One promising possibility is the development of circuits employing Esaki (tunnel) diodes, which are capable of switching at millimicrosecond speeds and may have adequate stability for quantitative pulse-height analysis.

An alternative approach to the pulsed accelerator problem takes advantage of the fact that the short bursts are separated by relatively long idle periods during which there are no input pulses. If the pulses occurring during the short bursts can be stored, in analog form, in a high-speed buffer memory, they can be measured with high precision and tallied at leisure during the idle periods between bursts. The value of such a buffer memory depends on its capacity and the rate at which it can accept input pulses. One possibility is to extend the concept of the pulse-stretcher buffer memory referred to earlier (see Art. 4.2 and Fig. 4.14) by employing a large number of such buffers in cascade. In the case of short bursts the data handling capacity of the instrument is thus increased in proportion to the number of buffers. This approach appears to be practical if a moderate number of pulses (perhaps 10) are to be recorded in each burst, but it is doubtful that anyone will consider building 100-pulse-stretcher buffers in order to record 100 pulses per burst.

The most promising buffer storage schemes in current use employ cathode-ray tubes or barrier-grid storage tubes in which charge patterns on an insulating surface are used as analog representations of the stored pulses. The first system of this type was reported by Cunningham [1] in 1954. The pulses to be measured are applied to one set of deflection plates (say, the vertical plates) of a standard cathode-ray tube. As the electron beam moves along the phosphor screen, it ejects secondary electrons, leaving the region traversed by the beam charged positively (see Art. 5.4). Of course, as the electron beam passes a point on the screen, the spray of secondary electrons partially neutralizes the positive charge established by the beam. The secondaries, however, spread over an area considerably larger than the cross section of the beam, so the rate of charge neutralization is lower than the initial charging rate. If the beam traverses the screen rapidly, therefore, its path is marked by a net positive charge. The vertical extent of the line of positive charge is determined by the amplitude of the pulse applied to the vertical plates. After a pulse has been "written" on the screen, a slow linear sweep voltage is applied to the same vertical deflection plates. During the sweep the beam moves sufficiently slowly for the secondary electrons to be able to remove the positive charge deposited during the writing operation, as well as that produced by the beam during the reading sweep, and to deposit a trail of negative charge. While the sweep traverses a region of the screen that has been charged positively in a writing operation, a small net negative current flows to the screen to establish the equilibrium negative charge. If a pickup electrode is mounted on the face of the cathode-ray tube and connected to the input of an amplifier, a small negative current is induced in the amplifier input resistance while the sweep traverses a positively charged portion of the screen. When the sweep reaches the end of the positively charged region, the net current to the screen drops to zero because the remainder of the screen is already charged to the equilibrium negative potential. Therefore, the current induced in the amplifier input resistance ends abruptly when the sweep voltage is equal to the amplitude of the signal that had previously been written on the screen, and the time at which this discontinuity in the read current occurs is a measure of the amplitude of the stored pulse. Thus it is seen that a signal can be written rapidly on a cathode-ray-tube screen and its amplitude measured at a later time.

So far we have shown how a single pulse can be stored on a cathode-ray-tube screen. A useful buffer for pulsed accelerator experiments must be able to store a number of pulses per burst. Cunningham found that several pulses could be written on the same vertical line on a cathode-ray tube and that individual discontinuities could still be recognized in the read signal corresponding to the peak amplitudes of the stored pulses, provided that no two pulses were the same size. A further increase in the storage capacity of a cathode-ray-tube buffer can be achieved with

the addition of horizontal deflection so that pulses can be written vertically at many locations on the screen.   The horizontal deflection voltage
can be a linear sweep, so that the pulses are randomly distributed across
the screen, or it can be a series of equal steps following the writing of each
pulse, so that the pulses are uniformly distributed in the horizontal
direction.

If the pulses are randomly distributed in the horizontal direction, it is
impractical to try to superimpose vertical reading sweeps on each of the
stored pulses.   In a system developed by Reaves [2] (see Fig. 9.2), reading is done with a set of evenly spaced horizontal sweeps, similar to a
television raster.   Each time the reading sweep crosses the positive trail
of a stored pulse, an impulse is induced on the pickup electrode at the
face of the cathode-ray tube.   The number of such impulses at each level

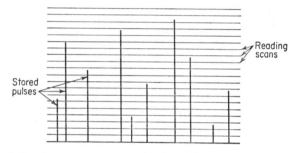

F<small>IG</small>. 9.2   Typical pulse-storage pattern in the cathode-ray-tube temporary storage
section of Reaves's [2] pulse-height analyzer.   The horizontal lines represent the
scanning pattern used to read the information stored.

of the horizontal sweep is a measure of the number of input pulses whose
amplitude exceeded that level.   These impulses can be counted and accumulated in the main instrument memory, in which a storage channel is
associated with each vertical level of the horizontal sweep.   The spectrum is then recorded in the form of an integral bias curve (see Art. 3.1).
The more familiar differential pulse-height distribution is obtained by
subtracting the counts stored in adjacent channels.

Reaves's horizontal reading scheme is successful only if each vertical
positive trail is detected every time it is crossed by the reading beam.   If
there are "dropouts" due to nonuniform writing, pulses will be lost in
some channels and added incorrectly in others.   If dropouts are to be
avoided, the read impulses must be large compared to the noise resulting
from nonuniformities in the secondary emission ratio of the phosphor
screen.   Reaves found that, with a type 5ADP1 cathode-ray tube, the
writing speed must be limited to about 1 in. per μsec to deposit sufficient
charge to prevent dropouts.

Dropouts due to nonuniform writing are much less serious in the case of vertical reading, because the gradual variations in the read signal when scanning a nonuniform positive trail are easily distinguished from the sharp discontinuity at the end of the trail. Higher writing speeds are, therefore, permissible, because it is only important that the read signal be well above the phosphor nonuniformity noise in the neighborhood of the pulse peaks. Since the writing beam moves relatively slowly in the neighborhood of the pulse peaks, even if the pulse edges are steep, shorter input pulses can be accommodated when the reading and writing sweeps are parallel than when they are perpendicular.

When reading and writing vertically, the horizontal spacing between pulses should be uniform, in order to simplify registration of the reading sweep on the stored pulses. Whether reading horizontally or vertically, uniform pulse spacing permits more efficient utilization of the storage space. Even with uniform spacing, however, accurate registration may be difficult to achieve because the horizontal steps must be made rapidly while writing. Fortunately, exact registration is not essential, particularly since horizontal spacing tolerances can be considerably increased by adding a small, high-frequency signal to the horizontal deflection voltage during reading to broaden the effective reading beam. The problems associated with parallel reading and writing are, therefore, not very severe, and this is the system that is most likely to be generally adopted [3,4].

The ultimate writing speed that can be achieved in a cathode-ray-tube buffer store is not uniquely determined, because it depends, in part, on the buffer capacity and the pulse-height resolution required. The essential requirement is that enough charge be deposited on the storage surface during the writing operation to produce a read signal greater than noise. Increasing the beam current decreases the time required to write a suitable charge signal, but it also increases the spot size and, therefore, decreases the resolution and storage capacity. Preliminary observations by Reaves [2] and Costrell and Brueckmann [4] indicate that it might be possible to obtain pulse-height resolution of the order of 1 per cent with flat-topped pulses, 2×10^{-9} sec wide at the peaks, on ordinary cathode-ray tubes.

In most cases the dominant source of noise is the nonuniformity of the storage surface. This leads to small spurious discontinuities in the pickup plate signals, even when scanning a blank section of the storage surface. It might be supposed, therefore, that better signal-to-noise ratios could be achieved on the uniform storage surfaces of barrier-grid storage tubes. Kandiah [5] has found, however, that the performance of a barrier-grid tube buffer can be limited by the spurious read signals resulting from nonuniformities in the secondary emission ratio of the barrier-grid wires. When reading from either the collector or the target assembly (see Art.

5.4), the signals from the barrier-grid wires cannot be distinguished from those from the storage surface. Kandiah, therefore, employs a unique reading arrangement which is insensitive to barrier-grid nonuniformities. The read signal is derived from the back plate, with the barrier grid grounded, so that the read amplifier is sensitive only to charge variations on the storage surface. While this effectively eliminates the barrier-grid noise, it results in a substantial decrease in read signal amplitude because of the large capacitance (about 0.001 μf) between the back plate and the barrier grid. It is necessary, therefore, to use a low-noise amplifier if the small amount of charge deposited by a short write signal is to be detected. The best results obtained using this reading arrangement (storage of 0.1-μsec pulses) seem rather less promising for high-speed storage than the results obtained with ordinary cathode-ray tubes. Barrier-grid tubes have much larger potential storage capacity, however, because of the absence of secondary electron spray effects and might be preferred, therefore, when many events must be stored in each accelerator burst.

REFERENCES

1. Cunningham, J.: A Multi-channel Pulse Height Analyzer Using a CR Storage Tube, *Natl. Bur. Standards Rept. No.* 3258, April, 1954.
2. Reaves, J.: Pulse Height Analyzer Using Electrostatic Storage, *Nuclear Instruments*, vol. 2, p. 136, 1958.
3. Pieper, G.: A Fast Storage System for Multichannel Pulse Height Analysis, *Nuclear Electronics*, Part I, p. 225, Proceedings of the International Symposium on Nuclear Electronics, organized by the French Society of Radio Electricians, Paris, 1958.
4. Costrell, L., and R. Brueckmann: Charge Storage Pulse-height Analyzers for Use with Pulsed Accelerators, *Nuclear Instruments*, vol. 3, p. 350, 1958.
5. Wells, F.: The Use of Electrostatic Storage Tubes for Fast Nuclear Data Storage, *Fast-pulse Techniques in Nuclear Counting*, UCRL-8706, p. 29, Proceedings of the Second Symposium on Advances in Fast-pulse Techniques for Nuclear Counting, held at the Lawrence Radiation Laboratory, Berkeley, Calif., February, 1959.

INDEX